How To Know
THE
Grasshoppers, Cockcroaches
And Their Allies

Pictured-Keys for identifying many of the
Grasshoppers, Crickets, Katydids, Earwigs,
Termites, Cockroaches, Praying Mantids,
Rock-crawlers, and Walkingsticks occur-
ring in North America, north of Mexico.

by

Jacques R. Helfer
Mendocino, California

All Illustrations Drawn
by
Jacques R. Helfer

WM. C. BROWN COMPANY PUBLISHERS
135 SOUTH L

THE PICTURED-KEY NATURE SERIES

"How to Know the Insects," Jaques, 1947

"Living Things—How to Know Them," Jaques, 1946

"How to Know the Trees," Jaques, 1946

"Plant Families—How to Know Them," Jaques, 1948

"How to Know the Economic Plants," Jaques, 1948, 1958

"How to Know the Spring Flowers," Cuthbert, 1943, 1949

"How to Know the Mosses and Liverworts," Conard, 1944, 1956

"How to Know the Land Birds," Jaques, 1947

"How to Know the Fall Flowers," Cuthbert, 1948

"How to Know the Immature Insects," Chu, 1949

"How to Know the Protozoa," Jahn, 1949

"How to Know the Mammals," Booth, 1949

"How to Know the Beetles," Jaques, 1951

"How to Know the Spiders," Kaston, 1952

"How to Know the Grasses," Pohl, 1953

"How to Know the Fresh-Water Algae," Prescott, 1954

"How to Know the Western Trees," Baerg, 1955

"How to Know the Seaweeds," Dawson, 1956

"How to Know the Freshwater Fishes," Eddy, 1957

"How to Know the Weeds," Jaques, 1959

"How to Know the Water Birds," Jaques-Ollivier, 1960

"How to Know the Butterflies," Ehrlich, 1961

"How to Know the Eastern Land Snails," Burch, 1962

"How to Know the Grasshoppers," Helfer, 1963

Other Subjects in Preparation

THE PURPOSE AND SCOPE OF THIS BOOK

 ERE for the first time a comprehensive cross section of all the U.S. grasshoppers, cockroaches, and allied insects is presented between the covers of a single volume. The insects treated here include some of the most important agricultural, building, and household pests in America. Information concerning these highly interesting and vitally important insects until now has been scattered through hundreds of technical books and papers, many of them rare and available only in the largest scientific libraries. Many species are figured here for the first time.

All of the diverse insects treated are basically similar in having chewing mouthparts and incomplete metamorphosis. Most have two pairs of wings, more often than not with the front pair, (the tegmina) somewhat thickened and leathery.

For convenience several related groups of insects, some of which have been more or less consistently treated as separate orders, are here considered together as components of a series which may be called Orthopteroides. The same meaning is embodied in the expression "Grasshoppers, Cockroaches, and their allies."

The total number of U.S. species of Orthopteroid insects is about 1300. Of these, 760 are mentioned in this book, with most of them pictured and described.

The keys presented are designed to enable almost anyone to correctly identify members of this group of insects. The language throughout has been kept as simple as possible with the introduction of a minimum of technical terms.

During the course of preparing this book I have had extensive loans of literature and authentically determined specimens from various individuals and institutions. Further, several leading American orthopterists have taken time out from their busy schedules to supply information in correspondence, and to read over portions of the manuscript. I am very grateful for the invaluable help they have given. Those who have been particularly helpful include Dr. A. B. Gurney, U.S. National Museum; Dr. I. La Rivers, University of Nevada; Dr. F. Strohecker, University of Miami; Dr. J. A. G. Rehn, Philadelphia Academy of Sciences; Dr. I. J. Cantrall, University of Michigan; Dr. E. R. Tinkham, Indio, California; Dr. W. L. Nutting, University of Arizona; Dr. W. W. Middlekauf, University of California, and Dr. K. McE. Kevan, Macdonald College, Quebec. All drawings are by Jacques R. Helfer.

Jacques R. Helfer

Mendocino, California
November, 1962

The accuracy and high excellence of this author's drawings make them truly noteworthy. They should be most helpful for entomological students. The data given for each species has likewise received exacting care. We wish we could have had a book like this years ago.

Editor

iv

CONTENTS

ABOUT GRASSHOPPERS, COCKROACHES, AND THEIR ALLIES

This assemblage of insects includes many of the strangest, most colorful, and most interesting creatures in the entire animal kingdom. Living fossils, insects that look like the twigs and leaves among which they dwell, fierce predators, efficient scavangers, tremendous jumpers, and powerful flyers, hitchhikers, cannibals, and insects that live as guests in ant colonies.

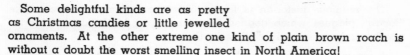

There are splendid little musicians among them, and some that live silent lives in snow banks and ice caves and in the hearts of rotten logs. There are social insects of which members of different looking castes carry out their important special duties.

There are insects that hiss and spread their colored wings in a threatening manner when disturbed, and others that are hard to find because they look like pebbles.

Some delightful kinds are as pretty as Christmas candies or little jewelled ornaments. At the other extreme one kind of plain brown roach is without a doubt the worst smelling insect in North America!

Acquaintance with these insects often begins on a childhood day when we wander in a warm sunny meadow, matching skill with baby grasshoppers; we trying to clap inexperienced hands over them, they keeping one jump ahead of us. And when we finally catch one we laugh to see it "spit tobacco juice" on our fingers. It often happens that an older child makes a pet of a praying mantis, or catches several grasshoppers and notices that there are "different kinds." Later he may save his catches to form an interesting collection.

A successful farmer must learn to recognize certain crickets and grasshoppers as presenting serious threats to his range and crops. He needs to be alert against the silent attack of termites in his buildings, and his wife may be concerned over cockroaches in the kitchen or earwigs in her prize dahlias.

The imaginative photographer discovers here a whole world of miniature subjects for his camera; curious stone-faced grasshoppers, fearsome mantids, weight for weight more terrible than the greatest dinosaurs, quaint katydids, all in a never-ending parade.

The religious historian is likely to see special significance in the "locust" plagues which goaded the Pharaoh, or in the cricket hordes which sorely tried early settlers in Utah.

A warm summer's day is brightened for the hiker by the flash and clatter of gaudy-winged grasshoppers. A warm summer's night rings with the trilling of crickets, punctuated at intervals, perhaps, by the dry "Zickkk" of a lanky kaytdid, watching from a nearby twig.

Members of this assemblage of quaint and curious insects are well represented in song and fable, rhyme and precept.

Such a richly diverse and interesting series of familiar insects as these may, as one can imagine, be studied from a great many points of view. The particular approach of this book is species identification.

While a fair percentage of the known forms of U.S. orthopteroid insects are mentioned in this book, some species are not mentioned here at all. There is always the possibility that a particular specimen represents a subspecies or minor population that looks somewhat different than the figure given. There may also be hybrids or even species thus far unknown to science, and obviously such forms cannot be found in the keys. Such puzzlers may be submitted for examination to experts such as are found at a few of the larger museums or universities.

Many of the characters used in the keys are best appreciated when a variety of different species is at hand for comparison. Therefore a good first step in using the keys in this book would be the collection for a full season of all possible kinds of grasshoppers, cockroaches, and their allies, and their preparation for study. Most specimens will be killed, pinned, and labeled in accordance with the instructions given in "How to Know the Insects." Cockroaches are pinned through the right tegmen, much as if they were beetles. Mantids are pinned through the right tegmen also.

Some colors may fade badly or be lost in ordinary handling. Dipping in weak (e.g. 5%) formalin for varying times may help to preserve difficult colors.

In preparing grasshoppers and katydids it is often desirable to slit the first three or four segments of the abdomen beneath, removing the internal contents with forceps, swabbing out with a little wad of cotton, and stuffing loosely with clean cotton. The side walls of small specimens are often simply sprung back into shape after the evisceration, and left to dry. Dehydration by refrigeration of the freshly killed and stuffed specimens will generally preserve difficult colors. Leave the specimens in the freezer for a few weeks or a month.

Great care must be taken when using killing agents, for these may be very harmful or even deadly if they are inhaled or if they get into the eyes or mouth, or even on the skin. Small children should never be allowed to use such substances. Carbon tetrachloride kills insects quickly but it is quite poisonous and great caution must be exercised if it is used. For small children ethyl acetate, chloroform, or rubbing alcohol may be used in insect collecting as these present fewer hazards. Alcohol fades the colors of many grasshoppers, katydids, etc., but is perfectly satisfactory for earwigs, termites, and many other dull-colored forms.

Camel crickets and other soft-bodied forms taken in molasses traps should have the molasses they have eaten removed. This is accomplished by evisceration or by slitting through the pleurites of one side into the crop and soaking out the molasses in a series of 40% to 50% alcohol rinses. Such a cricket is then specially prepared for pinning by giving it two thorough soakings in 95% alcohol, followed by two thorough soakings in synthetic methyl alcohol. This dehydrates it. Next the specimen is pinned and the appendages arranged, using a small piece of balsa wood as a pinning block. The specimen is then floated upside down in xylene for several hours until it hardens and becomes translucent.

Excellent specimens of such difficult subjects as termites and Jerusalem crickets may be prepared with the Volatile Solvent Technique. This involves starving the insect for a few days to clear the digestive tract, and killing in boiling water. The specimen is then placed in 70% to 80% ethyl alcohol for 24 hours, 90% to 100% ethyl alcohol for 24 hours, and anhydrous ethyl ether for more than 24 hours, following which it is pinned, the limbs arranged, and it is placed near a heat source. A 100 watt light globe is satisfactory. The distance between the specimen and the heat source must be such that the escaping vapors keep the body inflated to natural size while drying is progressing, but not so close that the specimen bursts.

When wings are present it is often necessary to spread the left ones, for example in the mantids, cockroaches, and many grasshoppers. Instructions are found on page 34 of "How to Know the Insects."

ARWIG wing veins are beautifully arranged, but the wings are delicate and usually tear badly when spreading is attempted. Perfect results are readily obtainable if the earwig is killed in about 3/16" of 70% alcohol in a petri dish. A 1" square is cut from a white blotter and dropped in the alcohol, the earwig being placed on top. The point of an insect pin is shoved through the right tegmen and into the blotting paper. This pin serves as a handle with which the specimen is held steady with the left hand. The head of a second insect pin is used to push and tease out the left wing. Eventually a critical point is reached when the double hinge suddenly snaps out straight and the wing is spread. Blotter and earwig are then lifted by the handle pin from the alcohol and transferred to a styrifoam pinning block. The pin is shoved down to its correct depth, a second smaller piece of blotting paper is placed over the spread wing and secured with pins, and the specimen placed to dry.

Collecting procedures for orthopteroid insects consist mainly of sweeping and beating vegetation, capturing with the aerial net, catching with the hands, and trapping with molasses jars set into the ground. Ant nests will need to be examined also, and rotten wood torn apart, loose bark removed from dead trees, rocks rolled and so on. Collecting at night near lights or with a headlamp or flashlight to track down songsters or expose nocturnal prowlers is profitable, especially during the summer and fall months. It is sometimes necessary to trample vegetation under the feet in order to force out individuals which have hidden. In marsh areas this will "drown out" the insects rather quickly. The widest possible variety of ecological conditions should be sampled as many species have rather specialized habits and are easily overlooked if collecting is not thorough.

When collecting, it is a good idea to persist until each species is represented by several specimens of each sex, and until one has gained a pretty good understanding of the size range and color variation to be expected in each species. The keys are sometimes easier to work if several specimens of a species are at hand. It often happens, too, that a careful examination of the day's catch reveals that what the inexperienced collector took to be mere variations of one or two species actually represent several species and genera.

creditable first goal for any collector would be to secure a complete series of all the species of grasshoppers, cockroaches, and their allies that occur within one or two miles of his home, or in his township or county. There should be representatives of both sexes wherever possible (some of these strange insects are able to reproduce through the females alone and males are seldom or never found). In the case of termites the different castes should be represented. The specimens should be unbroken, with the natural colors well preserved, and they should be neatly and uniformly mounted, accurately labeled, and correctly identified.

ATER on, trips to other parts of the country will enable one to make many splendid additions to the collection. It may be possible to arrange mutually helpful exchanges with collectors living in other parts of the country. Species which may be rather common in your area are sometimes great prizes to collectors elsewhere, and vice versa.

Some orthopteroides occur in rather limited areas and are rather uniform in size, color, and shape of their parts. Many other species, however, occur over large geographic areas, as from Atlantic to Pacific or from Canada to Mexico. Often one or more structural or color characters of such widespread species vary rather evenly and gradually across the range occupied by the species. This is called clinal variation. In some cases different characters of the species vary clinally at different rates or in different directions. Sometimes there are rather narrow regions, as along natural barriers, where variation becomes rather abrupt, resulting in stepped clines. There are instances of centripetal clinal variation, as about a mountain. In some cases it appears that at some time in the past colonies of certain species became isolated for evolutionarily significant periods of time, as by submergence of all but a few high areas of land. Later these somewhat differently evolved branches of a formerly homogeneous species appear to have reoccupied their ancestral ranges with the reemergence of the land. Interbreeding or hybridization may occur among such insects. In the West huge inland seas formerly existed which have now all but disappeared. Some forms appear to have changed to a greater or lesser extent in response to the increasing aridity. Some species appear to be particularly plastic in their response to altitude, moisture, average temperature, and other factors, and they form small populations of rather distinctive looking individuals. In the West, where life zones tend to be more sharply defined than elsewhere, there is a marked tendency for the formation of races. Most of these rather complex situations are only partly understood.

Various attempts have been made to apply scientific names to the subdivisions of species. Often the populations occuring at the opposite extremes of the range where clinal variation exists, have been called subspecies, with the populations of connecting areas referred to as "intermediates," sometimes with areas of "atypical" populations between the extremes and the intermediates. This can become quite complex and detailed, not to mention arbitrary, and such situations will not be discussed here, except to mention some of the "subspecies" briefly in passing.

As with other groups of insects, many of the largest, most colorful, and most highly specialized species are found in the tropical regions of the world while our forms tend to be somewhat less specialized and plainer colored. However we do have a fair number of colorful and considerably specialized species in our fauna, particularly in the more southerly states. We have many excellent examples of protective coloration and of special adaptations to particular modes of life.

Some species mentioned in this book occur in temperate and tropical regions all over the world, having been carried from their ancestral homes by early voyagers, and later to the New World by slave traders' ships and others. Likewise some of our species have been exported in return. Some of the cockroaches and earwigs among these transplanted species are important pests.

Some species are found in the adult stage throughout the year. Others are found as adults only in the spring, and still others persist until the first cold weather in the fall kills them. Some of our least collected forms appear in the spring and have disappeared before most entomologists take to the field.

The mantids, grylloblattids, and a few of the earwigs and jumping forms are predaceous. Many of the cockroaches and earwigs and a

6

few of the crickets and other types are primarily or incidentally scavangers. But most of the species treated here feed upon leaves of plants. Termites and some roaches eat wood, living in galleries and utilizing this unlikely material as food with the help of special protozoa or bacteria which live in large numbers in their digestive tracts. One minute roach species and a few minute crickets live with ants, and their food may consist at least in part of exudations from the bodies of the ants. Some of the termites eat fungi as well as wood.

Enemies of grasshoppers and related insects include fungous and bacterial diseases which may become epidemic, especially in prolonged warm, damp periods. There are also grasshopper mites (A and B), sarcophagid and tachinid flies, parasitic beetles, p a r a s i t i c worms, and birds, mammals, and numerous cold-blooded vertebrates which eat them as food.

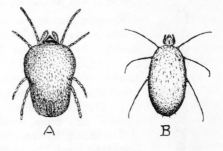

Poultry are sometimes permitted to run at large where they may catch grasshoppers as a substantial part of their diet. Quite a number of grasshoppers and cockroaches act as intermediate hosts of various parasitic worms. The birds become infected with these various worms, therefore, as a result of eating the insects.

Cockroaches which live about primitive drainage systems in buildings will come out at night to roam in search of food. They may easily carry disease germs to the food, bringing sickness to residents of such houses. Further, cockroaches may have pathogenic organisms in their bodies, and, if a roach is crushed carelessly as across a scratch on the skin, an infection may result.

ANY species of crickets and katydids have their tegmina equipped with ridges and resonating membranes used to produce sounds. They have the auditory organs located in the front tibiae. Many of these call only at night. Some deliberately synchronize their calls. Others deliberately alternate their notes. Some produce a ventriloquial effect by changing the angle of their tegmina while calling. Others achieve a similar effect by calling in a synchronized chorus, a given individual going silent when approached, such that the uninitiated collector is frustrated at following an ever receding quarry which he hears all about him. Some species produce two or even three different calls. Some produce long or short rhythmical trills while others sound off only irregularly and at long intervals. Usually the males do the calling, but females of some species are capable of limited sound production.

Many of the world's grasshoppers are silent, but in temperate regions many familiar species can produce sounds. This is usually accomplished when at rest by rubbing the hind femora against the tegmina, and when in flight by rubbing or snapping the wings. Various other sound-producing mechanisms also occur, for example the hind femur rubbing against a series of ridges or rasping plates on the sides of the abdomen. Grasshoppers are active and producing sounds mostly only during warm daylight hours, but a few continue calling at night.

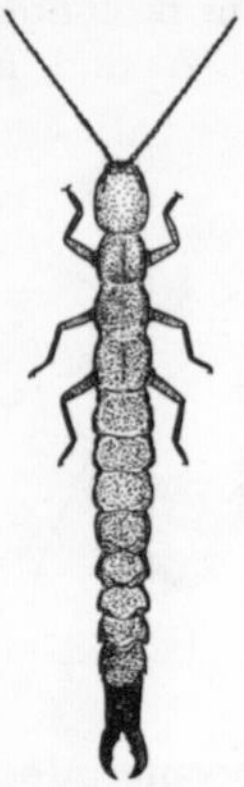

Certain insects belonging to other orders may bear a strong superficial resemblance to some of the Orthopteroids. Among these "look-alikes" are the japygids, classified as members of the order Diplura (Fig. 1). They somewhat resemble earwigs. These insects live in deep forest litter or in the soil, sometimes to a depth of several feet. They are whitish, delicate in structure, wingless, eyeless, and have terminal forceps. Certain members of the family *Mantispidae* of the order Neuroptera bear a striking resemblance to small praying mantids (Fig. 2). These insects have complete metamorphosis and the front wings are membranous. Many mantids have the front wings thickened. A few species of Hemiptera are easily mistaken for small walkingstick insects. Examination of the head reveals that the mouthparts are formed into a conspicuous sucking beak.

Figure 1

Figure 2

Plowing in late fall of fields which earlier that year were heavily infested with grasshoppers may result in the destruction of a high percentage of the eggs. The picturesque hopperdozers of yesteryear have yielded to modern insecticides such as aldrin, a mere two ounces of

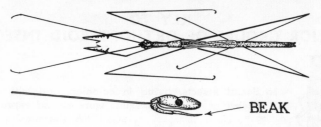

BEAK

Figure 3

which, in a half gallon of kerosene, sprayed over an acre will destroy practically all the grasshoppers in the treated area (and most of the other insect life besides). Coordinated grasshopper control programs are being undertaken with good success although they seldom prevent recurrences in succeeding years. A whole industry has sprung up to engage in repairing termite damage and preventing infestations by treating wood with creosote and other chemicals. Poison baits are used with considerable success in controling outbreaks of certain grasshoppers and katydids.

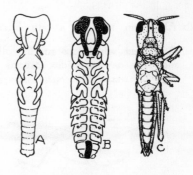

The immature stages of most Orthopteroids are very poorly known and any careful observer can make original observations on the appearance and behavior of some of the species in his area.

Three stages in the development of a grasshopper are shown, A and B in the egg, and C at the time of hatching.

KEY TO
MAJOR GROUPS OF ORTHOPTEROID INSECTS

1a Social insects, living in colonies, and with distinct castes as soldier, asexual worker, and reproductive ....ISOPTERA (termites) page 63

1b Not social (but sometimes gregarious), not colonial, and with no castes.............................2

Figure 4

2a Abdomen with strong horizontally movable forceps at end. Fig. 4.. ....DERMAPTERA (earwigs) page 13

2b Abdomen without strong horizontally movable forceps at end

(Timemas, which are small walkingstick insects, have small, strong movable asymmetrical forceps—like cerci at tip of abdomen (see Fig. 25, page 20)..3

3a Front coxae strongly elongate and front legs modified with spines for grasping prey. Fig. 5 MANTIDAE (mantids) page 25

COXA

Figure 5

3b Front legs not as described above............................4

4a Hind femora proportionally thicker than middle femora, modified for jumping, or (some mole crickets) with the hind femora less noticeably modified, but with the front tibiae strongly toothed (A), for digging. Fig. 6............7

Figure 6

4b Hind femora not proportionally thicker than middle femora, not modified for jumping, front tibiae not greatly modified for digging. . 5

5a Form oval in outline, body usually flattened, head partly or entirely concealed beneath pronotum....BLATTIDAE (cockroaches) page 35

5b Form not oval in outline, body not flattened, head visible from above 6

6a Cerci short, not jointed; body usually very slender and elongate .... PHASMIDAE (walkingstick insects) page 18

6b Cerci long, of several segments; body not especially slender or elongate .... GRYLLOBLATTIDAE (rock-crawlers) page 59

7a Pronotum (A) much prolonged behind, reaching nearly to or beyond tip of abdomen (small species) Fig. 7 .... TETRIGIDAE (pygmy grasshoppers) page 82

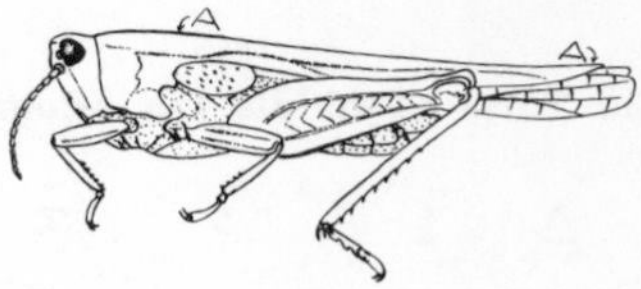

Figure 7

7b Pronotum much shorter, not reaching near tip of abdomen (small to large).. 8

8a Front legs and sometimes middle legs strongly flattened; front pair very short or shaped much differently than middle pair (fitted for digging—Fig. 6)... 16

8b Front and middle legs not as described above.................. 9

9a Southwestern desert grasshoppers having the following combination of characters: wingless, hearing organ not evident on abdomen or front tibia, lower basal lobe of hind femur longer than upper; ♂ with antenna longer than body, third abdominal tergite with a finely corrugated, thick, cylindrical stridulatory ridge; ♀ with antenna rather long (but shorter than body), ovipositor composed of four short, curved, horny sclerites whose tips diverge; mesonotum and metanotum well developed as rooflike plates which are free at the sides..
..... TANAOCERIDAE (desert long-horned grasshoppers) page 94

9b Without the above combination of characters.................. 10

10a Antenna short to moderately long, not reaching to end of abdomen or beyond 11

10b Antenna long, reaching nearly to end of abdomen or beyond...13

11a Wingless; head large, broad, smooth, and rounded in front, jaws very powerful; antenna reaching past middle of abdomen; front tibia with no hearing organ; limbs heavy; abdomen bulky; ground-inhabiting; western U.S. (ground crickets).................... 14

11b Winged (wings sometimes much reduced) or, if wingless, then otherwise without the above combination of characters....... 12

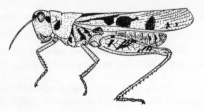

12a Antenna shorter than front femur; wingless.........
....EUMASTACIDAE (monkey grasshoppers) page 95

12b Antenna longer than front femur, or (♀ *Bootettix*) fully winged. Fig. 7½..ACRIDIDAE (grasshoppers) page 98

Figure 7½

13a Tarsi of middle leg 4-segmented (A) Fig. 8....................14

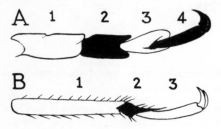

(The completely blind gopher burrow-inhabiting crickets *Typhloceutophilus* of Florida have all the tarsi 3-segmented but belong here, nevertheless.)

Figure 8

13b Tarsi of middle leg 3-segmented (B). Fig. 8....................
................................GRYLLIDAE (crickets) page 326

14a Front tibia with a hearing organ near base.................15

14b Front tibia without a hearing organ..........................
...GRYLLACRIDIDAE (cave, ground, and camel crickets) page 304

15a Hind tibia long, slender, and armed with numerous spines in each of two rows along dorsal side; fastigium usually more or less produced forward; ovipositor short or long; tegmina often resembling leaves.....................TETTIGONIIDAE, (katydids) page 262

15b Hind tibia short, stout, and armed with 8 or fewer spines in each of two rows along dorsal side; fastigium shallowly concave; ovipositor short; tegmina not leaflike..............................
........PROPHALANGOPSIDAE (hump-winged crickets) page 303

16a All tarsi 3-segmented; antenna composed of many small segments; length more than ½ inch (see Fig. 6)..........................
....................GRYLLOTALPIDAE (mole crickets) page 323

16b Front and middle tarsi 2-segmented, hind ones 1-segmented or absent; antenna composed of 12 or fewer elongate segments; length ½ inch or less..
........TRIDACTYLIDAE (sand or pygmy mole crickets) page 325

EARWIGS

About 500 kinds of earwigs are known, most being tropical. The most striking feature of earwigs is the forceps at the tip of the abdomen. These forceps are used variously for defence, for seizing and holding prey while eating, and for unfolding and folding the wings when such are present. They are probably not used as claspers during mating. About 20 species are known from our country, several having been accidentally introduced from elsewhere. Female earwigs guard their eggs and newly hatched young and carefully protect them from harm.

KEY TO EARWIGS

1a Second tarsal segment cylindrical (A) Fig. 9.....................4

1b Second tarsal segment lobed, prolonged beneath third (B) Fig. 9..2

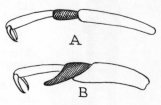

Figure 9

2a Antenna 12-segmented 3

2b Antenna 14-16-segmented, Fig. 10.................................
..........................*Doru lineare* (Eschscholtz) Linear earwig

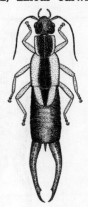

LENGTH: 8-15 mm. RANGE: New Jersey, southern Ontario, Michigan, Arizona, and California to South America.

Brown, pronotum and tegmina yellowish in part, limbs yellowish. Forceps of male well separated at base and with a distinct spine or tubercle. Hides in leaf bases of grasses and sedges during the day, and prowls at night.

D. aculeatum (Scudder), the Spine-tailed earwig, is common in the East, north to Michigan. It usually has the wings much reduced. A slenderer Florida form is called *D. aculeatum davisi* Rehn and Hebard.

Figure 10

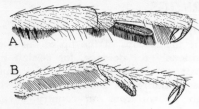

Figure 11

3a Lobe of second tarsal segment narrow, with long brush-like pubescence (A).

Figs. 11, 12........*Chelisoches morio* (Fabricius) Black earwig

Figure 12

LENGTH: 16-20 mm. RANGE: Tropical Pacific, California.

Blackish or brown, forceps variable in form. A common tropical form which has been established locally in California.

I found this insect commonly in New Guinea, during the war.

3b Lobe of second tarsal segment broad, with pubescence short, normal (B). Figs. 11, 13....*Forficula auricularia* Linnaeus European earwig

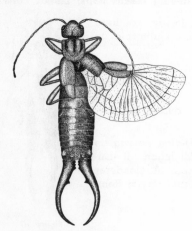

Figure 13

LENGTH: 11-17 mm. RANGE: Cosmopolitan, coast to coast in the U.S., and into British Columbia.

Blackish-brown with tegmina and appendages lighter. Has large beautiful wings but seldom flies. First firmly established in the U.S. in Rhode Island about 1912. Now a widespread pest in flowers, vegetables, fruits, about the house, etc., in many areas.

14

4a Antenna 14-24-segmented, combined
length of segments 4-5-6 usually
shorter than first (A). Fig. 14...5

4b Antenna 10-16-segmented, combined
length of segments 4-5-6 longer than
first (B). Fig. 14.................7

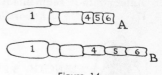

Figure 14

5a Male with apical forceps distinctly asymmetrical, the right arm much
more strongly curved than the left (see Fig. 16); wingless or
winged 6

5b Male with apical forceps symmetrical; winged. Fig. 15..........
........................*Labidura riparia* (Pallas) Riparian earwig

LENGTH: 18-26 mm. RANGE: Cosmopolitan. Texas
to North Carolina. Also Arizona and California.

Light brown and buffy, variable. A large species
found under litter along sea beaches and along rivers.
Produces a disagreeable odor.

I found it attracted to lights at a gasoline station
in Arizona.

Figure 15

6a Antenna 24-segmented; large, wingless species. Fig. 16..........
.....................*Anisolabis maritima* (Gene) Seaside earwig

LENGTH: 16-25 mm. RANGE: Atlantic, Gulf, and
southern California coasts. Also Vancouver Island.

Blackish-brown, legs and under surface lighter.
A large wingless species found under seashore
debris.

Figure 16

6b Antenna 15-16-segmented; smaller winged or wingless species. Fig. 17 . . . . *Euborellia annulipes* (Lucas) Ring-legged earwig

LENGTH: 9-13 mm. RANGE: Cosmopolitan. Vancover Island, North Carolina to Florida, Texas, and California.

Blackish-brown, legs and under surface lighter, legs usually ringed or with dark markings, third and fourth from last antennal segments usually pale. Tegmina and wings often absent. Common under debris and litter, and may invade houses. Mostly coastal.

Figure 17

E. cincticollis (Gerst.) is an African species which has been established in California since about 1946. Since then it has spread into Arizona. Similar to *E. annulipes* except that fully developed wings and tegmina, or at least small tegmina are present. Two further species of this genus, *Euborellia ambigua* (Borelli) and *E. stali* (Dohrn) are reported from the U.S.

7a Eye longer than side of head behind eye (A). Figs. 18, 19 . . . . *Vostox brunneipennis* (Serville) Brown-winged earwig

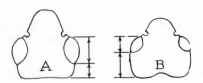

Figure 18

LENGTH: 9-12 mm. RANGE: Eastern U.S. to Texas and Arizona.

Brown to blackish, the abdomen, exposed portion of wing, and forceps often lighter. Usually uncommon, and mostly found under bark of dead trees.

Figure 19

7b Eye shorter than side of head behind eye (B). Fig. 18 8

8a Body thickly pubescent; length 7 mm. or less; fourth antennal segment as long as third. Fig. 20.. *Labia minor* **(Linnaeus) Least earwig**

LENGTH: 4-6 mm. RANGE: Galapagos Islands, Africa, Philippines, Madeira, Europe, southern Canada, and U.S.

Blackish, covered with fine yellowish pubescence. Legs brownish-yellow. Male with a tooth at middle of last ventral segment. A tiny introduced species which is now widespread. It flies about flowers and manure piles, especially on warm evenings.

Figure 20

8b Body sparsely pubescent; length 8 mm. or more; fourth antennal segment shorter than third.....................................9

9a Strongly shining red-brown; usually wingless. Fig. 21...........
.... *Prolabia pulchella* **(Serville) Handsome earwig**

LENGTH: 8-10 mm. RANGE: Southern U.S.

Common under tree bark, especially of pines. This is one of the few earwigs actually native to our country.

Figure 21

P. arachidia (Yersin) is a tropical cosmopolitan species which occurs in eastern U.S. It has the outer antennal segments strongly thickened and clublike. Wings are absent. A greasy household pest.

17

9b Weakly shining yellow-brown to blackish; usually winged. Fig. 22.
............Spongovostox apicidentatus (Caudell) Toothed earwig

LENGTH: 9-12 mm. RANGE: Southwestern U.S.

Prefers semi-desert or desert conditions. Found about dead cacti and dead leaves. A native species.

Figure 22

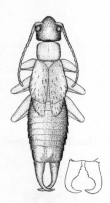

Foreign insects are constantly being intercepted by our Quarantine stations. From time to time one of these insects slips past the inspectors. and becomes established, often locally and often for a short time only, on our shores. One such earwig is *Pyragropsis buscki* (Caudell) Busck's earwig, Fig. 23, a native of the Carribean region, which has apparently become established in Florida. It has a well developed padlike arolium between the tarsal claws, conspicuous setae on the tegmina and exposed portions of the wings, and males have forceps of two distinct types (shown). It is light and dark brown colored.

Figure 23

WALKINGSTICKS

About 700 kinds of Phasmids are known, most being tropical. Some tropical forms are flattened and green colored so as to resemble leaves. Others are very spiny. Some are giants measuring more than 10 inches in length! When a leg is broken off a walkingstick has the useful ability to grow another to replace it. Phasmids are all vegetarians, but only one of our species is (sometimes) destructively common. Most of our species are long, slender, and twiglike, but the southwestern *Timemas* are more usual appearing insects and seem to be intermediate in some respects between walkingsticks and earwigs.

KEY TO WALKINGSTICKS

1a Antenna longer than front femur.............................2

1b Antenna shorter than front femur. Fig. 24......................
..*Parabacillus hesperus* Hebard Western short-horned walkingstick

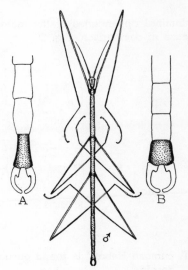

LENGTH: 63-90 mm. RANGE: Utah to California, Arizona, and Oregon.

Light to dark brown. Very slender. Only the first two antennal segments are distinct. Rather common on range grasses, but they also feed on burroweed (*Haplopappus*) and various species of *Sphaeralcea*. The last abdominal segment of the male (B, Fig 24) is about as long as wide.

Figure 24

P. coloradus (Scudder) occurs from Wyoming and Arizona to Kansas and Texas. It is similar to *hesperus* except that the last abdominal segment of the male (A, Fig. 24) is about twice as long as wide.

2a Large, slender; legs far apart, coxae visible from above; tarsi 5-segmented 3

2b Small, less than 1¼ inch long (32 mm.); broader; legs close together, coxae under body, not visible from above; tarsi 3-segmented. Fig. 25.
................*Timema californicum* Scudder California timema

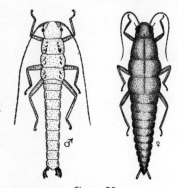

Figure 25

LENGTH: 12-25 mm. RANGE: California, north to Humboldt County.

Green, occasionally brown or pinkish. These run actively when disturbed and produce an unpleasant odor. Found on chaparral, especially *Ceanothus cuneatus* and *Cercocarpus*. Sometimes on fir. Taken by beating. Locally common, e.g. at Mount Diablo.

Five other species of *Timema* have been described. They are best distinguished by the shape of the abdominal appendages of the males. These are figured in a group for ease in comparison. Fig. 26.

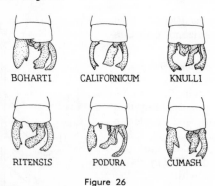

BOHARTI   CALIFORNICUM   KNULLI

RITENSIS   PODURA   CUMASH

Figure 26

T. cumash Hebard is found on oak *Quercus dumosa* in southern California.

T. podura Strohecker is found on *Ceanothus* and *Cercocarpus* in southern California.

T. ritensis Hebard is found in Arizona high on Mt. Wrightson and Mt. Lemmon.

T. knulli Strohecker is found in Monterey County, California. It is the largest timema, 20 mm. in the male, 27 mm. in the female.

T. boharti Tinkham is found on grass in the Borrego desert, California. It is striped gray in color. They sometimes hide under rocks.

3a Mesonotum four or more times as long as pronotum..............**4**

3b Mesonotum less than three times as long as pronotum. Fig. 27....
......*Anisomorpha buprestoides* (Stoll) Two-striped walkingstick

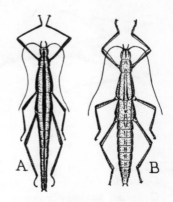

LENGTH: 39-77 mm. RANGE: Florida to southeast Georgia.

Male brownish-yellow, f e m a l e darker, both sexes with three black stripes. Rather common on grass or brush, under loose bark, and under boards, especially where moist. Adults may be found the year around. There are defensive glands under the pronotum which squirt a thick milky liquid at the collector. Take care and do not let any of this substance reach your eyes!

Figure 27

A. ferruginea (Beauvois) (B) is very similar but smaller, 30-36 mm., and has the stripes very pale and inconspicuous. It occurs from Texas to Florida, Virginia, and Illinois.

4a Tegmina and wings totally absent............................**5**

4b Tegmina and wings present. Fig. 28...........................
...................*Aplopus mayeri* Caudell Mayer's walkingstick

LENGTH: 83-127 mm. RANGE: Southern Florida and Keys.

Greenish to dark brown, marked with white. Head (A) with large spines, pronotum and mesonotum finely spined. Found on bay cedar *(Suriana maritima)* and other vegetation.

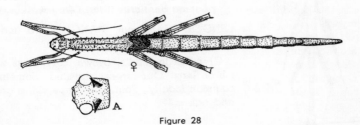

Figure 28

5a Middle femora spined or lobed, often swollen..................**6**

21

5b Middle femora simple, unarmed. Fig. 29.......................
..............*Pseudosermyle straminea* (Scudder) Gray walkingstick

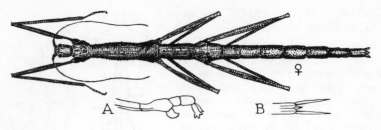

Figure 29

LENGTH: 40-75 mm. RANGE: Southern California to New Mexico and Colorado.

Greenish to gray-brown or whitish. Female longitudinally ridged and finely spined above, especially on thorax. Male smoother above and with cerci three-pronged at tip (A). Rather common on grass, rabbit weed, burroweed, sagebrush, etc.

P. strigata (Scudder), a similar species, occurs from eastern Texas to the lower Mississippi valley region. The female cerci (B) are long and slender, and the prongs of the male cercus are much more deeply cut than in *straminea*.

6a Middle and hind femora armed only with a spine near tip.......7

6b Middle and hind femora with median ridge of lower surface spined throughout. Fig. 30.......................*Megaphasma denticrus* (Stal) Giant walkingstick

LENGTH: 76-150 mm. RANGE: Iowa and Indiana to Texas and Louisiana.

Greenish to reddish-brown, sometimes whitish on legs. Our largest phasmid. Sometimes common locally. Found on grape vines, grass, and oak.

Figure 30

7a Middle femur and fifth abdominal segment conspicuously lobed. Fig. 31........*Sermyle mexicana* (Saussure) Mexican walkingstick

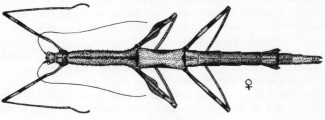

Figure 31

LENGTH: 85-90 mm. RANGE: Brownsville area of Texas.

Brownish to gray, mottled, and usually marked with whitish. Known only from females. Probably occurs on brush.

7b Middle femur and fifth abdominal segment not lobed............8

8a Head twice as long as wide or longer; hind femur with no spine beneath; middle femur not much swollen.......................9

8b Head little longer than wide; hind femur usually spined beneath; middle femur of male swollen. Fig. 32...........................
......................*Diapheromera femorata* (Say) Walkingstick

LENGTH: 68-101 mm. RANGE: Maine and southern Canada to Florida and Arizona.

Brownish or grayish to greenish, head vaguely striped. Middle femora of male usually banded. Sometimes occurs in tremendous numbers, defoliating oaks and other trees and shrubs. Usually abundant only every other year in a given locality. In a heavy infestation eggs and fecal pellets are dropped to the ground in great numbers, producing a pattering sound, like rain, accompanied by a peculiar seething sound of thousands of jaws chewing the leaves.

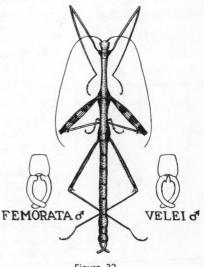

Figure 32

Several other species of *Diapheromera* occur, but mostly in small numbers. In fact some of them are among our scarcest Orthopteroids.

The differences that distinguish the various kinds are summarized below.

D. carolina Scudder, from North Carolina, is shorter than *femorata*, and the thorax bears a conspicuous median stripe.

D. persimilis Caudell, from Texas, on grass, is slenderer and the hind femur lacks the tooth which is customary in this genus.

D. torquata Hebard, from Chisos Mts., Texas, is also very slender and has the male cerci without any internal basal tooth. Further, the poculum, a normally symmetrical saclike structure beneath the aedeagus, is strongly twisted to the right.

D. covillea (R. & H.), from the more arid west Texas region, has hornlike spines on the head in both sexes, and the middle tibia of the male has numerous teeth on the lower margin. It occurs also on creosote brush in Arizona.

D. tamaulipensis (Rehn), from east central to south Texas, lacks the horns in the male sex. The ninth abdominal segment of the male is longer than wide in this species, as long as wide in *covillea*.

D. arizonensis Caudell, common on bear grass, spiny trees, and shrubs in Arizona, is yellowish or brown, the male with a green stripe on the back and a narrow black stripe beneath, on the thorax. Female greenish to brownish.

D. velii Walsh, from Minnesota to Texas and Louisiana, has the male femora usually unbanded, and the male cerci are armed with a slender spine internally at base as shown, instead of a blunt angle.

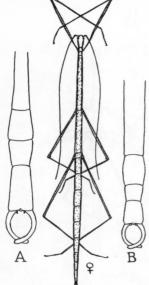

D. velii eucnemis Hebard is a Rio Grande Valley to west Texas subspecies or race in which the male poculum is strongly bilobed, the female femora are black at the ends, and it averages a little larger.

D. blatchleyi Caudell, from Kansas and Oklahoma to Virginia and Connecticut, lacks the tooth on the middle femur and has a blunt tooth at base of male cercus.

9a Male with last segment of abdomen **(A)** about twice as long as wide; cercus with a sharp tooth at base. Fig. 33.. ....*Manomera tenuescens* (Scudder) Slender-bodied walkingstick
LENGTH: 63-110 mm. RANGE: North Carolina to southern Florida.

Brown to green. Very slender throughout. Found on wire grass, huckleberry, saw palmetto, and other low vegetation. More active at night. The female has the last abdominal segment longer than the pronotum.

Figure 33

24

9b Male with last segment of abdomen (B) only a little longer than wide; cercus with a blunt, oblique tooth at base. See Fig. 33B....
Manomera brachypyga Rehn and Hebard Short-rumped walkingstick
LENGTH: 69-93 mm. RANGE: Florida.

Brown to green. Similar to above and the two species occur together in Florida. Here the female has the last abdominal segment equal to the pronotum in length. Found mainly on undergrowth in pine woods. As with most walkingsticks the collecting is best on warm nights using lights.

PRAYING MANTIDS

OST of the more than 1500 known species of mantids are tropical. All are predaceous. Some tropical species are colored and shaped in wonderfully exact imitation of certain types of flowers (Figure 34) among which they wait for their prey. After mating the female mantid is very likely to eat her mate. Mantids are among the most remarkable of all insects, easily able to turn their triangular heads in various directions, and waiting motionless with front legs folded until the moment when they suddenly flash out to clamp a hapless insect in the death trap of their grasp. Mantids are related to cockroaches but date only from the Cenozoic era while roaches are a much more ancient group.

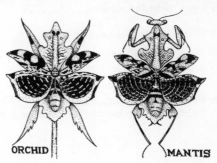

ORCHID   MANTIS

Figure 34

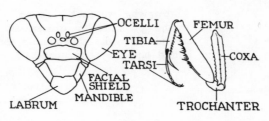

OCELLI   FEMUR
TIBIA
EYE   COXA
TARSI
FACIAL
SHIELD
MANDIBLE
LABRUM   TROCHANTER

Figure 35

25

KEY TO PRAYING MANTIDS

1a Head without hornlike process in front.........................2

1b Head with a hornlike process in front. Fig. 36.................
............*Pseudovates arizonae* Hebard Arizona unicorn mantis

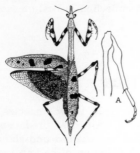

LENGTH: 64-77 mm. RANGE: South central to southeastern Arizona.

Green, tegmina with brown markings, wing extensively brown with yellow veinlets. Found sparingly on grasslands, in dense shaded vegetation, and in low, moist spots where vegetation is rank. Middle leg (A) and hind legs lobed.

Figure 36

Phyllovates chlorophaea (Blanchard) ranges from Central America to southeastern Texas. It is much like *Pseudovates arizonae* but the middle and hind legs are not lobed.

2a Eyes rounded above..4

2b Eyes conical, pointed above. Fig. 37A........................3

3a Eyes very narrow, head narrow (A); front limbs small. Fig. 37....
Yersiniops sophronicum (Rehn and Hebard) Yersin's ground mantis

LENGTH: 13-15 mm. RANGE: Southwestern desert areas.

Brownish, wingless. Found running on ground on bare or grassy slopes. These mantids have the hind femora somewhat enlarged and they can jump several inches.

Figure 37

26

3b Eyes broader, more divergent, head broader (A); front limbs longer.
Fig. 38......*Yersiniops solitarium* (Scudder) Horned ground mantis

LENGTH: 18-25 mm. RANGE: Arizona
to Rocky Mountains.

Brownish, wingless. Found running
on ground in rather bare, rocky places.
They sometimes spit up quantities of
brown liquid when caught. These mantids commonly jump a few inches.

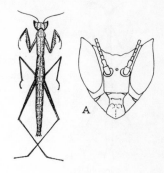

Figure 38

4a Pronotum much longer than wide................................5

4b Pronotum about as long as wide. Fig. 39........................
...................*Mantoida maya* S. and Z. Little Yucatan mantis

LENGTH: 15-17 mm. RANGE: Southern Florida,
Yucatan.

Brownish, pronotum marked with black. Tegmina long. Found running on ground under
dense brush. Uncommon.

Figure 39

5a Antenna threadlike...6

**5b Antenna thick, especially at base. Fig. 40.......................
.... *Brunneria borealis* Scudder Brunner's mantis**

Figure 40

LENGTH: 65-90 mm. RANGE: North Carolina to Texas.

Green, elongate, sides of pronotum conspicuously toothed. Tegmina much reduced. Only females are known.

6a Larger, 36 mm. or more, or front tibia with one or more dorsal teeth; pronotum usually much longer than front coxa.................7

**6b Small, 32 mm. or less; front tibia with no dorsal tooth; pronotum slightly longer than front coxa. Fig. 41 ....
.... *Litaneutra minor* (Scudder) Minor ground mantis**

Figure 41

LENGTH: 25-32 mm. RANGE: British Columbia to North Dakota, Texas, and Mexico.

Reddish or yellowish-brown to blackish. Variable. Male tegmina usually long but sometimes short. Female tegmina short. Male wing often with a dark central blotch. Found on ground or sometimes on vegetation. Moderately common.

7a Pronotum distinctly narrowed ahead of point at which front legs are attached; form narrower.......................................8

7b Pronotum not narrowed ahead of point at which front legs are attached; form broad. Fig. 42.....................................
........................*Gonatista grisea* (Fabricius) Grizzled mantis

LENGTH: 36-40 mm. RANGE: South Carolina to Florida and Cuba.

Mottled gray, green, and brown. Females are especially well camouflaged as they wait motionless on bark of trees. A broad species, the female abdomen is lobed at the sides.

Figure 42

8a Front tibia with few teeth, with at least one dorsal tooth, and measuring less than one-half as long as front femur.................9

8b Front tibia with several teeth, with no dorsal tooth, and measuring more than one-half as long as front femur....................11

9a Hind portion of pronotum less than three times as long as front portion 10

9b Hind portion of pronotum three to four times as long as front portion. Fig. 43.......*Thesprotia graminis* (Scudder) Grass-like mantis

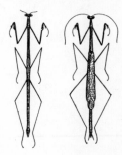

LENGTH: 47-56 mm. RANGE: Florida to Mississippi.

Brownish, extremely slender. The wingless female looks like a dead pine needle. Found on grasses, etc., or on beds of pine needles where it cannot be seen until it moves. Taken by sweeping vegetation.

Figure 43

**10a Hind portion of pronotum twice as long as front portion; more slender. Fig. 44...
...........Oligonicella mexicana (S. and Z.) Slim Mexican mantis**

LENGTH: 32-45 mm. RANGE: Arizona to Guatemala.

Brownish, very slender. Female wingless. Front femur (A) very slender. Found mostly on flowers such as the composite *Gymnolomia annua*, and at lights.

Figure 44

**10b Hind portion of pronotum not much longer than front portion; less slender. Fig. 45...
...............*Oligonicella scudderi* (Saussure) Scudder's mantis**

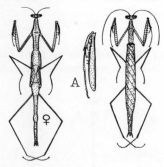

LENGTH: 26-37 mm. RANGE: Nebraska to Texas and Florida.

Brownish, slender. Female with tegmina and wings reduced. Front femur (A) a little thicker than in *O. mexicana*. Found on ground, on grass, and on other low vegetation.

Figure 45

11a Wing not brick-red; facial shield without a pair of tubercles....12

11b Wing more or less extensively dull brick-red with dark markings; facial shield with a pair of tubercles. Fig. 46....................
....................*Iris oratoria* (Linnaeus) Mediterranean mantis

LENGTH: 45-54 mm. RANGE: Southern California, Mediterranean.

Green or brownish above. Front femur (A) with five teeth on the outer margin (the tooth at end is not counted). The female wings and tegmina are often somewhat shorter than in the male, exposing a fourth to a half of the abdomen. Introduced about 1933 and

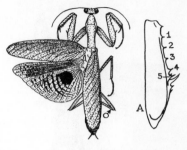

Figure 46

now well established in California north to San Jose. On vegetation in cotton fields. At lights.

12a Facial shield more than twice as wide as high (see Fig. 35).....15

12b Facial shield less than twice as wide as high.................13

13a Front coxa with no large spot; green color of tegmina usually sharply confined to costal area..............................14

13b Front coxa with a large black-ringed spot near base, beneath; green color of tegmen not sharply confined to costal area. Fig. 47.
....................*Mantis religiosa* Linnaeus European mantis

LENGTH: 47-65 mm. RANGE: New York to Ontario, North Africa, South Europe, and temperate Asia.

Green or brown, the color spreading far back over the tegmina. First introduced about 1899, probably on nursery stock at Rochester, New York. Often deliberately introduced to other areas since then and specimens may turn up almost anywhere. The egg mass is about ⅝" wide by 1¼" long, narrowed at one end.

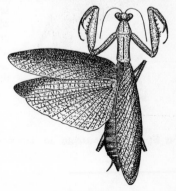

Figure 47

**14a Smaller; hind wing narrower from front to rear, lightly marbled.
Fig. 48...*Tenodera angustipennis* Saussure Narrow-winged mantis**

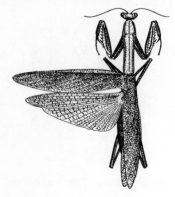

LENGTH: 70-75 mm. RANGE: New York to Virginia. Asia.

Green. Known to have been present in the U.S. as early as 1926. Has been deliberately introduced in many places. The elongate egg masses are usually placed on woody stems or twigs having a diameter of at least that of the egg mass.

Figure 48

**14b Larger; hind wing broader from front to rear, heavily marbled.
Fig. 49......*Tenodera aridifolia sinensis* Saussure Chinese mantis**

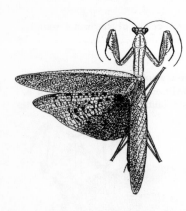

LENGTH: 77-103 mm. RANGE: Connecticut to Virginia, Illinois, California. Also eastern Asia and nearby islands.

Green. Known to have been present in the U.S. as early as 1896. Often deliberately introduced to new areas and specimens may turn up almost anywhere. This is our largest mantis. The large, rounded egg masses measure about 1" by 1¼" to 1½", and are commonly placed on stems of weeds such as goldenrod as well as on twigs and small branches. These large mantids make interesting pets.

Figure 49

15a Species occurring in eastern United States...................16

15b Species occurring in southwestern United States..............17

16a Larger, 58 mm. or more; form more elongate, abdomen of female nearly parallel-sided. Fig. 50...................................
............Stagmomantis floridensis Davis Larger Florida mantis

LENGTH: 58-71 mm. RANGE: Florida.

Green (or brown in cabinet specimens) more or less mottled darker. Female with tegmina shorter than pronotum. Occurs in about equal numbers with the next species in Florida.

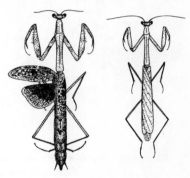

Figure 50

A fine collection of mantids of the world can be very interesting indeed as there are many strange and bizarre species. In New Guinea one common fast-running wingless mantis scurrys around to the other side of a tree trunk when you try to catch it. Sometimes they dodge many times before being caught.

16b Smaller, 57 mm. or less; form less elongate, abdomen of female strongly widened at middle. Fig. 51...........................
..............Stagmomantis carolina (Johannson) Carolina mantis

LENGTH: 48-57 mm. RANGE: New Jersey and Indiana to Utah, and Florida to Central America and Cuba.

Green or brown, more or less mottled darker. Female tegmina longer than pronotum. A common species occurring over a wide area. Found about gardens, orchards, borders of cultivated fields, and in forest undergrowth.

Figure 51

17a Abdomen of male with four dark cross-bands. Fig. 52...........
......*Stagmomantis californica* Rehn and Hebard California mantis

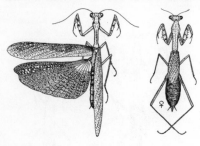

LENGTH: 45-50 mm. RANGE: California to Colorado and Texas.

Green, yellowish, or brownish. Male wing brownish with pale mottling and cross veinlets, purplish at base. Female wing brown, purple, and orange-yellow. Common on bushes and low vegetation, and often attracted to lights.

Figure 52

17b Abdomen of male with no dark crossbands. Fig. 53.............
................*Stagmomantis limbata* (Hahn) Bordered mantis

LENGTH: 45-50 mm. RANGE: Arizona to Texas and Mexico.

Green, yellowish, or brownish. Male wing clear except opaque stripe along front edge. Female tegmina usually green, wing thickly spotted with lemon yellow. A common mantis on low vegetation, especially flowering plants and bushes.

Figure 53

S. gracilipes Rehn is an uncommon Arizona species which is much like the other Stagmomantis species except quite a bit slenderer. Males are brown or green, females usually golden or yellowish. It measures 58-61 mm. in length.

COCKROACHES

ABOUT 55 species of this large and mostly tropical group are recorded from continental United States. Many more species occur in the South than in colder sections. Cockroaches much like those we have today are known as fossils from as far back as the middle Silurian period, which means they lived about 365 million years ago.

Four kinds of cockroaches, the German, the Brown-banded, the American, and the Oriental, are common household pests in many areas. Careful carpentry when building and good housekeeping thereafter will discourage roaches by depriving them of cracks and openings for concealment, and crumbs of food. Various modern insecticides are effective in the control of cockroaches.

Some cockroaches lay eggs in capsules. The female may carry the egg capsule at the end of her abdomen for some days. Other kinds are ovoviviparous, that is the eggs hatch within the female's body and the young are "born alive." Some cockroaches are able to reproduce parthenogenetically, that is without any males being necessary, eggs laid by the females giving rise to new generations consisting of all females.

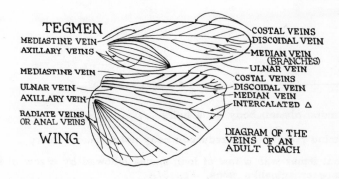

TEGMEN
MEDIASTINE VEIN
AXILLARY VEINS
MEDIASTINE VEIN
ULNAR VEIN
AXILLARY VEIN
RADIATE VEINS
OR ANAL VEINS
WING

COSTAL VEINS
DISCOIDAL VEIN
MEDIAN VEIN
(BRANCHES)
ULNAR VEIN
COSTAL VEINS
DISCOIDAL VEIN
MEDIAN VEIN
INTERCALATED △

DIAGRAM OF THE
VEINS OF AN
ADULT ROACH

Figure 54

KEY TO COCKROACHES

1a Length greater than 3 mm.; almost never found in ant nests....2

1b Length less than 3 mm.; living with ants. Fig. 55. . . . .
. . . .*Attaphila fungicola* Wheeler Ant cockroach

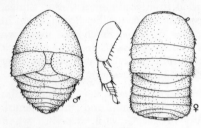

Figure 55

LENGTH: 2.45-2.7 mm. RANGE: Texas.

Rather strongly convex above. Amber yellow to brownish. Tegmina reduced in male, absent in female. Antennal segments except second and third decidedly longer than wide. Antennae usually bitten off short by the ants.

This, our smallest cockroach, lives in the fungus gardens of the ant *Atta fervens* Say.

2a Wingless or wing with intercalated triangle absent or inconspicuous **3**

2b Wing with large intercalated triangle or appendicular field **45**

3a Front femur with one or a few to many spines on ventral margin, usually plus one or more at tip. Fig. 56B. **4**

3b Front femur with no spines on ventral margin or with only one or a few spines at tip (often with rows of stiff hairs which should not be confused with spines which are much heavier). Fig. 56A. . . .**35**

Figure 56

4a Tegmina absent; body quite hairy **43b**

4b Tegmina present (often reduced); body not unusually hairy **5**

5a Front femur with a row of long spines followed by a row of short spines or spinelike setae. Fig. 57A **6**

Figure 57

5b Front femur with a row of spines which decrease gradually in size and length, or with only a few spines along margin. Fig. 57B. . . .**21**

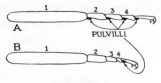

Figure 58

6a First four tarsal segments with pulvilli (A); pronotum not strikingly marked. Fig. 58A..............8

6b Fourth tarsal segment only with a pulvillus (B); pronotum with distinct striking markings. Fig. 58B...........................7

7a Tegmina and abdomen with a pattern of markings. Fig. 59.......
...............*Aglaopteryx gemma* Hebard Little gem cockroach

LENGTH: 7.5-9.7 mm. RANGE: Texas to Florida.

Glossy yellowish to brownish with dark markings. Front femur as in A. Sexes similar. A pretty species found under signs on trees and about vegetation.

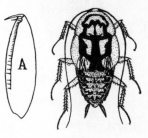

Figure 59

7b Tegmina and abdomen with no pattern of markings. Fig. 60......
...............*Euthlastoblatta abortiva* Caudell Fragile cockroach

LENGTH: 8.7-10.5 mm. RANGE: Brownsville area of Texas.

Glossy brown, pronotum strikingly marked with buff. Tegmina brown, lighter in male, exposing part of abdomen in female. Not uncommon in wood rat nests and in leaves and dry litter on the ground along the Rio Grande River.

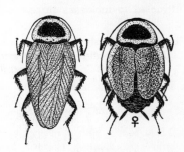

Figure 60

8a Male with sixth and sometimes seventh dorsal abdominal segment specialized at middle; median segment not specialized...........9

8b Male without specialization at middle of sixth or seventh dorsal abdominal segments, but often with median segment specialized at middle 10

9a Blackish-brown above with orange-brown legs; male with sixth and seventh dorsal abdominal segments highly specialized, subgenital plate strongly asymmetrical, one style more than twice as large as the other (A). Fig. 61..
........*Ischnoptera deropeltiformis* (Brunner) Dark wood cockroach

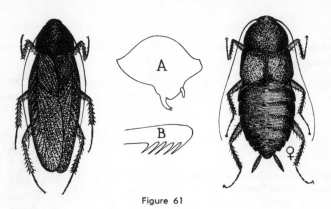

Figure 61

LENGTH: 11.7-17.8 mm. RANGE: Eastern U. S., north to New Jersey, west to Kansas and Texas.

Usually shining blackish-brown above, but tegmina of male sometimes paler. Sixth dorsal abdominal segment of male bearing a pair of small, median, comb-like structures (B). Found in woodland areas under cover in damp litter and rubbish and under bark and stones. Attracted to molasses traps.

9b Pale brownish; male with sixth dorsal abdominal segment specialized; subgential plate not strongly asymmetrical. Fig. 62.........
.......................*Latiblatella rehni* Hebard Rehn's cockroach

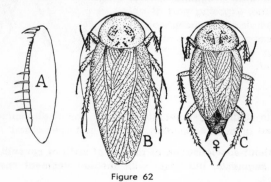

Figure 62

LENGTH: 10:5-12.9 mm. RANGE: Extreme southeastern Florida.

Glossy pale brown, pronotum with small specks of dark brown. Sexes similar. Taken under signs on pine trees and at lights.

A shows the front femur. B is the male.

L. lucifrons Hebard the Pale-headed cockroach, found in the Huachuca and Santa Rita Mts., Arizona, is similar except the female (C) has the tegmina shorter than the abdomen. In June it feeds on pollen and dead insects on *Yucca elata* flower stalks.

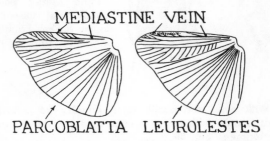

Figure 63

10a Wing with mediastine vein reaching to near apex; sexes similar; median segment of male unspecialized. Figs. 63, 64..............
.................*Leurolestes pallidus* (Brunner) Pallid cockroach

LENGTH: 15.2-20 mm. RANGE: Tropical. Florida Keys.

Glossy light translucent brown, tegmina yellowish on sides at front. Pronotum with dark brown central blotch. The cerci are short and 10-segmented. Found in old burlap sacks, in cracks, under boards, and in houses. Probably a native of the West Indies.

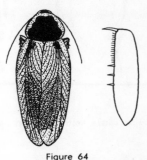

Figure 64

10b Wing with mediastine vein reaching about halfway to apex; females usually with tegmina and wings much reduced; males often with median segment specialized...................................11

11a Abdomen of male with dorsal surface unspecialized...........12

11b Abdomen of male with one or two segments of dorsal surface specialized 13

12a Male with eyes much farther apart than ocelli; head pale colored; female with tegmina separated by less than the width of one tegmen. Fig. 65.......*Parcoblatta desertae* (R. & H.) Desert cockroach

LENGTH: 11.3-13.8 mm. RANGE: Texas, Ft. Davis, and Chisos Mts., southwest to Presidio.

Male glossy pale brownish, female light russet-brownish, abdomen darker. Found under rocks on desert and at lights.

Figure 65

12b Male with eyes and ocelli about equally far apart; head dark colored; female with tegmina separated by about twice the width of one tegmen. Fig. 66...
..............*Parcoblatta bolliana* (S. & Z.) Boll's wood cockroach

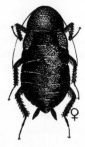

LENGTH: 9-12.8 mm. RANGE: New Mexico to Nebraska, North Carolina, and Georgia.

Male glossy pale brownish, female shining blackish-brown. Occurs beneath the pine needle layer of the forest floor, occasionally at lights. Visits molasses traps.

Figure 66

13a Male with median segment alone specialized. Fig. 67.........14

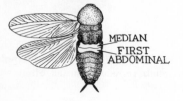

MEDIAN
FIRST
ABDOMINAL

Figure 67

13b Male with median segment and first dorsal abdominal segment specialized. Fig. 67.........19

14a Median segment with a single broad specialized area at middle 15

14b Median segment with paired specialized areas.................17

15a Specialized area a moderately large median patch of minute scattered hairs. Fig. 68...
...........*Parcoblatta virginica* (Brunner) Virginia wood cockroach

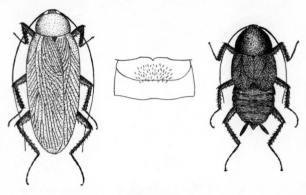

Figure 68

LENGTH: 10.3-14.7. RANGE: Maine to North Carolina and Alabama, west to Minnesota and Kansas.

Male glossy pale brownish, pronotum slightly darker; female hazel-brown, abdomen darker. Common about borders of woods and cultivated fields, under loose bark, and under cover on the ground. Males often come to lights.

15b Specialized area a tuft of hairs which are stuck together.......16
16a Tuft of hairs small and square; remainder of median segment showing little specialization. Fig. 69...................................
........*Parcoblatta americana* (Scudder) Western wood cockroach

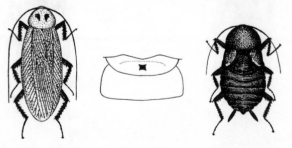

Figure 69

LENGTH: 8.8-14.8. RANGE: Oregon to Lower California, Nevada, and Arizona.

Male glossy brown, female much darker. Specimens from arid areas tend to be smaller and paler. Found under rocks on grassy slopes. Often found at lights. Attracted to molasses traps.

16b Tuft of hairs larger and distinctly transverse; remainder of median segment further specialized. Fig. 70............................
...............*Parcoblatta zebra* Hebard Banded wood cockroach

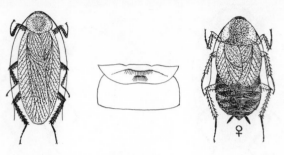

Figure 70

LENGTH: 11.5-16 mm. RANGE: Indiana and Illinois to Texas, Louisiana, and Tennessee.

Male glossy light brownish above, female a little darker generally, black-brown on broad middle area of abdomen. Found on pine tree, under a sign, at light, and in cavity of a sweet gum tree.

17a Paired specialized areas consisting of weak ridges which have tufts of hairs marking short more strongly angulated faces.....18

17b Paired specialized areas consisting of strong fuzzy ridges, portions of which overhang a concave area of the median segment. Fig. 71.
.............*Parcoblatta divisa* (S. & Z.) Southern wood cockroach

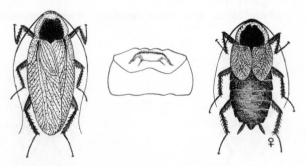

Figure 71

LENGTH: 12.7-17.8 mm. RANGE: Pennsylvania to Louisiana.

Male glossy light brownish above, central portion of pronotum darker, female a little darker, sometimes with tegmina reaching beyond end of abdomen. Found mostly under signs on trees; a few in molasses traps, or at lights.

P. pennsylvanica (De Geer) which occurs from Quebec to Texas and Georgia, is very similar to *divisa* but the male has both the median and first abdominal segments modified with overhanging ridges. Females average larger, are more solidly colored, and have the side margins of the pronotum more contrastingly pale than *divisa*. It is attracted to molasses jars in forested areas, and flies to lights. Sometimes becomes a pest in houses.

18a Male with tegmina markedly broader than pronotum; cerci with inner angles of segments 6-9 briefly, acutely produced (B). Fig. 72. ....*Parcoblatta uhleriana* (Saussure) Uhler's wood cockroach

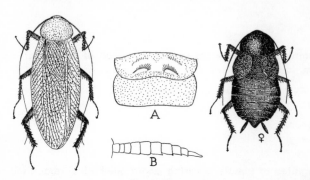

Figure 72

LENGTH: 9.8-16.5 mm. RANGE: Massachusetts and Michigan to Iowa and Florida.

Male glossy light brownish above, female shining blackish with reduced, separated tegmina. Specialized abdominal segments of male as in "A." Found under cover in wooded areas. Females common in molasses traps. Males common at lights.

18b Male with tegmina little broader than pronotum; cerci with all segments simple (B). Fig. 73...................................
.......*Parcoblatta fulvescens* (S. and Z.) Fulvous wood cockroach

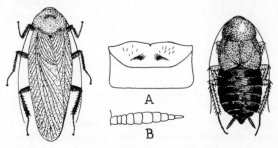

Figure 73

LENGTH: 10.8-16.5 mm. RANGE: Long Island, New York, to Florida Keys, Texas, Kansas, and Iowa.

Male glossy light brownish above, female orange-brown above with abdomen darker. Fairly similar to *P. uhleriana* but here the male is more slender and the tegmina of the female are much larger. Specialized abdominal segments of male as in "A." Fairly common in dry sandy areas, under cover as in open pine woods. Attracted to molasses and lights.

19a Tegmina of female covering most or all of abdomen; male 12.2-18 mm. in length..20

19b Tegmina of female covering about one-half of abdomen; male 17.5-21.5 mm. in length. Fig. 74....................................
................*Parcoblatta lata* (Brunner) Broad wood cockroach

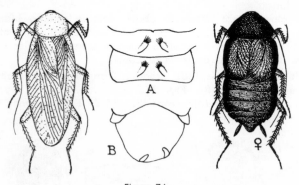

Figure 74

LENGTH: 15.7-22 mm. RANGE: Delaware and Maryland to Missouri and Texas.

Male glossy light brownish above, female much broader, light orange-brown, abdomen darker. Male subgenital plate as shown (B) and with specialized areas of median and first abdominal segments (A) weak. Found mostly under signs on pine trees and under loose bark.

20a Tegmina of female shorter than abdomen. Fig. 75.............
..............*Parcoblatta notha* (R. & H.) Arizona wood cockroach

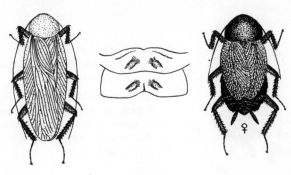

Figure 75

LENGTH: 14-18 mm. RANGE: Arizona; Prescott to Baboquivari and
Huachuca Mts., and Safford.

Male glossy light brownish above, female a little darker. Found
under bark in wooded areas. Occasional in houses. Attracted to
molasses.

20b Tegmina of female longer than abdomen. Fig. 76..............
..........*Parcoblatta caudelli* Hebard Caudell's wood cockroach

LENGTH: 10.7-16 mm. RANGE:
Virginia and District of Columbia to Indiana and Texas.

Sexes similar, glossy light brownish above. Very little is known
of the habits of this cockroach.

(A) shows the median and first
abdominal segments of the male.
(B) shows the male subgenital
plate.

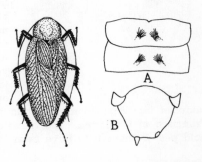

Figure 76

45

21a Body above blackish with numerous light yellowish markings; tegmina much reduced. Fig. 77.....................................
.............*Neostylopyga rhombifolia* (Stoll) Harlequin cockroach

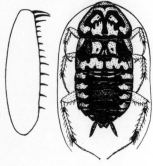

LENGTH: 20-25.3 mm. RANGE: Mainly tropical, Asia, Mexico, Arizona (Tucson, Nogales).

This handsome cockroach is a household pest in Asia and western Mexico. Front femur shown. The ancestral home of this insect was probably the Indo-Malayan region.

Figure 77

21b Body lacking intricate color pattern of above; tegmina either reduced, absent, or entire.....................................22

22a Pronotum and tegmina marked with large brown spots; limbs very slender. Fig. 78...
........*Supella supellectilium* (Serville) Brown-banded cockroach

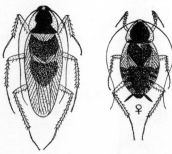

LENGTH: 10-12 mm. RANGE: Tropical regions of the world. Florida, Arizona, and California.

Glossy light yellowish-brown with large darker brown areas on tegmina and pronotum. Variable. Female broader with tegmina not quite covering abdomen. Wing with small intercalated triangle and costal veins thickened at ends. From 1903 to at least 1917 this was known only from Florida in the U. S. Introduced into Arizona in 1933 and now present as far North as San Francisco in California. The ancestral home of this important household pest is thought to have been in Africa.

Figure 78

22b Not as described above.....................................23

23a Rather small and light colored with two dark stripes on pronotum. Fig. 79...........*Blatella germanica* (Linnaeus) German cockroach

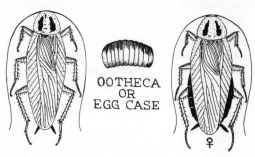

Figure 79

LENGTH: 10.5-12.8 mm. RANGE: Cosmopolitan.

Pale brownish-yellow, stripes on pronotum dark brown. Female similar except a little larger and broader than male. An important household pest which prefers the bathroom and kitchen. Common in commercial establishments. Leaves a "roachy" odor. The ancestral home of this insect is now believed to have been northeastern Africa, from which it was disseminated by commerce in early times.

B. vaga Hebard the Field cockroach is similar to the German cockroach except for its more olive general coloration and black face. It is common in southern Arizona in irrigated sections. In very dry weather it sometimes becomes a nuisance around plumbing fixtures. Remove vegetation around house to control.

23b Not as described above.....................................24

24a Brown, pronotum and tegmina with broad cream border; styles of male (A) highly specialized. Fig. 80...........................
***Pseudomops septentrionalis* Hebard Pale-bordered field cockroach**

LENGTH: 9-15 mm. RANGE: Texas, Mexico.

Glossy russet to brownish-black with pale borders. This elegant insect is most often found on the foliage of heavy weeds and about flowers. Also occurs in ground litter. The male styles (A) are shown as they appear from directly behind the cockroach.

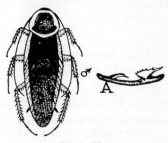

Figure 80

24b Not colored as above; styles of male not as shown above......25

25a Length more than 10 mm......................................26

25b Length less than 10 mm.; pale, pronotum with small dark pattern; tegmina not completely covering abdomen. Fig. 81..............
............*Cariblatta lutea* (S. and Z) Small yellow cockroach

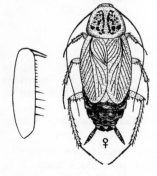

LENGTH: 5.8-9.5 mm. RANGE: Roanoak Island, North Carolina to Louisiana and Florida.

Pale buff, pronotum ornamented with brown. Sexes similar in general appearance. Common in winter and spring under cover on ground, especially where dry and sandy. Occasionally on foliage of brush.

Figure 81

C. *lutea minima* Hebard the Least yellow cockroach, of southern Florida and the Keys, averages a little smaller, is paler, and has the tegmina, especially of the male, a little shorter. The wings are vestigal and the produced portion of the male subgenital plate (between styles) is about as long as wide (three times wider than long in the typical form). Both forms occur in similar situations.

26a Front femur with many spines on ventral margin plus one or more at tip 27

26b Front femur with one or a few spines on ventral margin plus one or more at tip..34

27a Length 14 mm. or less; male with styles of subgenital plate terminal, heavy, and asymmetrical (A); female with tegmina reduced, superficially resembling a female *Parcoblatta*. Fig. 82............
........................*Symploce lita* Hebard Smooth cockroach

LENGTH: 11-14 mm. RANGE: Florida and Mexico.

Glossy light brownish. The discoidal veins of male tegmina and wings conspicuously branched, and the sixth dorsal abdominal segment bears a hairy sculptured median area. A household pest in the tropics.

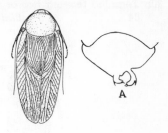

Figure 82

27b Length 18 mm. or more; male with styles of subgenital plate slender, elongate, equal, and symmetrical; female not resembling a Parcoblatta **28**

28a Tegmina much reduced, exposing most of abdomen...........**29**

28b Tegmina covering most or all of abdomen, not much reduced....**30**

29a Tegmina small, widely separated scales which are distinctly longer than wide; length less than 25 mm...........................**30**

29b Tegmina fairly large, wider than long; length 30 mm. or more. Fig. 83...........*Eurycotis floridana* **(Walker) Stinking cockroach**

LENGTH: 30-39.5 mm. RANGE: Mississippi and Georgia to Florida Keys.

Glossy claret-brown to blackish, more or less paler at sides. The tegmina are much too short to reach the median segment. Common under cover, in cavities in limestone, under bark, etc. Adults of both sexes are able to emit a repulsive smelling greasy liquid. These are the champion "stinkers" among our U. S. insects. (A) shows tip of male abdomen.

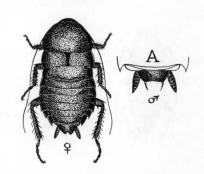

Figure 83

E. lixa Rehn, known from Key West, Florida, is similar but black and has small narrow tegmina, twice as long as wide.

30a Tegmina longer than abdomen..............................**31**

30b Tegmina leaving two or more segments of abdomen exposed. Fig. 84 . . . . *Blatta orientalis* Linnaeus Oriental cockroach

Figure 84

LENGTH: 18-24 mm. RANGE: Cosmopolitan.

Shining blackish-brown. Gregarious. This important household pest prefers warm moist locations. It moves outside in warm weather. The original home of this insect is believed to have been .in North Africa, from whence it was carried in ships in ancient times.

31a Color above entirely shining blackish-brown. Fig. 85 . . . . *Periplaneta fuliginosa* (Serville) Smoky brown cockroach

LENGTH: 24.5-32.5 mm. RANGE: Texas to northern Florida.

Common out of doors, under cover such as signs on trees, especially about towns. Common on wharves at night at Jacksonville. Probably East Asian in origin as its closest relative is a native there.

Figure 85

31b Color above not entirely shining blackish-brown 32

32a Tegmina reddish-brown with conspicuous yellow stripes at sides in front; pronotum yellowish with base and one or two large, clear-cut spots blackish-brown. Fig. 86.................................
........*Periplaneta australasiae* (Fabricius) **Australian cockroach**

LENGTH: 23-29 mm. RANGE: Tropical. Florida.

This handsome cockroach is a house and garden pest in much of its range. Found in Florida under signs in trees, in pitcher plant *Sarracenia*, and in houses. Several of our cockroaches which are widespread pests were named in the early days of entomology and designated as "Oriental," "German," "American," "Australian," etc., on the basis of what were then thought to be the homes of these insects. More recently extensive field work in many parts of the world has shown that many of the old ideas were incorrect. The ancestral home of *P. australasiae* was almost certainly tropical Africa.

Figure 86

32b Tegmina entirely reddish-brown; pronotum with markings less sharply defined 33

33a Male with last abdominal segment deeply notched at middle, and posterior half thin, clear, and translucent, projecting back as a hood over the ventral plate (Fig. 88A); median segment unspecialized. Fig. 87...
..........*Periplaneta americana* (Linnaeus) **American cockroach**

LENGTH: 27.8-34.2 mm. RANGE: Cosmopolitan. In eastern U. S. north to New York City.

Tegmina glossy reddish-brown, paler toward sides and tips. Pronotum paler with base and more or less distinct central markings darker. An important household pest, also common about wharves, in sewers, etc. They prefer warm, moist locations. In warm weather they move to outbuildings, under porches, etc. Originally probably from tropical Africa.

Figure 87

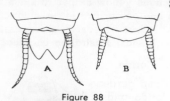

Figure 88

33b Male with last dorsal abdominal segment entirely sclerotized and opaque, only slightly notched at tip (Fig. 88B); median segment with a broad shallow median channel with a tuft of silky hairs. Fig. 89......
..........*Periplaneta brunnea* Burmeister Southern brown cockroach

Figure 89

LENGTH: 25.1-33 mm. RANGE: Circumtropical, Florida and Texas.

Tegmina glossy reddish-brown, paler toward sides and tips. Pronotum with darker central markings more diffuse than those of *P. americana*. Female slightly smaller and less elongate than *P. americana*, with the cerci shorter and the last dorsal abdominal segment much less deeply notched. A household pest, also found under cover out of doors. Probably tropical African in origin.

34a Tegmina long; front femur as in "A." Fig. 90...................
...........*Blaberus craniifer* Burmeister Death's head cockroach

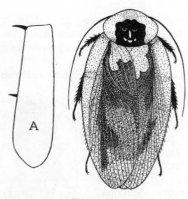

Figure 90

LENGTH: 42.7-58.8 mm. RANGE: Tropical America. Key West, Florida.

Pronotum dull yellowish with central black-brown marking somewhat suggesting a "death's head." Tegmina brown, variably yellowish at base, in middle, and along costal margin. Rarely the facelike pronotal marking is indistinct. Found under boards and other cover. Our largest cockroach.

34b Tegmina reduced, covering median segment at sides; front femur shown. Fig. 91...
..........*Hemiblabera tenebricosa* R. & H. Broad keys cockroach

LENGTH: 37-39 mm. RANGE: Florida Keys, Dade County, and West Indies.

Glossy claret-brown, paler at sides. A large, very broad cockroach, the habits of which appear to be little known at present.

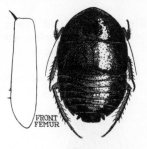

Figure 91

35a General color not pale green....................................36
35b General color pale green. Fig. 92...............................
................Panchlora nivea (Linnaeus) Cuban cockroach

LENGTH: 12.2-18 mm. RANGE: Greater Antilles, Mexico, and Central America. Brownsville, Texas.

Pale translucent Paris green, occiput, pronotum, and front half of tegmina with a pale submarginal line. Tegmen often with a tiny brown spot about one third from tip (shown). Sexes similar. Often brought to our cities in bunches of bananas, but established only in the Brownsville area.

Figure 92

36a Large (38-53 mm.); hind margins of middle and hind femora each with one short apical spine only, front femur as shown (B); tip of male abdomen as shown (A). Fig. 93.........................
............Leucophaea maderae (Fabricius) Madeira cockroach

LENGTH: 38-53 mm. RANGE: West Africa, South and Central America, West Indies, Java, Hawaii, Philippines, and Fiji. Eastern U. S.

Glossy pale brown with darker markings. The male subgenital plate (SGP) is shown. Probably originated in West Africa. Ovoviviparous. It stridulates by rubbing the pronotum and tegmina together. It has an offensive odor when handled.

Figure 93

53

36b Not as above..**37**

37a Tegmina light brown, pronotum dark brown, pale at front; basal fourth of tegmina with numerous small round pits, many in double rows; front femur bordered with stiff hairs and a single stout spine as shown. Fig. 94..
..........*Pycnoscelis surinamensis* (Linnaeus) Surinam cockroach

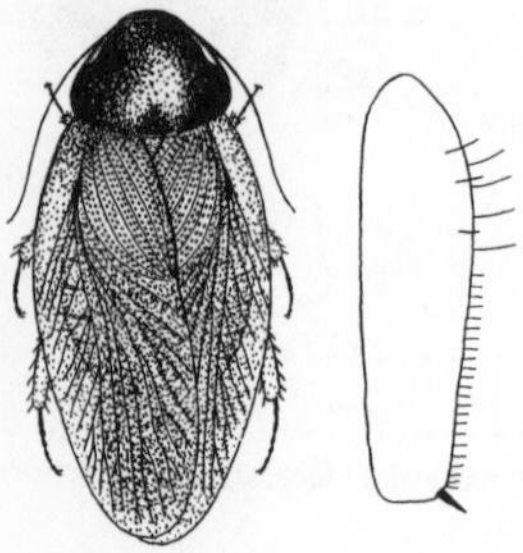

LENGTH: 16.3-23 mm. RANGE: Circumtropical, Texas to Florida. Commonly adventive elsewhere.

Shining, sexes similar (but males usually not found). Taken under cover, in litter and debris. Occasionally establishes itself in heated areas such as greenhouses in more northerly localities. Probably originated in Asia. This species is both parthenogenetic and ovoviviparous.

Figure 94

37b Not as characterized above................................**38**

38a Pronotum and tegmina pale brownish; pronotum with dark central blotch, with intricate pale markings, and a dark band at each side. Basal third of discoidal vein pigmented brown. Fig. 95..........
..............*Nauphoeta cinerea* Saussure Cinereous cockroach

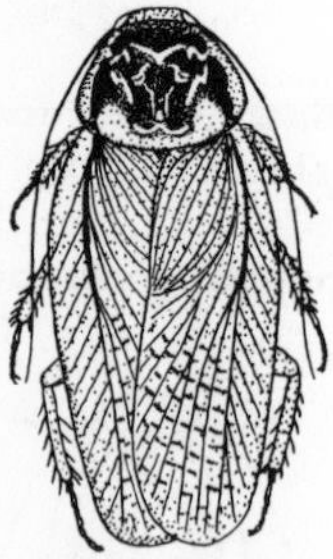

LENGTH: 23-24 mm. RANGE: Tropical. Florida.

Sexes similar. The ancestral home of this pretty insect was probably in East Africa. It is found especially in feed storage and manufacturing plants. It is ovoviviparous.

Figure 95

38b Not as described above.....................................**39**

39a Size quite small, 4.8-6.5 mm................................**40**

39b Size larger...**41**

40a Tegmina divided obliquely into an opaque, hairy, outer basal portion and with the remainder very thin; pronotum uniform in coloration. Fig. 96...
..........*Holocompsa nitidula* (Fabricius) Small hairy cockroach

LENGTH: 4.8-6.2 mm. RANGE: American tropics, Key West, Florida.

Male pronotum and base of tegmina black, feebly greenish, remainder of tegmina clear, almost colorless. Female similar except pronotum yellowish to orange-brownish, basal portion of tegmina greener, and remainder of tegmina faintly brownish. Uncommon. Found in folds of burlap in a fruit store and between boards in a wood shed.

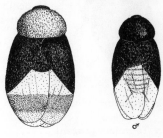

Figure 96

40b Tegmina not obliquely divided into an opaque, hairy half and a thin half; pronotum with a darker central area. Fig. 97............
...............*Compsodes schwarzi* (Caudell) Schwarz' cockroach

LENGTH: 5.3-6.5 mm. RANGE: Santa Rita and Catalina Mts., Arizona, Brownsville area, Texas, Sinaloa, and Lower California.

Glossy, pronotum pale brownish, central area a little darker; tegmina pale brownish, sides of tegmina and pronotum transparent. Male subgenital plate shown. A conspicuous diagonal vein on each tegmen.

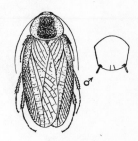

Figure 97

C. cucullatus (S. & Z), the Small hooded roach, is a diminutive pale brownish species which has the pronotum hoodlike in front, concealing the head. It measures 3.5 mm. and is a native of Guatemala. Specimens came to light at Paradise Key, Florida.

41a Pronotum with front edge greatly thickened and projecting slightly over the head as a hood; tegmina absent in both sexes. Fig. 98..
......*Cryptocercus punctulatus* Scudder Brown hooded cockroach

LENGTH: 23.5-29 mm. RANGE: New York to Georgia and Washington to California.

Shining blackish-brown. Sexes similar. The ocelli are absent. Front femur shown. Found in wet rotten wood of various trees.

Figure 98

41b Pronotum with front edge not greatly thickened; tegmina present or absent 42
42a Tegmina present 43
42b Tegmina absent 44
43a Cerci segmented, evenly tapering; middle and hind femora each with a long heavy spine at tip; front tibia with nine spines at tip; middle and hind tibiae each with six spines at tip (*Arenivaga*)..44
43b Cerci not segmented, not evenly tapering; middle and hind femora very hairy but with no spines; front tibia with seven spines at tip (A). Fig. 99...
.....*Eremoblatta subdiaphana* (Scudder) Hairy desert cockroach

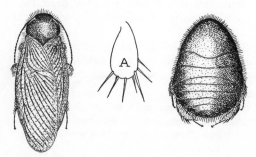

Figure 99

LENGTH: 8.7-12.3 mm. RANGE: Deserts of California, Arizona, Nevada, and New Mexico.

Glossy brown above, male with front margin of pronotum pale; female wingless, densely clothed with yellowish hairs. Mostly taken at lights.

44a Length of male twice greatest width; Florida species. Fig. 100...
............*Arenivaga floridensis* Caudell Florida sand cockroach

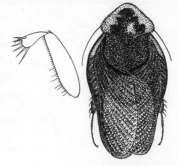

LENGTH: 13-17 mm. RANGE: Florida.

Male dark brown except pale around front of pronotum. Very broad. Female wingless, broadly oval, blackish except orange-brown around front of pronotum. Found on ground under cabbage palmetto leaves, flying low over sandy road, and taken in malt trap.

Figure 100

44b Length of male more than twice greatest width; species occurring in southwest. Fig. 101...
............*Arenivaga bolliana* (Saussure) Boll's sand cockroach

LENGTH: 15.7-23.8 mm. RANGE: Texas.

Female black except pronotum usually brown at front; male brown with surface of concealed genital plate shagreened. The front femur is hairy at base, followed on ventral margin by a closely set row of stiff, almost spine-like hairs; body hairy. Found in wood rat (*Neotoma*) nests. Males at lights.

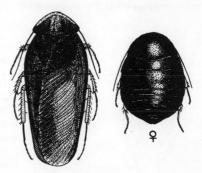

Figure 101

Several additional species of *Arenivaga* are known from southwestern desert areas. They are common about sand dunes and may be taken at night by sweeping them with the hand from their little burrows which are easily recognized as serpentine ridges, like miniature mole runs.

45a Front femur with 3 spines at middle on ventral margin, and two spines at tip. Fig. 102...
............*Ectobius pallidus* (Olivier) Spotted Mediterranean cockroach

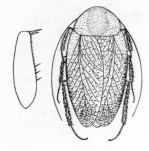

LENGTH: 8-9 mm. RANGE: Massachusetts. Lapland to North Africa.

Glossy light yellowish-brown with numerous darker specks. The wing has a conspicuous intercalated triangle. This insect appears to have become established in Massachusetts about 1951 and it occurs in and about houses and under cover outside.

Figure 102

45b Front femur with a fringe of stiff hairs and one spine at tip....46

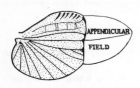

46a Oval, convex; tegmina with relatively few veins; appendicular field of wing very large (Fig. 103); subgenital plate of male (A) with styles small as shown. Fig. 104.....................*Plectoptera poeyi* (Saussure) Florida beetle cockroach

Figure 103

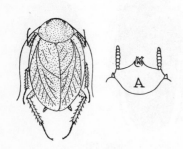

LENGTH: 5-5.7 mm. RANGE: Key West, Florida, and Cuba.

Glossy, uniformly translucent yellowish. Shaped like a Hydrophilid beetle. This small insect has been beaten from foliage, especially of holly *(Ilex cassine)*. The tarsal claws are delicate, each one armed with two microscopic teeth at middle, inside.

Figure 104

46b More elongate, depressed; tegmina with numerous veins; intercalated triangle of wing not as large; subgenital plate of male with styles larger, concave, as shown. Fig. 105....................
......*Chorisoneura texansis* S. & Z. Small yellow Texas cockroach

LENGTH: 7.3-8.4 mm. RANGE: Texas to North Carolina and Florida.

Glossy translucent yellowish, sides of pronotum and tegmina transparent. Found under dead leaves in oak forest and beaten from foliage of oak and bayberry. Occasional at light.

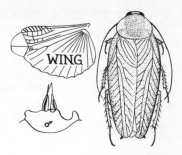

Figure 105

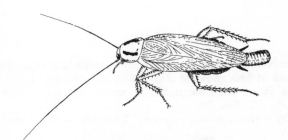

ROCK CRAWLERS

RYLLOBLATTIDS or rock crawlers are very remarkable insects which are of great interest to scientists. The group is known to occur only in Japan, Siberia, northwestern U.S., and western Canada. Rock crawlers are found under rocks, especially at the edges of snowfields, in the eternal darkness of ice caves, in talus slopes, in rotten logs, and crawling around on snow. They are active at temperatures of —2.5° to 11.3° C., become lethargic at lower temperatures, and are fatally injured by the heat at 20.5° to 26° C. Cultures are maintained at around 0° to 5° C. These predaceous insects probably require several years to reach maturity. Study of both internal and external anatomy indicates that these "living fossil" insects are very primitive in themselves, and that they are rather closely related to both crickets and roaches (as the name "Grylloblattid" implies), and perhaps to termites as well. Our species are yellow-brownish to grayish in color. They all have five-segmented tarsi, and differ in various structural details. Last instar nymphs are difficult to tell from adults.

59

KEY TO ROCK CRAWLERS (GRYLLOBLATTIDS)

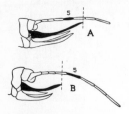

Figure 106

1a Dorsal valve of ovipositor reaching to middle of cercus or at least to apical half of fifth segment (A); antenna of adult composed of 36 segments or less, of nymph not more than 30. Fig. 106.............2

1b Dorsal valve of ovipositor not reaching to middle of cercus, or beyond base of fifth segment (Fig. 106B); antenna of adult often composed of 39 or more segments, of nearly mature nymph usually more than 30. Fig. 107...
......*Grylloblatta sculleni* Gurney Scullen's Cascade rock crawler

Figure 107

Figure 108

LENGTH: 23 mm. RANGE: Cascade Mts., Oregon, vicinity of Three Sisters.

Light amber, paler beneath, setae, tibial spines, and tarsal claws brown. Compound eye black. Found in moist broken rock at lower margin of melting snow at about 6,600 feet. Nymphs have up to 32 segments in antennae.

G. barberi Caudell Barber's rock crawler (Fig. 108), known only from nymphs, is similar to *sculleni* except antennae of nymphs with 36-40 segments, and color grayish. It was found in the Feather River region of northern California.

2a Apical half of male supra-anal plate symmetrical or nearly so. Fig. 109A, 110..........*Grylloblatta campodeiformis* Walker Northern rock crawler

Figure 109

LENGTH: 16.5-30 mm. RANGE: Montana and Wyoming to Alberta and British Columbia.

Amber yellowish. Found in rotten logs, on and near snow, about margins of glacial bogs, and among rocks near snow. 3,500 to 10,000 feet. Antennae usually with fewer than 30 segments.

Figure 110

G. c. occidentalis Silvestri occurs in British Columbia and Washington (Mt. Baker). It is similar to the above except antenna with 32-36 segments.

2b Apical half of male supra-anal plate asymmetrical (B). Fig. 109...3

3a Stylus of male attached laterally Fig. 112 (A); male supra-anal plate with left hind corner conspicuously developed, lobe-like Fig. 112 (C); segments of cerci comparatively short. Fig. 111. .... *Gryllo-blatta rothi* Gurney Roth's Cascade rock crawler

Figure 111

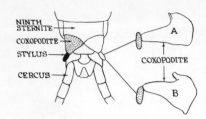

LENGTH: 14.5-16 mm. RANGE: Crater Lake and Happy Valley, 15-20 miles south of Sisters, Oregon.

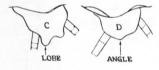

Figure 112

Yellowish to brownish. Found under stone at 6,500 feet, and in middle of rotten log at 6,400 feet.

3b Stylus of male attached at end Fig. 112 (B); male supra-anal plate with left hind corner angular, not lobelike Fig. 112 (D); segments of cerci comparatively long and slender, especially those near tip. Fig. 113. . *Grylloblatta bifratrilecta* Gurney Sonora Pass rock crawler

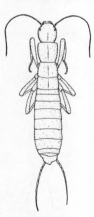

LENGTH: 17-20 mm. RANGE: Sonora Pass area, California.

Yellowish. Found from 8,600 to 10,000 feet. Among rocks, especially near or protruding from snow, and found crawling on snow. Numerous specimens were taken in July. Summer and Fall are good times to collect rock crawlers.

Figure 113

TERMITES

ERMITE fossils tell us that these wood-eating social insects have been present since ancient times. A few kinds have footholds in southern Canada, but the majority of the 1500 or so known species are tropical. They do $40,000,000.00 or more damage yearly in the U.S.

Winged termites leave the termitarium on colonizing flights which end when they break off their wings across special weak sutures and pair off in little chambers which they gnaw or dig. Males are recognized by their narrower and more numerous apical sternites, and sub-anal styles (Fig. 114).

Kings and queens of three distinct types are found. First form reproductives develop from winged individuals which pair off and found new colonies. They have wing stubs. Second form kings and queens possess only short wing pads.

They develop from nymphs which had short wing pads. They can reproduce their second form type but no winged forms . Third form kings and queens have no trace of wings or wing pads.

Wood thoroughly treated with Copper sulphate, Zinc chloride, Creosote, Pentachlorophenol, or Copper naphthenate is pretty well protected from termite attacks.

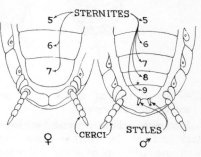

Figure 114

KEY TO TERMITES

1a Wing with conspicuous oblique cross-veins between "radial sector" veins (A); head with no fontanelle. Fig. 115 2

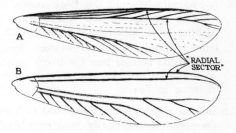

Figure 115

1b Wing with no conspicuous oblique cross veins between "radial sector" veins (B); head with fontanelle often present. Fig. 115...12

2a Soldier with antenna composed of more than 20 segments and with cerci prominent and composed of 3 or more segments; ocelli absent (Family: *Hodotermitidae*). Fig. 116..............*Zootermopsis angusticollis* (Hagen) Light-colored Pacific coast damp-wood termite

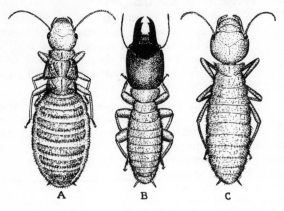

Figure 116

LENGTH: to tips of wings 23-26 mm. RANGE: British Columbia to southern California.

Brownish, wings grayish, soldier (B) with head reddish becoming black in front. No worker caste. First form queens (A) bearing wing stubs are only moderately enlarged. Most of the individuals seen when a colony is opened are pale colored nymphs (C) of various stages and, in season, winged reproductives awaiting the proper time to swarm out. Large worker-like forms without wing pads are either potential soldiers or wingless third form reproductives. These termites mine moist wood in the forest and also damage buildings, utility poles, fence posts, etc.

Z. *nevadensis* (Hagen) the Dark-colored Pacific coast damp-wood termite is similar to the above except darker colored, averaging smaller, and occurring a little farther to the East.

Z. *laticeps* (Banks) the Southwestern damp-wood termite is again similar but the soldier has the head broader and the pronotum pointed at the sides in front. It mines dying cottonwoods from southeastern Arizona to Texas.

2b Soldier with antenna composed of fewer than 20 segments and with cerci small, indistinctly segmented; ocelli usually present (Family: *Kalotermitidae*) 3

3a Front wing with median vein running about midway between radial sector and cubitus (A); soldier with third segment of antenna more or less conspicuously specialized and longer than adjoining segments. Fig. 117...4

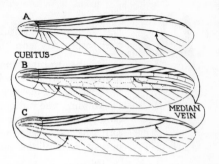

Figure 117

3b Front wing with median vein running much closer to radial sector (B) or uniting with it (C); soldier with third segment of antenna small. Fig. 117..9

4a Soldier with third segment of antenna as long as combined length of next 4 segments (Fig. 118A). Fig. 119.................*Procryptotermes hubbardi* (Banks) Light-colored western dry-wood termite

LENGTH: to tips of wings: 13 mm., soldier 6-8 mm. RANGE: Southeastern California, western Mexico, and Arizona.

Pale brownish-yellow, wing pale with yellowish veins, soldier with head brown, darker in front. Very destructive in houses, furniture, dead and living trees, etc. Colonizing flights occur at night between June

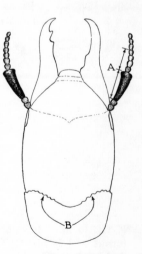

Figure 118

and December. Withstands rather high temperatures and rather dry conditions.

In the tropics some moisture-loving termites dig tunnels down as much as 80 feet into the ground to find water. Others heat their colonies with masses of rotting vegetation, or orient their high, narrow colony structures in a North-South direction so that only the narrow edge is presented to the sun at the hottest time of the day.

(B) of Fig. 118 draws attention to the dentate front margin of the pronotum.

Figure 119

4b Soldier with third segment of antenna shorter than combined length of next four segments...5

5a Soldier with third segment of antenna as long as combined length of next 3 segments. Fig. 120...................................
..*Kalotermes minor* Hagen Dark-colored western dry-wood termite

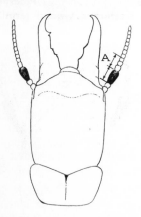

Figure 120

LENGTH: to tips of wings: 11-12 mm., soldier 8-10 mm. RANGE: California and Lower California to Arizona and Utah.
Reddish-brown, wings blackish, soldier dark reddish-brown, mandibles black, abdomen and legs lighter, as usual. This very destructive

termite attacks buildings, furniture, utility poles, piled lumber, living trees and shrubs, etc. Swarming occurs mostly from about September to November and takes place on hot sunshiny days. The wings are broken off by leverlike prying.

Some other kinds of termites lose their wings during flight and the wingless insects come tumbling down. In the tropics termites commonly destroy books, linoleum, wallpaper, and clothing.

5b Soldier with third segment much shorter than combined length of next three segments..6

6a Soldier with third segment of antenna about as long as combined length of next 2 segments; eye light-colored (A). Fig. 121........7

6b Soldier with third segment of antenna only slightly longer than fourth; eye black (B). Fig. 121B...............................
........................*Kalotermes jouteli* Banks   Joutel's termite

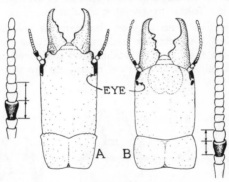

Figure 121

LENGTH: 10 mm. without wings, soldier 9-13 mm. RANGE: Southern Florida and the Keys, West Indies, and Mexico.

Yellowish, brighter on head, soldier head brown with black mandibles. Swarming occurs in late autumn. Reproductive individuals of all three forms have been found in colonies of this termite, none of them much enlarged. This termite requires much moisture and it has been noted as destructive in damp foundation timbers of buildings

Most termites are tropical. Some, like this, extend their range only into our southernmost areas.

7a Pronotum of soldier with fine teeth along front margin. Fig. 121A
....................*Kalotermes snyderi* Light   Snyder's termite

LENGTH: to tips of wings 11-12 mm., soldier 8-10 mm. RANGE: Florida to Virginia and Texas.

Brownish to yellowish, wings pale with brown marginal veins. Soldier head yellowish, pale brownish in front, mandibles black. Small flights occur at night in May and June and these swarming individuals often fly to lights. Attacks buildings, especially underpinning, utility poles, dead tree branches, and logs. Termites are able to digest wood with the aid of various micro-organisms in their digestive tracts. Different kinds of protozoa have evolved in various termite species.

7b Pronotum of soldier with front margin smooth...................8

8a Soldier with pronotum distinctly wider than head, and with mandibles about as long as width of head. Fig. 122A.................
Kalotermes approximatus Banks Dark southeastern dry-wood termite
LENGTH: to tips of wings: 11-12 mm., soldier 7-8 mm. RANGE: Northern Florida, Mississippi, Louisiana, and Virginia.

Pale brownish, soldier head yellowish, darker in front, mandibles black. Flights occur in daytime from August to October. Occasionally attacks buildings. Taken in sweet gum trunks.

From an objective point of view the termites' role in nature is the breaking down of the complex cellulose molecules into simpler substances which are then readily assimilated and used by other organisms. When the cellulose in question makes up the wood of our homes a conflict of interest arises.

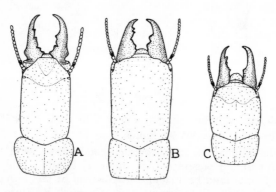

Figure 122

8b Soldier with pronotum about as wide as head, and with mandibles distinctly shorter than width of head. Fig. 122 B, C...............
..........*Kalotermes schwarzi* Banks Southern dry-wood termite
LENGTH: to tips of wings 15-16 mm., of body 8-9 mm., soldier 7-10 mm. RANGE: Florida and Cuba.

Pale brown, pronotum dark on hind corners. Soldier head brown, darker in front, mandibles black. Long and short-headed soldiers are found. Common and destructive in southern Florida in buildings, utility poles (including crossarms and insulator pegs), and in dead wood in nature. Colonizing flights occur in April and May.

When a reproductive or soldier dies or is removed from a termite colony, a nymph (now freed from the physiological restraint imposed by the inhibitory chemical or "social hormone" of the more specialized individual) develops in a few weeks to replace the casualty.

9a Head of soldier short, but little longer than wide, boxlike, and strongly excavated in front...**10**

9b Head decidedly longer than wide, more flattened, and not strongly excavated in front...**11**

10a Head of soldier rough in front. Fig. 123C................*Cryptotermes brevis* (Walker) **Tropical rough-headed power-post termite**

LENGTH: to tips of wings: 11 mm., soldier 3-3.5 mm. RANGE: Florida, West Indies, Mexico, Central and South America.

Brownish, soldier brownish with head darker in front and mandibles black. A common very destructive species in buildings and wooden objects or other cellulose materials in Florida. It not only destroys floors, furniture, etc., but annoys during the process by dropping little pellets from its workings. Swarming occurs in May and June. Moderately enlarged queens occur. This is one of the kinds of termites that can honeycomb wooden structures beyond repair, reducing the interior of a board to a powdery ruin while leaving a thin shell of nearly normal-appearing exterior.

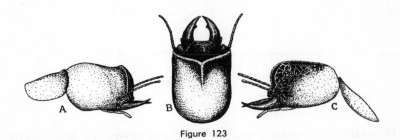

Figure 123

10b Head of soldier smooth. Fig. 123 A, B.........................
Cryptotermes cavifrons Banks **Smooth-headed powder-post termite**

LENGTH: to tips of wings: 8.5-9 mm., soldier 3.5-4.5 mm. RANGE: Southern Florida.

Dull pale brownish, wings clear, soldier brownish-yellow with reddish head, black in front. Swarms in April and May. Infests dry wood in nature, and sometimes attacks buildings. Large first form queens are common.

Calcaritermes nearcticus (Snyder) of Florida is small and similar in habits to the powder-post termites though preferring damper wood. The wing membrane is smoky and there are but few cross veins between the radial sector veins. The soldier's head is excavated in front and the front tibiae have spurs at the tips. Not destructive to man-made structures.

11a Soldier with antenna composed of 16-19 segments (A); body length 10-12 mm. Fig. 124A..
...*Neotermes castaneus* (Burmeister) Southern damp-wood termite
LENGTH: to tips of wings 15 mm., soldier 10-12 mm. RANGE: Florida and West Indies.

Pale brownish, soldier head darker in front with mandibles black. Colonizing flights from May to August. Infests logs, stumps, moist dead branches, etc. Attacks branches, trunks, and roots of trees including citrus and avocado.

An interesting thing to know about termite soldiers is that they may be of either sex. Though normally sterile, a few freak soldiers have been found which were able to lay eggs.

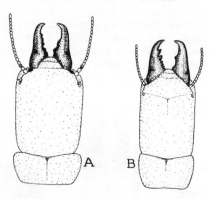

Figure 124

11b Soldier with antenna composed of 14 segments (B); body length 8-9 mm. Fig. 124B..
..*Paraneotermes simplicicornis* (Banks) Desert damp-wood termite
LENGTH: to tip of wings 11-12 mm. RANGE: Southern California and Lower California to Texas.

Brownish, soldier head yellowish, darkened in front, mandibles black. Swarming occurs in daytime from September to November in California. Essentially subterranean, they establish runways in the soil. They attack decayed wood from the soil, and attack utility poles, citrus trees, dead roots, buried wood, etc. Trees under attack die suddenly as they are cut entirely across, horizontally, below ground level. Shelter tubes are often constructed on stems of shrubs under attack.

12a Front wing scale distinctly larger than and reaching about to base of hind one; pronotum of soldier and worker flat, not elevated in front (Family: *Rhinotermitidae*)..............................13

12b Front wing scale about the same size as hind one and not reaching its base; pronotum of soldier and worker narrow and elevated in middle at front (Family: *Termitidae*).....................17

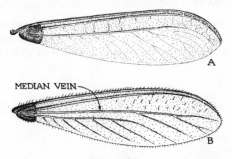

Figure 125

13a Wing with median vein absent (Fig. 125A); fontanelle very distinct; soldier (Fig. 126B) with head distinctly wider behind than at front and with labrum broadly rounded at apex. Fig. 126............
.....*Prorhinotermes simplex* (Hagen) Florida damp-wood termite

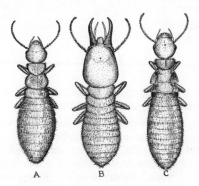

Figure 126

LENGTH: to tip of wings 9 mm., soldier 5.5-6.5 mm. RANGE: Coast and Keys of Dade and Broward Counties, Florida.

Pale brownish, soldier (B) yellowish, mandibles red-brown except base. Flights occur at about dusk from October through January. Occurs in logs in tidal mangrove swamps and in coastal pine woods. Attacks woodwork and wall paper. Builds shelter tubes up walls, etc. Third form queens (A) are common in colonies of this termite. This is the only non-subterranean member of the family *Rhinotermitidae*.

A flight of termites occuring inside or outside a building is good evidence and fair warning that an attack is under way.

13b Wing with median vein present (Fig. 125B); fontanelle often indistinct; soldier with head not much widened behind and with labrum very narrowly rounded at apex...............................**14**

14a Ocellus of winged form separated from eye by more than diameter of ocellus (Fig. 127A); soldier about 6.7 mm. in length. Fig. 127..
.....*Reticulitermes flavipes* (Kollar) Eastern subterranean termite

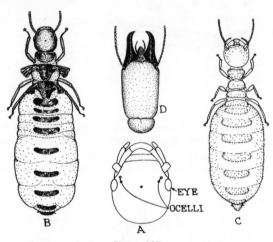

Figure 127

LENGTH: to tip of wings 10 mm., soldier 4.5 mm. RANGE: Ontario to Guatemala, West to Arizona and Utah.

Brown to blackish, wings grayish, soldier yellowish, head (D) darker in front. Very destructive to building foundations, utility poles, fence posts, stored materials, shrubs, flowers, and crops. Living trees are sometimes attacked. It often builds shelter tubes across concrete, etc., and up the trunks of trees. Swarms occur in daytime between February and November. Reticulitermes termites are subterranean and they dig tunnels to reach additional supplies of food.

(B) is a first form queen, (C) is a third form queen.

14b Ocellus of winged form closer to eye than diameter of ocellus; soldier smaller **15**

15a Species occurring in West; soldier (Fig. 128E) with head fully twice as long as wide. Fig. 128.....................................
....*Reticulitermes hesperus* Banks Western subterranean termite

LENGTH: to tip of wings 9 mm., soldier 5 mm. RANGE: British Columbia to Mexico, East to Idaho and Nevada.

Brown to blackish, wings dark; soldier head yellowish, mandibles black toward tips. Colonizing flights occur in daytime following the first Fall rains, and again from February to June. A very destructive species which requires damp earth as in cool, moist, and shaded areas, for its activities. Constructs covered runways across concrete foundations, etc., to get at wood. Often builds emergence towers.

In newly established colonies of many termite species the first soldiers are often dwarfs.

Queens of nearctic termites are able to walk about. The more extremely enlarged queens of some tropical termites are immobile and remain for many years in a special "royal cell," producing eggs at the prodigious rate of several thousand per day.

Heterotermes aureus (Snyder) (Fig. 128D) the Desert subterranean termite, occurs in Arizona, southern California, and Lower California. It mines dead cacti and other desert plants and also attacks wooden buildings, utility poles, and posts. Constructs small rounded shelter tubes over inedible objects to reach wood.

15b Species occurring in eastern U.S.............................16

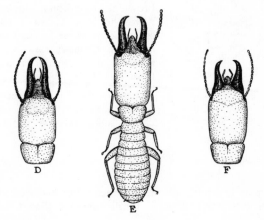

Figure 128

16a Tibiae of winged form blackish; soldier with gula less than twice as wide in front as at middle (Fig. 129B). Fig. 128F..............
.....*Reticulitermes tibialis* Banks Arid land subterranean termite

LENGTH: to tip of wings: 9.5-10 mm., soldier 3.5-4.5 mm. RANGE: California, Oregon, and Montana to Missouri, Arkansas, Texas, and Mexico.

Shining blackish, soldier head dull brownish-yellow, mandibles black toward tips. Requires open, sunny sites. Flights occur in daytime from March to December, the exact time depending upon local conditions. In areas where this and the similar *R. hesperus* (Fig. 128E) occur together the soldiers of *R. tibialis* (Fig. 128F) are markedly more pugnacious. A destructive species which prefers drier conditions than *R. hesperus*. Subterranean termites do a certain amount of good from mankind's point of view by aerating, turning, and fertilizing the soil.

16b Tibiae of winged form pale; soldier with gula fully twice as wide in front as at middle (A). Fig. 129....................*Reticulitermes virginicus* **Banks   Light southeastern subterranean termite**

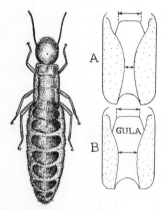

LENGTH: to tip of wings: 8 mm., soldier 3.5 mm. RANGE: Philadelphia to Florida, Texas, and Oklahoma.

Shining dark brown; soldier head brownish, mandibles black toward tips. A second form queen in shown. Colonizing flights occur in May and June and again in October and November. Six species of *Recticulitermes* are known from the U. S.

R. arenincola Goellner occurs in sandy places around Boston and Chicago, and has but little economic importance.

Figure 129

R. hageni Banks is small, like *R. virginicus*, but less common. It tolerates drier conditions than *R. virginicus* and flies from August to February.

17a Soldier caste present...**18**

17b Soldier caste absent. Fig. 130...............................
.... *Anoplotermes fumosus* Hagen   Soldierless termite

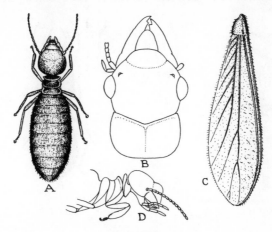

Figure 130

LENGTH: to tip of wings: 7.5 mm. RANGE: New Mexico, southwestern Texas, and northern Mexico.

Brown, wings dark, workers (A) a dirty gray color. Flights occur in August. The jaws of the reproductives (B) are exceptionally large. Often occurs with other termites in burrows in the ground, in cow chips, and in buried or partly buried logs. Not destructive to man-made structures.

This is an example of a termite that associates with other termites. Certain kinds of beetles and other insects are regularly found living in termite colonies.

18a Soldier with large conspicuous mandibles....................19

18b Soldier with head drawn out into a nose-like projection; mandibles degenerate, minute 23

19a Winged form 12 mm. or less in length, counting wings; soldier with mandibles shorter and curved throughout.....................20

19b Winged form 13 mm. or more in length, counting wings; soldier with mandibles rather long and nearly straight except incurved at tips. Fig. 131, 132A, C.....................................
Gnathamitermes tubiformans (Buckley) Tube-forming desert termite

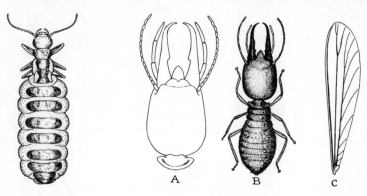

Figure 131   Figure 132

LENGTH: to tip of wings: 9 mm., soldier head 2.4 mm. Total length of soldier 5-5.5 mm. RANGE: Western Texas and Mexico.

Brown, wings brownish; soldier with abdomen gray, legs white, mandibles red-brown from beyond basal third to tips. Flights occur in daytime in spring or summer, after a rain. This common and destructive subterranean termite eats roots of grass and other vegetation. Working at night it constructs thin-walled tubes and spreads thin earth-like mortar over vegetation. Often found in cow chips.

Some tropical termites build interesting toadstool-shaped nests or pagodalike multiples. Others build intricate series of sloping rooflike structures many feet high on trees.

G. perplexus (Banks) (Fig. 132B) is a similar species which occurs from California to Nevada, Arizona, and Texas.

20a Mandible of soldier with inner tooth past middle..............21

20b Mandible of soldier with inner tooth at or before middle.......22

21a Mandible of soldier rather heavy, and with inner tooth well beyond middle. Fig. 133A..
..............*Amitermes snyderi* Light Snyder's desert termite

LENGTH: probably less than 12 mm. to tip of wings. RANGE: Mojave and Colorado deserts of California.

This little known termite occurs at elevations of 1,000-2,000 feet and is known to attack roots of desert trees and shrubs, partly buried pine and redwood, and fallen yucca branches. The

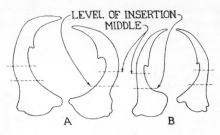

Figure 133

mandibles of the soldier are distinctive. Quite a lot remains to be learned about our desert termites. In several cases not all of the castes have yet been found.

21b Mandible of soldier rather slender and with inner tooth not as far beyond middle. Fig. 133B......................................
..........*Amitermes silvestrianus* Light Silvestri's desert termite

LENGTH: to tip of wings: under 12 mm., head of soldier 2.2 mm. RANGE: Coachella Valley, California.

Shining light brown, soldier yellowish with abdomen gray, legs whitish, and mandibles red-brown from basal third to tips.

The eight or more U. S. species of *Amitermes* are similar and best distinguished at present by the mandibles of the soldiers. *A. silvestrianus* works in wood in or on the ground, building thick brownish encrusting galleries over the wood. Not known to be of any particular economic importance.

22a Mandible of soldier with inner tooth narrow and abruptly projecting from both sides of its base. Fig. 134 B, C.................
........*Amitermes wheeleri* (Desneux) Wheeler's desert termite

LENGTH: to tip of wings less than 12 mm., soldier head 2 mm. RANGE: California, Nevada, Arizona, Texas, and Mexico.

Brownish; soldier yellowish, abdomen gray, legs pale yellowish, mandibles red-brown from basal third to tips. Destructive in buildings, utility poles, fence posts, etc. Found in cow chips, dead cacti, etc. Flies in later afternoon or at night in May, June, and October, often following rains. They will fly to lights.

In collecting termites it is well to open the colony and put 50 to 100 individuals including all obviously different castes in a vial of alcohol for later study. A rather detailed investigation of the colony then follows, with additional selected specimens being added to the sample. Small colonies may be collected in their entirety.

(A) shows a worker.

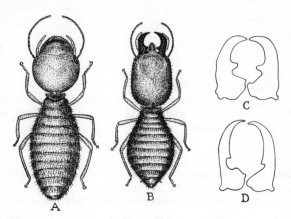

Figure 134

22b **Mandible of soldier with inner tooth very broad, sloping gradually from tip of mandible to its point and abruptly projecting only on side of base nearest head. Fig. 134D..........................**

..................*Amitermes minimus* Light Least desert termite

LENGTH: to tips of wings less than 12 mm., head of reproductive less than .95 mm. wide. RANGE: Texas, Arizona, Nevada, and California.

Blackish, soldier yellowish, abdomen grayish, mandibles red-brown from basal third to tips. A small destructive species of relatively wide range. It damages utility poles, etc., building hard crusty galleries over the buried wood. Flights were noted in July (Texas) and September (California).

Amitermes termites contain relatively few protozoa in their digestive tracts, and perhaps the large numbers of bacteria or special enzymes act here to enable them to utilize cellulose as food.

23a **Head of soldier conspicuously constricted at middle. Figs. 135, 136A, C** ....*Tenuiro-
stritermes tenuirostris* (Desneux) Southwestern nasutiform termite

LENGTH: to tip of wings: 18-20 mm., soldier (total length) 3 mm. RANGE: Arizona, Texas, and Mexico.

Pale brownish-yellow, front and abdominal segments browner; soldier head reddish-brown with mostly black beak. Flights occur about dusk during warm rains in June and July. Found under rocks and in ground.

T. cinereus (Buckley) is a similar form occurring in irrigated sections of southwestern Texas under stones or cow chips. They attack plants above ground at night.

SECOND FORM
QUEEN

Figure 135

Most nasutiform termite soldiers have only the chemical warfare syringes on their heads to battle with, but some tropical species have huge jaws as well. Some nasutes squirt a thin liquid which vaporizes quickly to a puff of poisonous gas. Others squirt a sticky entangling and repelling substance. This chemical warfare apparatus has an effective range against ants of up to ½ inch.

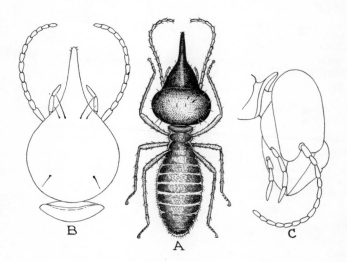

Figure 136

23b Head of soldier not constricted at middle. Fig. 136B.............
..*Nasutitermes corniger* (Motschulsky) Tropical nasutiform termite

LENGTH: 7 mm.; soldier head 1.5 mm. RANGE: South and Central America, Florida, and (?) Texas.

Reddish-brown; soldier brownish-yellow, head brown, legs pale yellowish. A common destructive tropical species. Specimens labelled "Texas" are in the national museum. In its tropical home country it builds large round termitaria in trees. It always maintains contact with the ground when attacking wood to assure an adequate moisture supply.

Raiding ants are deadly enemies of termites.

ZORAPTERA

 ORAPTERA is a small order of which only about 17 species have been named for the entire world. We have two species in the United States. Zorapterans are gregarious insects of small size. There are two very different forms or castes of each sex. One form is winged, moderately sclerotized, and has compound eyes and ocelli. The other form is wingless, feebly sclerotized, and completely blind. When wings are present they commonly break off, leaving stubs, after maturity is reached,

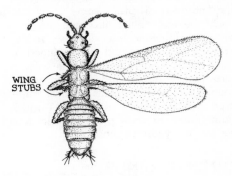

WING
STUBS

Figure 137

but the breaks do not occur at special sutures such as those found in termites. Zorapterans occur under bark and in rotting wood. *Zorotypus hubbardi* Caudell (both castes figured) is amber colored and about 2 mm. in length. It is sometimes common in colonies of *Reticulitermes flavipes* and *Prorhinotermes simplex*. Also taken in old sawdust piles. It occurs from Washington, D.C. to Florida and Texas. *Z. snyderi* Caudell is darker, more active, and has been found in Florida and Jamaica.

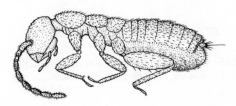

Figure 138

PYGMY GRASSHOPPERS

THE TETRIGIDAE are small grasshoppers of widespread occurrence, especially in moist habitats, but also in rather dry habitats, especially in the North. Adults are found throughout the year, emerging from "hibernation" for brief activity on sunny days in winter. In the North there may be only one annual brood, while in the South there may be two. In the laboratory 4 annual broods are possible. Females sometimes reproduce parthenogenetically, the offspring being mostly females in such cases. The eggs from one female may produce offspring some of which have the pronotum reaching past the end of the abdomen (long-winged), and others of which have the pronotum too short to reach the end of the abdomen (short-winged). Long and short-winged individuals of the same species may look rather different. The color patterns of pygmy grasshoppers are quite variable, and serve to camouflage them effectively. Occasional specimens are found which appear green because they are covered with a growth of algae. Tetrigid food consists of algae, rich organic muck, or other plant material found on the ground. Adults may live for two years or more.

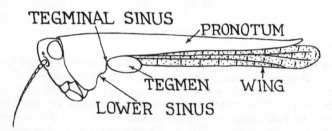

Figure 139

KEY TO PYGMY GRASSHOPPERS

1a Antenna 12-15-segmented; middle femur usually compressed and narrowly ridged above, not channeled above...................2

1b Antenna 19-22-segmented; middle femur with a broad, shallow channel above 13

2a Ridges of frontal costa weakly
    divergent below. Fig. 140A..4

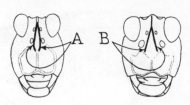

2b Ridges of frontal costa strongly
    divergent below. Fig. 140B..3

Figure 140

3a Pronotum arched in profile with median ridge rather high and nar-
    row, tegminal sinus usually weakly indicated; tegmina small,
    shorter than middle femur, usually more or less concealed under
    the pronotum. Fig. 141...
    Neotettix proavus Rehn and Hebard, Fork-faced pygmy grasshopper

LENGTH: 8.1-10.5 mm.
RANGE: Southeastern
states.

Brownish or grayish,
usually with black marks
on pronotum above teg-
mina. Neotenic. About
98% are brachypronotal
with tegmina much re-
duced and usually con-

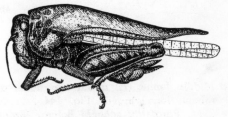

Figure 141

cealed. About 2% are macropronotal, with tegmina exposed and tegminal sinus moderately well developed. Adults May to September.
Overwinter as nymphs. Apparently single-brooded. Found in deciduous forest areas.

N. nullisinus (Hancock) occurs in the Brownsville and Houston, Texas
areas. It is similar to *proavus* but has the head narrower and the
middle femora proportionally shorter and broader.

3b Pronotum not arched in profile, with median ridge lower and not as
    narrow, tegminal sinus well developed; tegmina larger, as long as
    middle femur, exposed. Fig. 142................................
    ...*Neotettix femoratus* (Scudder) Short-legged pygmy grasshopper

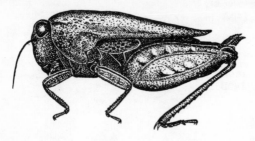

Figure 142

LENGTH: 7.2-10.5 mm. RANGE: Texas and Oklahoma to the Atlantic, Pennsylvania to Florida.

Brownish, grayish, or variously patterned. Structurally variable, many individuals being more or less robust and coarsely sculptured.

About 66% are short-winged (brachypronotal). Common in dry and wet habitats.

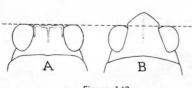

Figure 143

4a Fastigium distinctly produced forward of eyes when viewed from above. Fig. 143B 8

4b Fastigium about even with eyes when viewed from above. Fig. 143A. Middle femur often lobed beneath. 5

5a Middle femur (A) about two times as long as wide; form rather robust; long-winged. Fig. 144.....................................
......*Paratettix schochi* Bolivar Broad-legged pygmy grasshopper

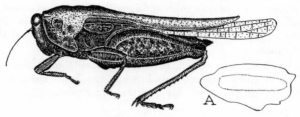

Figure 144

LENGTH: 8-12 mm. RANGE: Southern Arizona to Central America.

Brownish, sometimes with more or less distinct markings. Uncommon. Found in canyons of the Baboquivari Mountains. On sand in a wash below a deep pool about a mile above the dam in Brown Canyon at about 5,500 feet.

Some tropical tetrigids have bizarre outgrowths on their bodies which probably help to camouflage them.

5b Middle femur about three times as long as wide; form more slender; long-winged or short-winged.....................................6

6a Middle femur distinctly lobed above and below. Fig. 145........
......*Paratettix mexicanus* (Saussure) Mexican pygmy grasshopper

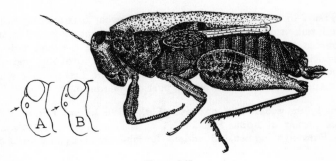

Figure 145

LENGTH: 7-12.3 mm. RANGE: Western and extreme southern U.S. to Panama.

Unusually variable in morphological details and color. The pronotum is usually marked at the sides above the tegmina with black patches. Usually grayish, brownish, or blackish, with small black markings. Found at elevations from —150 to +7,500 feet, along streams and in other damp areas. Long-winged or short-winged. Profile of face as in "B."

P. cuculatus (Burmeister) occurs from Washington and Oregon to Texas, east to the Atlantic, and north into Ontario. Similar to *mexicanus* (with which it sometimes occurs) except area between antennae more abruptly convex in profile "A," pronotum lower in profile, middle femur slenderer in proportion, and all specimens long-winged.

6b Middle femur sometimes irregular, but not distinctly lobed........7

7a Fastigium as wide as one eye or narrower (A); lateral ridges of pronotum weak at front. Fig. 146.................................
..........*Paratettix aztecus* (Saussure) Aztec pygmy grasshopper

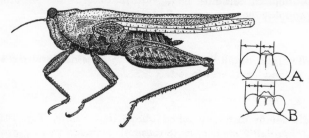

Figure 146

LENGTH: 9-15 mm. RANGE: West and southwest to Texas and Arkansas.

Dull red, gray, or brown, usually with numerous small markings. Sometimes with large pronotal blotch at front or a broad pale stripe. All specimens are long-winged. Common on gravelly margins of streams, often occurring with *P. mexicanus*. The fastigium is widest in specimens from the northwestern part of its range.

7b Fastigium wider than one eye (Fig. 146B); lateral ridges of pronotum strong at front. Fig. 147....................................
...*Paratettix rugosus* (Scudder) **Rough-backed pygmy grasshopper**

Figure 147

LENGTH: 9-14 mm. RANGE: Florida and Texas.

Brownish or blackish, sometimes marked with a large tan blotch or band. Middle femur as in "A." Many individuals have black markings at the sides of the pronotum, above the tegmina. All are long-winged. Pronotum granulose and tuberculate or rugose. Damp areas.

P. brevipennis (Hancock), from central Texas, occurs both long and short-winged. It has the hind femur very robust (2.1 to 2.4 :: 1), and the scapular area of the pronotum (above tegmen, on side) of about equal width throughout.

P. toltecus (Saussure), from Texas, occurs both long and short-winged. It has the hind femur as in *rugosus*, i.e. 2.6 to 2.8 :: 1, and the scapular area of the pronotum narrowed in front as in *rugosus*. It has the middle femur (B) proportionally shorter, the pronotal surface less roughened, and the lateral ridges of the pronotum sharper in front.

8a Pronotum strongly angularly produced forward at middle when viewed from above (Fig. 148P); median ridge of pronotum more or less compressed and strongly raised..........................9

8b Pronotum not strongly angularly produced forward at middle when viewed from above; median ridge low to moderately developed...10

9a Pronotum (P) with front margin at middle bluntly angled (A); fastigium (F) projecting in front of eye a distance equal to width of eye as seen from side, and with median ridge low. Fig. 148........
.........*Nomotettix parvus* Morse Low-ridged pygmy grasshopper

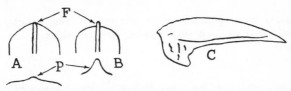

Figure 148

LENGTH: 6.3-9.2 mm. RANGE: Minnesota, Kansas, and Illinois.

Dull, dark-colored, sometimes variously marked or patterned. The face is more oblique in profile than the following species. Found in damp areas as along streams.

Tetrix sierrana Rehn and Grant, from the California Sierra, has the pronotum bluntly, angularly produced in front as viewed from above, and the median ridge of the pronotum is rather thin and high. *Nomotettix* does not occur west of the great plains.

9b Pronotum (P) with front margin acutely angled (B); fastigium (F) projecting in front of eye a distance equal to $\frac{1}{2}$ the width of eye or less, as seen from side, and with median ridge high. Fig. 149..
.......*Nomotettix cristatus* (Scudder) Crested pygmy grasshopper

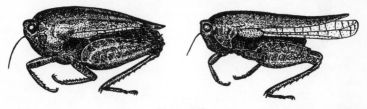

Figure 149

LENGTH: 6-11 mm. RANGE: Eastern half of U.S. and adjacent parts of southern Canada.

Dull, dark colored, sometimes variously marked or patterned. The face is less oblique in profile than *parvus*. Both long-winged (macropronotal) and short-winged (brachypronotal) individuals occur. Found in drier areas such as old fields, hillsides, openings in woods, etc.

The subspecies *compressus* Morse is found in dry or moist places from New York to northern Florida and Texas. It has the pronotum (Fig. 148, C) with the median ridge rather thin, high, and strongly arched.

The subspecies *floridanus* Hancock is found in dry or moist places from Florida to Virginia. In cross section the pronotum is rather rooflike, without as high and thin median ridge as *compressus*.

10a Pronotum with median ridge strong, surface usually distinctly higher along midline and sloping toward sides...............11

10b Pronotum with median ridge feeble, surface depressed, nearly flat. Fig. 150...*Tetrix arenosus* Burmeister Sanded pygmy grasshopper

LENGTH: 9-14 mm. RANGE: Texas to Ontario and east to the Atlantic.

Grayish, brownish, or blackish, sometimes with a large whitish area across widest part of pronotum. Rather variable. Florida specimens are slenderer and more roughly sculptured. Common in dry and moist areas.

Figure 150

11a Fastigium (Fig. 153A) with median ridge distinctly to sharply raised as seen from above, front rather strongly incurved just below fastigium as seen in profile.................................12

11b Fastigium (A) with median ridge low, scarcely at all raised as seen from above, front nearly straight to feebly incurved just below fastigium as seen in profile. Fig. 151.........................
.....*Tetrix subulata* (Linnaeus) Awl-shaped pygmy grasshopper

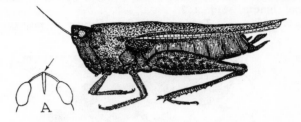

Figure 151

LENGTH: 7-13.5 mm. RANGE: Europe and boreal America, south to Pennsylvania in the East and to California and Arizona in the West.

Color often uniformly dark, varying to variously striped or spotted. Usually about 94% macropronotal, but in British Columbia as many as 40% may be brachypronotal. Common in moist meadows and about lake margins.

Color patterns of tetrigids are inherited in definite genetically controlled ways.

12a Fastigium strongly produced forward as seen in profile; hind femur proportionally less robust; first segment of hind tarsi rather long and slender. Fig. 152...
..........*Tetrix brunneri* (Bolivar) Brunner's pygmy grasshopper

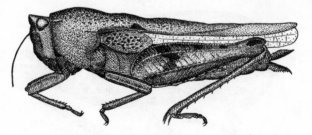

Figure 152

LENGTH: 7.5-10.9 mm. RANGE: Labrador to Alaska and South to Oregon, Utah, Colorado, Michigan, and New York.

Blackish to yellowish, often variously marked. Generally about 80% are brachypronotal, a few being intermediate in pronotal length, the rest macropronotal. Nearly all specimens from Utah and Colorado are brachypronotal. Adults April to August. Boreal. Locally sometimes moderately common in damp areas.

12b Fastigium moderately produced forward as seen in profile, hind femur proportionately more robust; first segment of hind tarsi of normal length. Fig. 153...
.....................*Tetrix ornata* Say Ornate pygmy grasshopper

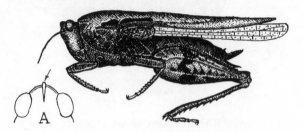

Figure 153

LENGTH: 7.5-12 mm. RANGE: Alberta to Ontario and south to Texas, New Mexico, Kansas, Mississippi, and North Carolina.

Blackish to brownish or variously marked. Either macropronotal or brachypronotal. Common in dry and moist areas. Adults may be found the year around but are most plentiful in fall and spring.

13a Body markedly swollen looking, robust; pronotum strongly arched in profile at front, not reaching past tip of abdomen, lateral ridges absent in front of shoulders. Fig. 154.........................
...............*Paxilla obesa* (Scudder) Obese pygmy grasshopper

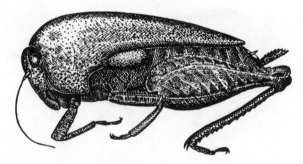

Figure 154

LENGTH: 9-14.5 mm. RANGE: Florida to South Carolina and Mississippi.
Dark brown with lighter patches. About 10% of specimens have the upper surface of the pronotum much lighter than the rest of the body.

Found locally in moist areas, often where pitcher plant and sundew grow.

Populations of tetrigids commonly include a variety of strikingly marked individuals whose genetically controlled distinctive color patterns occur in rather fixed frequencies. Such recurring color variants are referred to as chromatomorphs.

13b Body rather slender to only moderately swollen; pronotum low in profile, not strongly arched, often reaching past abdomen, lateral ridges present in front of shoulders..........................14

14a Tegmina and wings minute, concealed; hind margin of lateral lobe of pronotum lacking a distinct tegminal sinus. Fig. 155..........
....*Tettigidea empedonepia* Hubbell Neotenic pygmy grasshopper

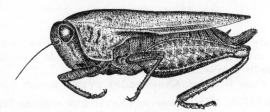

Figure 155

LENGTH: 8.8-12 mm. RANGE: Northern Florida.

Yellowish, reddish, or grayish-brown, markings inconspicuous. Neotenic, the antennal segments appear to number only 19 and the wings do not develop normally. This remarkable, apparently relict species has been taken only in Torreya Ravine, Camp Torreya, Liberty County.

Tetrigids have been used successfully as laboratory animals in the study of genetics.

14b Tegmina and wings normally developed; hind margin of lateral lobe of pronotum with a distinct tegminal sinus...............15

15a Pronotum (P) pointed at front when viewed from above. Fig. 156..
...........*Tettigidea armata* Morse Armored pygmy grasshopper

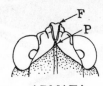
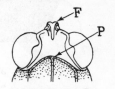

PRORSA   ARMATA   LATERALIS

Figure 156

LENGTH: 11-15 mm. RANGE: New York to Florida and west to Texas and Oklahoma.

Dark brown to blackish, pronotum usually coarsely granulose, sometimes cream or tan, hind femur sometimes with pale bands. Found mostly about wet mucky areas, often where shady. About 55% of specimens are "short-winged."

T. acuta Morse which occurs from New York to Florida and Louisiana is usually darker and has the median ridge of the pronotum lower and more evenly curved with the general texture of the pronotum less strongly granulose. It is found in salt, brackish, or fresh water marsh and swamp areas. About 3% of specimens are "short-winged."

15b Pronotum (P) obtusely angled or rounded at front when viewed from above 16

16a Head rather evenly narrowed to fastigium (F), when viewed from above, eyes not prominent. Angle of fastigium and face rather sharp and narrowly marked. Fig. 156.........................
.....*Tettigidea prorsa* Scudder Cone-headed pygmy grasshopper

LENGTH: 8-12 mm. RANGE: New Jersey to Florida and west to Tennessee and Louisiana.

Cream or brownish above, blackish on sides of pronotum and legs, median ridge of pronotum sometimes black. Found in low boggy areas and wet meadows in pine woods. Local. About 3% of individuals are macropronotal (long-winged).

16b Head uneven in outline to fastigium Fig. 156 (F), when viewed from above, eyes prominent; angle of fastigium and face more rounded and less sharply marked. Fig. 157.....................
........*Tettigidea lateralis* (Say) Black-sided pygmy grasshopper

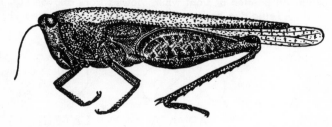

Figure 157

LENGTH: 9-16 mm. RANGE: Arizona and Colorado to Manitoba and the Atlantic.

Variably black, gray, brownish, or cream. Hind femur often with a light colored spot. Often common in both dry and wet areas. Sometimes occurs in migratory swarms. Specimens from Arizona, New Mexico, Nebraska, and Colorado have the eyes less prominent and less globose, with the space between them wider. The median ridge of the fastigium is also wider, and the lower front is proportionally broader. These have been called *T. lateralis* subspecies *cazieri* Rehn and Grant.

DESERT LONG-HORNED GRASSHOPPERS

ANAOCERIDS are strange, nocturnal, uncommon, wingless grasshoppers which are found only in our semiarid southwestern deserts. They are so peculiar that it was not until 1955 that their systematic placement, in a new family, was finally decided in two independent papers by Dirsh in England and Tinkham in California. Prior to that they were thought to be aberrant monkey grasshoppers or lubbers.

Although considered great "rarities" until recently, Tanocerids may be collected easily enough on desert vegetation at night. May seems to be a good time for adults. Easter vacation would be a good time to go after them.

KEY TO DESERT LONG-HORNED GRASSHOPPERS

1a Pronotum and basal abdominal segments with prominent fin-like crests along midline; form slender; antenna heavy at base and tapering gradually to tip; hind femur proportionally longer, reaching past end of abdomen, and margined above by a high narrow ridge. Fig. 158..*Mohavacris timberlakei* Rehn Timberlake's desert long-horned grasshopper

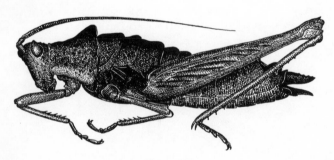

Figure 158

LENGTH: 18-25 mm. RANGE: Mojave desert area, California.

Grayish marked with black, sometimes mostly black. Adults April and May. On sagebrush (*Artemesia*), chamise (*Adenostema*) and *Erigonum*. This is the only species of the subfamily *Mohavacrinae*.

94

1b Pronotum and basal abdominal segments without crests along midline; form rather heavy; antenna heavy in basal two segments, then abruptly thread-like to tip; hind femur proportionally shorter, not reaching end of abdomen, and margined above by a low broad ridge. Fig. 159...*Tanaocerus koebelei* Bruner Koebele's desert long-horned grasshopper

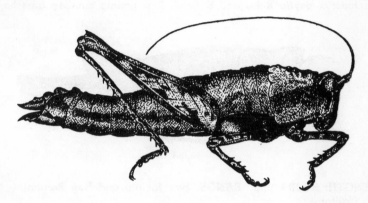

Figure 159

LENGTH: 12.5-22 mm. RANGE: Southern California, Arizona, and Nevada.

Pale gray, lightly marked with blackish. On *Franseria dumosa*, *Erigonum* and other desert plants. The males are tremendous jumpers. Adults December to May.

The subspecies *ablatus* Rehn was described from Whitewater Canyon, Coachella Valley, California. It is larger than the typical *koebelei* and has the hind margin of the pronotum crenulated or with rather regularly spaced small notches.

MONKEY GRASSHOPPERS

EUMASTACIDAE is a small family of mostly tropical grasshoppers. Our few species are found mostly on bushes or trees in our southwestern states. They perch with hind legs akimbo and short antennae raised alertly, ready to give a quick silent leap to another bush if disturbed. Wingless, slender-limbed, and with long, narrow, pointed heads, these are among our most highly specialized grasshoppers. Adults are usually markedly harder and less likely to shrivel than last instar nymphs which they otherwise much resemble.

KEY TO MONKEY GRASSHOPPERS

1a Tarsal claws symmetrical, the claws equal and the arolium directed
    midway between them; head and pronotum comparatively robust..2

1b Tarsal claws asymmetrical, the external claw very small and the
    arolium directed toward the small claw; head and pronotum com-
    paratively slender. Fig. 160............................*Psycho-
    mastax psylla* Rehn and Hebard San Jacinto monkey grasshopper

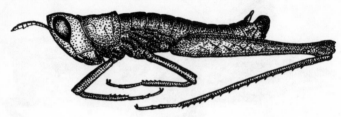

Figure 160

LENGTH: 9.6-18.1 mm. RANGE: San Jacinto and San Bernadino Mts.,
California.

Brownish with light and dark markings. Found at altitudes of 6,500-
7,500 feet on spiny chaparral. The subspecies *inyo* Rehn and Grant occurs in September at 9,500 feet or higher in the White Mountains of
California, on gooseberry, with bristle-cone pines present. The heads
of the females of *psylla* (A) and the other two species are shown
diagrammatically from the front. Fig. 161.

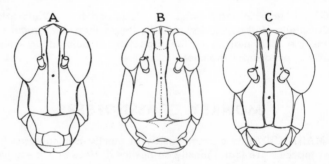

Figure 161

P. robusta Rehn and Grant (B) occurs on the eastern side of southern
    Sierra Nevada Mts., California, and Charleston Mountains, Nevada.
    It is more robust.

P. deserticola Rehn and Grant (C) occurs in the Mojave desert and adjacent San Bernadino Mts., California. It has the hind femur about 5.2 times as long as greatest width (6 or more times in *psylla* and *robusta*). The subspecies *P. deserticola indigena* Rehn and Grant occurs in the Belted Range, Nye County, Nevada. The single known female has a body length of 25.2 mm. as compared to 11.3-14.3 mm. in typical *deserticola*.

2a Cercus of male not curved down at tip; legs very long and slender, hind femur 6.6 or more times as long as greatest width. Fig. 162.. ....*Eumorsea balli* Hebard Ball's monkey grasshopper

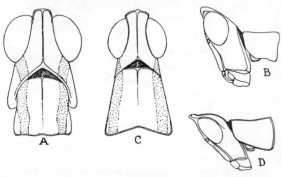

Figure 162

LENGTH: 11.8-21 mm. RANGE: Huachuca and Santa Rita Mountains and Glenn Oaks, Arizona.

Brown with light and dark markings. Taken on Mexican pinyon pine and on "low weeds, herbs, and bushes at some distance from pines." Specimens have been taken at altitudes of 5,000-9,000 feet.

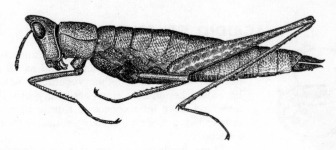

Figure 163

E. pinaleno Rehn and Grant, Pinaleno monkey grasshopper, occurs in the Graham Mountains, Arizona. It is 11.7-22 mm. in length, colored much as *balli*, but has the hind femur of the male 8.4 times as long as greatest width (about 6.6 in *balli*). A and B show the head and pronotum of *balli* from top and side, C and D show *pinaleno* for comparison.

2b Cercus of male curved down at the tip; legs less slender, hind femur less than 6.5 times as long as greatest width. Fig. 164......
......*Morsea californica* Scudder Chaparral monkey grasshopper

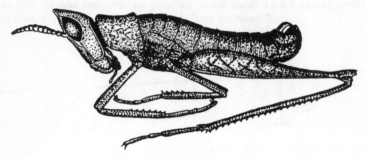

Figure 164

LENGTH: 8.2-19 mm. RANGE: California, Arizona, Nevada, and Utah.

Grayish or brownish, varying to blackish or greenish, with dark markings, often speckled. Found from 750 to 7,500 feet in chaparral areas. Very alert and nimble, these delicate little grasshoppers often lead the collector on a merry chase through scratchy chaparral. They sometimes come to light at night. Five subspecies are recognized: *tamalpaisensis* Rehn and Hebard (shown) in the San Francisco region and southward; *piute* Rehn and Grant in the Great Basin and Range Province of California, Arizona, Nevada, and Utah; *kaibabensis* Rehn and Grant, north of Grand Canyon; *dumicola* Rehn and Grant, south of Grand Canyon; and typical *californica* in southern California.

ACRIDID GRASSHOPPERS

OME kinds of grasshoppers become ruinously numerous and destructive at times, and as all grasshoppers eat grass or other vegetation none can be called beneficial. However many are uncommon and have little economic significance, some, indeed being among our scarcest and least known insects.

Many kinds are so variable as to render difficult their absolute differentiation in simple keys. While many species are quite distinctive and easily recognized, many others exist as members of apparently relatively recently evolved groups of closely related species wherein the most reliable structural characters (used by experts in separating them) are found in the male aedeagi. Geography is a help to the amateur in separating these.

In recent years much study has been given to the problem of higher groups of grasshoppers. Some of our grasshoppers have been found to possess contradictory sets of "important" structural characters and the old subfamilies of band-winged and slant-faced grasshoppers (Oedipodinae and Acridinae) are not now thought to be as separate and distinct as in past years.

KEY TO ACRIDID GRASSHOPPERS

1a Hind tibia with both inner and outer immovable spines at tip (A). (Ignore the calcaria, which are movable). Fig. 165............2

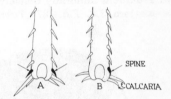

Figure 165

1b Hind tibia with only the inner immovable spine at tip, outer one absent (B). (Ignore the calcaria, which are movable.) Fig. 165....7

2a Pronotum about equally long at sides and at middle, with hind margin nearly straight across as seen from above, and with three nearly equally strong smooth longitudinal ridges. Fig. 166.......
................*Brachystola magna* (Girard) Lubber grasshopper

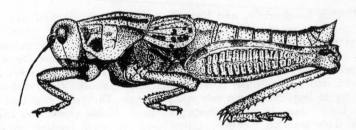

Figure 166

LENGTH: 38-79 mm. RANGE: Montana, North Dakota, and Minnesota to Arizona, Texas, and Mexico.

Grayish-green or brown, marked with brown, greenish, or bluish, and black. Tegmina much reduced, pink with small black spots. Often common, especially on rocky or gravelly soil with scanty grass and coarse weeds. Sometimes destructively common. Often seen on roads feeding on their dead. The colors of this large and interesting species may be rather well preserved if the specimens are gutted and stuffed as soon as killed, and then dried out under refrigeration. Adults August to October.

2b Pronotum much longer at middle than at sides with hind margin angling back strongly to midline as seen from above, and with one dominant median longitudinal ridge or no strong longitudinal ridges at all..3

3a Wing red with black border.....................................4

3b Wing not red with black border.............................5

4a Pronotum uniformly densely punctate; male capable of flight; southwestern U.S. Fig. 167..*Taeniopoda eques* (Burmeister) Horse lubber

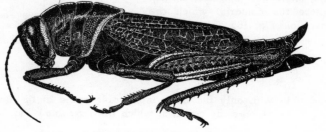

Figure 167

LENGTH: 38-64 mm. RANGE: Arizona to Texas, Mexico, Honduras, and Costa Rica.

Shining black above and beneath, conspicuously marked with yellow and orange, tegmina black with network of yellowish veins. The wings are rose-red with black borders. These spectacular grasshoppers are common and occasionally destructive. They are usually found on grasslands and into the live oak belt. They feed on mesquite, burroweed, and various other desert shrubs and annuals. When disturbed they try to leap and flutter into spiny bushes. They also hiss and display their wings in a threatening manner. Males sometimes loudly clack their tegmina together. Often seen on roads feeding on their dead. Adults August to November.

4b Pronotum much smoother and less punctured on prozona of lateral lobes than elsewhere; neither sex capable of flight; southeastern U.S. Fig. 168..
......*Romalea microptera* (Beauvois) Eastern lubber grasshopper

Figure 168

LENGTH: 50-70. RANGE: North Carolina and Tennessee to Florida and Louisiana.

Dull yellow with numerous black markings and a reddish stripe on tegmen, varying to mostly black with only the median ridge and edges of pronotum and hind margins of abdominal segments dull yellow. The wings are red with black borders. Common in roadside vegetation, along railroad rights of way, edges of fields, etc. These spectacular grasshoppers are sometimes destructive in truck crops. When disturbed they hiss and spread and buzz their wings. When picked up they exude an evil-smelling frothy brown liquid from their mesothoracic spiracles. Adults June to November.

5a Tegmina and wings fully developed, reaching well beyond end of body. Good fliers. Fig. 169 . . . .
. . . .*Tytthotyle maculata* (Bruner) Furnace heat lubber

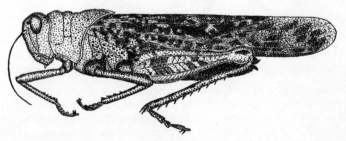

Figure 169

LENGTH: 22-48.5 mm. RANGE: California, Nevada, Utah, and Arizona.

Variegated browns on a whitish or yellowish ground. Sometimes chalky pale blue, green, or pink colors are present. The wing is yellowish to greenish. Found in the hottest parts of the desert at the hottest time of the year. In such furnacelike areas as Death Valley and

Needles it occurs from 225 feet below sea level over blistering hot slopes and up torrid valleys to 4,800 feet above sea level. The preferred host plant is creosote bush. It occurs in rocky, gravelly, silt, or lava areas. It is a capable if not exceptional flier. Adults April to September.

Spaniacris deserticola (Bruner) has recently been transferred to the Romaleinae. It lacks the external spine at tip of hind tibia and so does not run here in the key. See page 147.

5b Tegmina and wings reduced, not reaching to end of body, non-flying ground-dwellers **6**

6a Pronotum with a high median crest; fastigium conspicuously projecting forward. Fig. 170....................................
.............*Dracotettix monstrosus* Bruner Gray dragon lubber

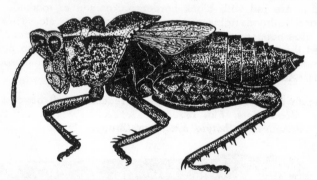

Figure 170

LENGTH: 18-45 mm. RANGE: West central to southern California.

Various browns or grays, the pronotum often whitish in part. The color of females is especially variable. Found on rocky or gravelly mountain areas with sparse grass and other scattered plants. Males are active but females rely on their camouflage to escape detection. ▪This is one of our most distinctive-looking grasshoppers and a great prize to collectors. Adults are present through most of the year. They are sometimes found under bark or other cover in winter.

D. plutonius Bruner is similar except less specialized. For example the crest on the metazona of the pronotum is lower, and the fastigium does not project forward as much. It occurs uncommonly from 4,500-6,000 feet in the mountains between Owens Valley and Death Valley, California. Adults in April and May.

6b Pronotum flattened and rough with no median crest; fastigium not conspicuously projecting forward. Fig. 171.........................
...............*Phrynotettix robustus* (Bruner) Robust toad lubber

LENGTH: 27-56 mm. RANGE: New Mexico, Texas, and Mexico.

Variegated browns and whites. Found in gravelly or rocky areas with sparse grass. These strange rough grasshoppers look like pebbles and wait until nearly stepped on before jumping. Four subspecies are known, three of which occur north of Mexico. Adults March to November, and some adults live through winter.

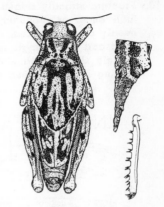

Figure 171

P. tshivavensis (Haldeman) the Chihuahua toad lubber, is a brown to gray or mahogany-red species which breaks into five subspecies. It occurs on gravelly soil with scanty grass in Arizona, New Mexico, Texas, and Mexico. The subspecies *pusillus* Rehn and Grant is relatively small (18.2-32 mm.) and occurs on the Mogollon Plateau and other elevated areas of central New Mexico and Arizona. Adults June to November. The odd-looking name "tshivavensis" is based on a transliteration of Chihuahua, a city and state in Mexico.

7a Prosternum even at middle, bearing no tubercle or spine-like structure................8

7b Prosternum modified at middle with a tubercle or spine-like structure. Fig. 172..........
..........Section 2, page 151

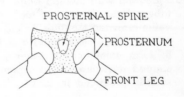

PROSTERNAL SPINE

PROSTERNUM

FRONT LEG

Figure 172

8a Wing colored and with a marginal or submarginal band (Fig. 173A) ....Section 1, page 104

8b Wing clear to faintly washed with color but not banded, sometimes entirely brown, sometimes smoky at tip.................9

9a Tegmina and wings long, reaching near or past tip of abdomen..10

9b Tegmina and wings short, not reaching near tip of abdomen.....
....Section 2, page 151

10a Prontum strongly ridged along midline, or median ridge cut more than once, or pronotum tuberculate. Tegmen with veins rather evenly closely spaced, no rows of very large cells being formed; head and facial angle often similar to Fig. 173 A; form never extremely slender and elongate with sword-shaped antennae; often making loud snapping, crackling, or buzzing noises in flight.....
....Section 1, page 105

INTERCALARY VEIN

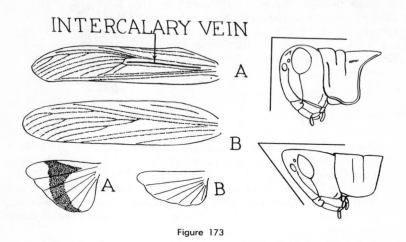

Figure 173

10b Pronotum with median ridge low, usually cut but once, usually not tuberculate. Tegmen of male sometimes with some of longitudinal veins crowded together, or cross-veins widely spaced, forming rows of very large cells; head and facial angle often similar to Fig. 173 B; form sometimes extremely slender and elongate with sword-shaped antennae; no conspicuous snapping, crackling, or buzzing sounds produced in flight..................Section 2, page 151

SECTION 1 — ACRIDIDAE

In this artificial key section are found the band-winged grasshoppers and their allies which are usually placed as subfamily *Oedipodinae*, plus a few other forms which have colored or banded wings, but which are otherwise rather clearly members of the traditional subfamily *Acridinae*. The *Acridinae* form the first part of Section 2 in this key.

KEY TO SECTION 1, ACRIDID GRASSHOPPERS

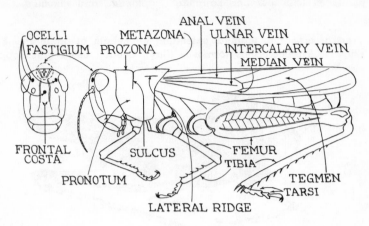

Figure 174

1a Pronotum with a high semicircular crest on midline; hind tibia with
   more than 12 spines in outer row.............................2

1b Pronotum without a high semicircular crest on midline; hind tibia
   with fewer than 12 spines in outer row........................3

2a Crest of pronontum smooth, developed over metazona only. Fig.
   175..... *Acrolophitus variegatus* Bruner Smooth-crested grasshopper

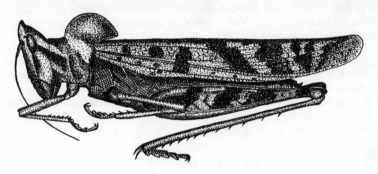

Figure 175

LENGTH: 46-50 mm. RANGE: Texas, New Mexico.

Green, mottled, hairy, antenna red, wing disc yellowish, head and
pronotum with pale stripes. A large, handsome, clumsy species.

A. hirtipes (Say) Green fool grasshopper, is similar except smaller
(33-43 mm.) and plain green. It occurs from Alberta and Saskatche-

wan to Texas, on sandy areas of river valleys, feeding on various plants as *Lithospernum*, *Lappula*, *Cryptantha*, and *Phasuba*.

2b Crest of pronotum toothed, extending full length of pronotum. Fig. 176...... *Tropidolophus formosus* **(Say) Great crested grasshopper**

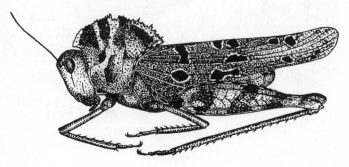

Figure 176

LENGTH: 37-45 mm. RANGE: Arizona to Wyoming, Kansas, Oklahoma, Texas, and Mexico.

Green with brownish markings. Wing orange with imperfect black band. June to October. On low-growing *Malvaceae* such as *Malvastrum* and *Sphaeralcea*, and Horse nettle in areas of sparse to dense grass. Makes a rather high-pitched rattle-clicking sound in flight. A fancied resemblance to the fin-backed dinosaur *Dimetrodon* prompts some collectors to nick-name this the "Dinosaur grasshopper." A very similar-looking species occurs in Iran.

3a Head elevated, fastigium pointed, antenna long and red, pronotum saddle-shaped. Fig. 177..
Pedioscirtetes nevadensis **Thomas Nevada point-headed grasshopper**

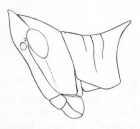

LENGTH: 25-32 mm. RANGE: Arizona, Nevada, and Idaho.

Green, wing yellow with black band. Tegmen with intercalary vein. Adults in July and August. Usually uncommon. Usu-

Figure 177

ally on Colorado rubber plant *Actinia richardsoni*, but sometimes on other plants.

P. *maculipennis* (Scudder) (Fig. 178) the Texas point-headed grasshopper, measures 25-34 mm., and is grayish mottled with brown. The wing is dark brown or blackish. Tegmen without an intercalary vein. Adults occur from June to September on low rocky hills of Lower Sonoran Zone. Feeds on a low gray matlike plant *Coldenia canescens*. Ranges from Arizona and Texas to Mexico.

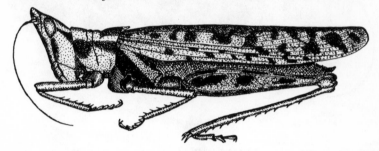

Figure 178

Pedioscirtetes and *Acrolophitus* are classified as slant-faced grasshoppers of subfamily ACRIDINAE.

3b Head sometimes elevated, but fastigium not pointed.............4

4a Pronotum with median ridge distinct throughout its length, entire or cut by one sulcus...5

4b Pronotum with median ridge indistinct in some part of its length, or cut by two or three sulci.................................20

5a Wings usually brightly colored and with a dark band, sometimes pale-colored with only a portion of a dark band evident, or wing largely black 9

5b Wings not brightly colored or banded, at most appearing somewhat smoky or faintly yellowish....................................6

6a Sexes similar, females larger than males but similarly colored...7

6b Sexes dissimilar, females larger than males and usually very differently colored 8

7a Pronotum usually with lateral ridges distinct and uninterrupted to metazona; tegmen usually brownish with a straw stripe along anal vein, and dark spots. Fig. 179..................................
....*Camnula pellucida* (Scudder) Clear-winged grasshopper

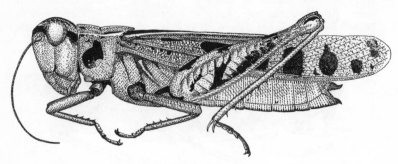

Figure 179

LENGTH: 19-32 mm. RANGE: Widespread, Newfoundland to British Columbia, south to Virginia, Texas, and California.

Yellowish-brown to blackish, occasionally magenta, marked as described above, body lighter. Hind tibia yellowish. Sometimes injurious in grassy areas. Nymphs or adults sometimes migrate in hordes for short distances and may be quite destructive. A summer species.

7b Pronotum with lateral ridges indistinct or interrupted about one-third from front, displaced out of line at point of interruption; tegmen about as in *Camnula* or brownish with three dark cross-bands. Fig. 180..
...........*Encoptolophus sordidus* (Burmeister) Dusky grasshopper

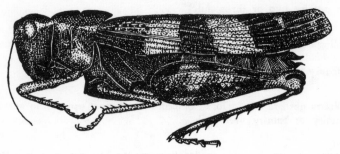

Figure 180

LENGTH: 18-32 mm. RANGE: Ontario and Alberta to Mexico and North Carolina.

Brownish, tegmina banded darker, pronotum often with a faint pale "X" mark. Wing faintly yellowish toward base, outer half faintly smoky. A common summer and fall species of dry upland grassy meadows. It often makes a harsh buzzing sound in flight. The subspecies *costalis* (Scudder) occurs from Alberta and Manitoba to Texas and Arizona. The head and thorax are variably gray to greenish-white, the tegmina brown to greenish with dark bands.

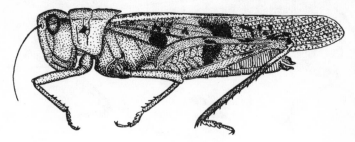

Figure 181

E. subgracilis Caudell, Fig. 181, 22-33 mm., occurs from South Dakota to southern California and Mexico. It is slender, pale, and marked with brown, green, or reddish. Frequents cultivated fields and damp desert flats. Sometimes destructive in alfalfa and truck crops.

8a Frontal costa deeply grooved above and below ocellus; fastigium deeply excavated; tegmina and wings of female sometimes much reduced. Fig. 182...
...*Chimarocephala pacifica* Thomas Painted meadow grasshopper

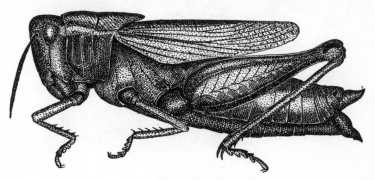

Figure 182

LENGTH: 16-23 mm. RANGE: California.
Female green or red or both with black marks. Tegmina and wings somewhat shortened. Male brown, long-winged. A gaudy early

spring form occurring in grassy areas. The subspecies *incisa* Caudell (Fig. 183) also occurs in California. Both sexes are long-winged, and the pronotal ridge has a notch. The colors are much as above. Sometimes marked with whitish. The male usually has an orange spot on top of hind femur. Often associated with filaree.

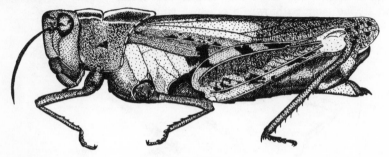

Figure 183

8b Frontal costa not deeply grooved both above and below ocellus; fastigium shallowly excavated; tegmina and wings reaching tip of abdomen, functional in both sexes. Fig. 184....................
....*Chortophaga viridifasciata* (De Geer) Green-striped grasshopper

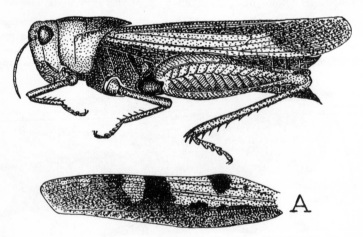

Figure 184

LENGTH: 24-36 mm. RANGE: Widespread, British Columbia and Ontario to Arizona, Mexico, and Florida.

Females usually green with a brownish streak on tegmen, males brown. Colors of sexes occasionally reversed. Wing faintly yellowish

110

basally, faintly smoky toward tip. An early spring species (stragglers may persist until November) in grassy areas. Both sexes fly and crackle in flight. The subspecies *australior* Rehn and Hebard, Southern green-striped grasshopper, occurs from Florida to Georgia. It has the fastigium proportionally wider and the tegmina often spotted (Fig. 184A). Variants which are largely reddish-purple have been found.

9a Pronotum with median ridge almost always arcuately raised, entire or feebly nicked by principal sulcus; interspace of metasternum longer than wide in male, narrower than space between mesosternal lobes in female; colored disc of wing large with band narrow; general color not strongly speckled. Figs. 185 and 187B. . . . .
. . . .*Arphia sulphurea* (Fabricius) Sulphur-winged grasshopper

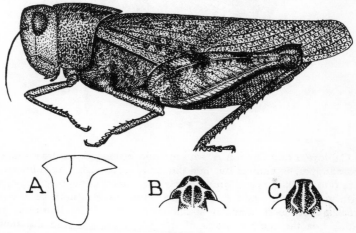

Figure 185

LENGTH: 17-30 mm. RANGE: Ontario to Florida and Nebraska, commoner east of Mississippi River.

Blackish to brown or mottled greenish or grayish, wing yellow with black band and spur. Tegmina often with a clay-yellow median stripe. Abundant in June in upland meadows, on rocky hillsides, etc. About July it is replaced by the appreciably larger *A. xanthoptera* (Burmeister) the Autumn yellow-winged grasshopper which ranges from New England to Florida, Nebraska, and Texas. This has the frontal costa strongly narrowed above the antennae and not or only feebly sulcate below the ocellus. In the western part of its range red-winged individuals occur. The pronotum is as in "A." *A. pseudonietana* (Thomas), Red-winged grasshopper, 30-35 mm., ranges from British Columbia to Michigan, Mexico, and California. It is black or brown, speckled,

111

sometimes with white on head. The fastigium (C) is shown beside that of *sulphurea* (B). Wing rich red with band and spur black. Crackles in flight. A more robust blackish subspecies *crassa* Bruner, Southwestern red-winged grasshopper, occurs in Arizona, Texas, and Mexico.

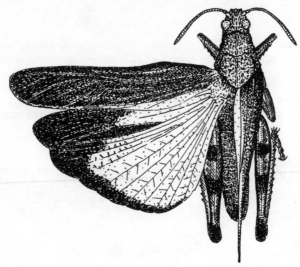

Figure 186

In California and Oregon *A. saussureana* Bruner, Saussure's red-winged grasshopper, is similar but has the body yellowish. *A. behrensi* Saussure (Fig. 186), Behrens' grasshopper is a common yellow-winged spring form in California, and *A. granulata* Saussure, Southern yellow-winged grasshopper, is a common southeastern (especially Floridan) species which has the median ridge of the pronotum low and the metazona thickly granulated. *A. conspersa* Scudder, Speckled rangeland grasshopper, 25-32 mm., ranges from Alaska to eastern Texas and Mexico. The wing is red, pink, orange, or yellow with a rather narrow brown crossband. Hind tibia pale, a little darker in apical two-thirds.

9b Pronotum with median ridge either rather strongly raised and deeply cut by principal sulcus or low and variously cut; interspace of metasternum as long as wide in male, wider than long in female; colored disc of wing sometimes small with band wide; general body color sometimes strongly speckled............................**10**

10a Color plain brown; wing orange with black marginal band; antenna flattened; fastigium tuberculate, with no median ridge; hind tibia not marked with orange; hind femur abruptly narrowed at posterior third. Fig. 187...

..........*Tomonotus ferruginosus* Bruner Oak-leaf grasshopper

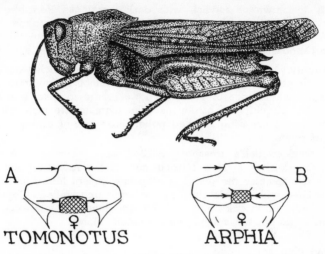

A   B

TOMONOTUS   ARPHIA

Figure 187

LENGTH: 28-38 mm. RANGE: Southeastern Arizona to Mexico.

Brown with black-banded orange wing; general appearance of an *Arphia*. Hind tibia blue. April to August. Usually found on dead oak leaves in live oak belt.

10b Without this combination of characters........................11

11a Pronotum with median ridge rather strongly raised, at least on prozona, and deeply cut by principal sulcus; form never robust....12

11b Pronotum with median ridge rather low and not deeply cut by principal sulcus; form sometimes quite robust.................16

12a Hind tibia partly or entirely orange. Fig. 188...................
.......*Spharagemon collare* (Scudder) Mottled sand grasshopper

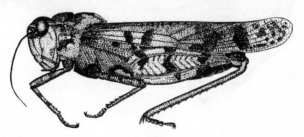

Figure 188

LENGTH: 30-38 mm. RANGE: Alberta and Montana to Arizona, and east to Atlantic and Gulf coasts.

113

Gray to brown or reddish with dark markings. Variable. Wing yellow with black band and short spur. Hind tibia orange or red. Median ridge of pronotum high, sharp, and obliquely cut by sulcus. June to October in mixed grass-herbaceous areas. Crackles in flight.

S. *equale* (Say) Say's grasshopper, ranges from Saskatchewan to British Columbia, Oregon, Utah, Texas, and Illinois. Similar to *collare* except median ridge of pronotum lower, more rooflike, less deeply and not obliquely cut by sulcus. The tegmina are more distinctly banded and the wing is often paler. Bare soil of arid plains and along roads.

S. *bolli* Scudder Boll's grasshopper, 26-28 mm., occurs from Manitoba and the Dakotas to New Mexico, east to the Atlantic coast. Variable, it resembles the above two species except hind tibia marked near base with a pale ring and a black ring. July to September. On sandy soil in oak bluffs and dry woodlands. New Mexico specimens represent the subspecies *inornatum* Morse.

12b Hind tibia not orange..13

13a Wing disc yellow, yellowish, or greenish-yellow with a more or less distinct dark band......................................14

13b Wing disc not yellow or yellowish..........................15

14a Frontal costa deeply grooved above and below ocellus; wing disc pale yellow or greenish-yellow. Fig. 189.......................
..........*Microtes occidentalis* (Bruner) Little buzzer grasshopper

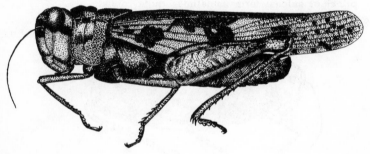

Figure 189

LENGTH: 16-18 mm. RANGE: California.

Brownish with blackish markings. Wing color varies to faintly greenish. Occurs in coastal dune areas near Monterey north to Marin County. Flies with a buzzing sound.

14b Frontal costa not grooved above ocellus, shallowly grooved below' wing disc bright yellow. Fig. 190........................
.....................*Lactista oslari* Caudell Oslar's grasshopper

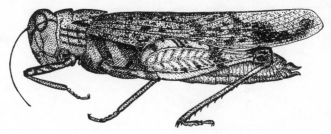

Figure 190

LENGTH: 25-38 mm. RANGE: California to Mexico and New Mexico.

Dark gray, wing bright yellow with dark band and dark tip. Hind
tibia pale blue with pale ring near base. Most frequently on bare
rocky slopes where palo verde and saguaro grow (Arizona). March
to October.

15a Pronotum with median ridge about equally high on prozona and
metazona; wing disc black and margin pale. Fig. 191.........
............*Dissosteira carolina* (Linnaeus) Carolina grasshopper

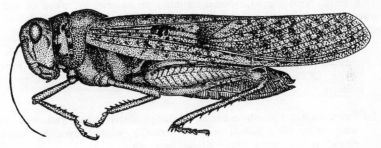

Figure 191

LENGTH: 38-52 mm. RANGE: Widespread. Alaska and British Columbia to Nova Scotia, Florida, and California.

Grayish or brownish to black, tegmina usually with numerous dark
specks, wing black to base with outer margin pale yellowish. Often
common from July to October in towns, along roads, and about cultivated areas. Gregarious. Flight somewhat butterfly-like.

D. *longipennis* (Thomas) the High plains grasshopper, 38-48 mm., occurs from Wyoming and South Dakota to Texas. Similar to *carolina*

except tegmen with distinct dark blotches, wing with black fading out near base, and with outer margin transparent, not yellowish. Wary. Sometimes destructively common on the range.

15b Pronotum with median ridge much higher on prozona; wing, reddish with dark band. Fig. 192 (B)...........................*Dissosteira pictipennis* Brunner California rose-winged grasshopper

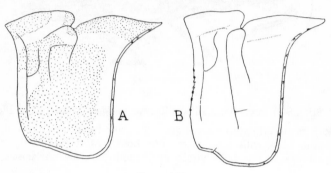

Figure 192

LENGTH: 21-34 mm. RANGE: California to southern Oregon.

Brownish or grayish with darker markings, anal vein of tegmen often pale. Variable. Common on bare spots and in areas of scanty grass.

D. spurcata (Saussure) (A) Pale-winged grasshopper, 33-41 mm., ranges from California to Washington, Idaho, and Utah. Yellowish or grayish to brown, more or less distinctly marked with darker brown. Wary. Often common in range areas. Often preferring ridges and hilltops.

16a Form rather robust; medium to large sized; wing yellow or reddish with dark band; tegmen usually with brownish "leopard spots" and a pale stripe along anal vein.....................19

16b Form slender; small to medium sized; wing yellow or orange with dark band; tegmen speckled or spotted but without "leopard spots"; sometimes with pale stripe along anal vein.................17

17a Hind tibia reddish in part or insect speckled in appearance....18

17b Hind tibia not reddish; insect not speckled in appearance; tegmen with dark band in line with band on hind femur. Fig. 193.......
........*Platylactista aztecus* (Saussure) Aztec range grasshopper

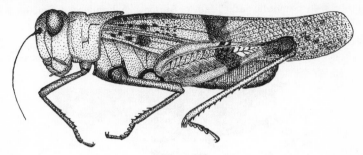

Figure 193

LENGTH: 19-25 mm. RANGE: Arizona to Texas and Mexico.

Light gray, cream, or brown to red-brown, wing yellow with dark band; hind tibia green. Sometimes destructively common on grasslands but usually found in desert areas.

18a Speckled; tibia pale, not reddish. Fig. 194......................
.....................*Scirtetica ritensis* **Rehn   Lichen grasshopper**

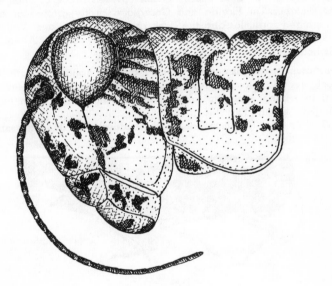

Figure 194

LENGTH: 18-25 mm. RANGE: Arizona.

Gray-green, spotted and mottled black; wing orange with black band and long spur. Hind tibia pale with dark mottlings. Occurs on

117

lichen-covered, north-facing cliffs and rock slides where they are extremely well camouflaged. June to August. A handsome species which is seldom collected.

18b Not speckled; tibia reddish. Fig. 195...........................
..............*Scirtetica marmorata* (Harris) Marbled grasshopper

Figure 195

LENGTH: 33-38 mm. RANGE: Ontario to New Jersey and Michigan.

Grayish, reddish, or brown, variably barred and mottled darker. Hind tibia red with dark and light rings at base. Wing disc small, yellow, band broad, spur short. Lichen covered areas in open woods. July to October. In Florida and Georgia a pretty orange or chrome yellow-winged form, lacking the dark ring on hind tibia, is called subspecies *picta* (Scudder). It is common in sandy areas. A noisy, accomplished flier.

19a Pronotum with prozona and metazona about equal in length; frontal costa feebly sulcate below ocellus, and not narrowed near antennal insertions; inner apical spur of hind tibia more than twice as long as outer. Fig. 196..
..............*Hippiscus rugosus* (Scudder) Wrinkled grasshopper

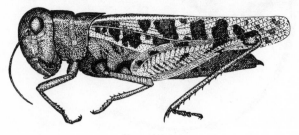

Figure 196

LENGTH: 35-51 mm. RANGE: Texas, Arizona, and Northern Mexico to Montana and the Atlantic coast.

Large and robust. Brownish, tegmen spotted darker. Wing pale yellow or orange with dark band and spur. Adults July to November, commonest from September to November. Grassy areas, especially in open woods.

19b Pronotum with prozona considerably shorter than metazona; frontal costa strongly sulcate below ocellus and narrowed between or above antennal insertions; inner apical spur of hind tibia less than twice as long as outer. Fig. 197...............................
......*Pardalophora apiculata* (Harris) Coral-winged grasshopper

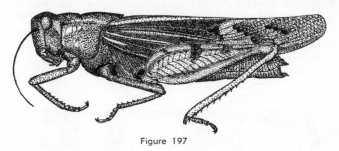

Figure 197

LENGTH: 25-44 mm. RANGE: Hudson Bay to Montana, Wyoming, Missouri, and North Carolina.

Brownish to greenish with dark blotches. Wing red or occasionally yellow, with dark band and spur. Hind margin of pronotum acute-angled. Hind tibia yellowish or orange. Occurs in grassy areas, especially where dry and sandy. April to July. Females hide and are reluctant to fly.

P. phoenicoptera (Burmeister) Orange-winged grasshopper, 31-45 mm., occurs from Florida to Texas, Kansas, Illinois, and Pennsylvania. Hind angle of pronotum right or obtuse. Brownish or greenish, wing yellow or orange with dark band and spur. Hind tibia yellow or orange. In meadows, open woods, and grain fields. Females hide and are reluctant to fly.

P. haldemanii (Scudder) Haldeman's grasshopper, 27-46 mm., Montana to Utah, New Mexico, Texas, and Michigan. It is gray brown with dark spots. Wing usually red, sometimes yellow or pinkish with dark band and spur. Hind tibia yellow or reddish. June to August in dry grassy areas where vegetation is heaviest. Fly with a whirring sound but no stridulation.

P. saussurei (Scudder) Saussure's grasshopper, 50-61 mm., Texas to New Mexico and Kansas, is similar to *haldemanii* but larger with median ridge of pronotum stronger, metazona sharply acute behind, and hind femur proportionally broader.

20a Size medium to large; form more or less robust; tegminal markings often of "leopard spot" type; pronotum rather roughly sculptured, with median ridge low, and lateral ridges evident, at least on metazona; wings colored and banded........................21

20b Size small to medium large; form more or less slender; tegminal markings various, usually not of "leopard spot" type; pronotum usually rather feebly sculptured, with median ridge sometimes high, or often nearly obliterated, and lateral ridges often obliterated; wing sometimes not colored or banded......................25

21a Fastigium vaguely sculptured; frontal costa grading into front shortly below ocellus, not deeply sulcate; hind tibia often blue; wing usually blue or greenish with band but with no spur extending inward. Fig. 198...
........Leprus robustus Hebard. Robust blue-winged grasshopper

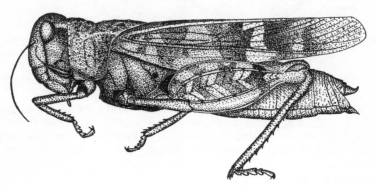

Figure 198

LENGTH: 37-45 mm. RANGE: Arizona to Texas and Colorado.

Robust. Reddish-brown or grayish-brown, tegmina banded. Wing pale bluish-green. Hind tibia pale blue. Late August to December in desert grasslands and on rocky hillsides and ridges.

L. cyaneous Cockerell. Cockerell's blue-winged grasshopper, found in about the same area, is similar but has the wing disc blue. March to September.

L. wheeleri (Thomas) Wheeler's blue-winged grasshopper, occurs in Texas, overlapping into New Mexico and Oklahoma. It is found on sandy adobe flats and often flies to lights. Otherwise similar to above.

L. glaucipennis Scudder. Scudder's blue-winged grasshopper, 19-33 mm., occurs from southern California and Channel Islands to Mexico. Hind angle of metazona of pronotum acute, longitudinal ridges sharp, and surface sharply tuberculate. Wing and hind tibia bluish.

21b Fastigium distinctly sculptured; frontal costa distinct below ocellus and often deeply sulcate; hind tibia not blue; wing disc not blue or greenish, wing band usually with a spur extending inward...**22**

22a Female very robust, often with shortened tegmina and wings; hind femur with broad flanges above and below, as pictured; brownish, and usually with hind tibia red, and usually with a red spot inside at end of hind femur. Fig. 199..................................
Agymnastes ingens (Scudder) Lubberly band-winged grasshopper

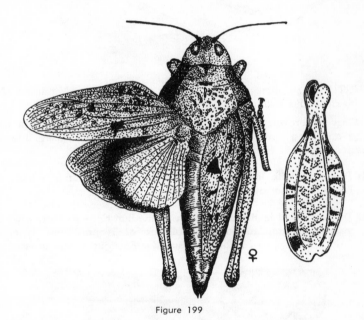

Figure 199

LENGTH: 30-45 mm. RANGE: Northern and central California to Nevada.

Grayish or brownish. Wing yellow or orange with black band. Hind femur blue inside basally. Pronotum rough. The female looks like a pebble and is very reluctant to move. Males are long-winged and active. Rocky hillsides and mountain ridges. Except for the peculiar females these are much like *Xanthippus* in general appearance. Some females have the tegmina reaching the tip of the abdomen. May to July.

22b Sexes similar, tegmina and wings long; colors not as above....**23**

121

23a **Pronotum with lateral lobes wider at bottom than in middle. Fig. 200....** *Cratypedes neglectus* **(Thomas) Pronotal range grasshopper**

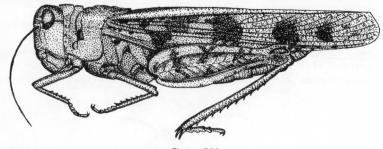

Figure 200

LENGTH: 27-38 mm. RANGE: British Columbia to Manitoba, New Mexico, and California.

Gray or brown, anal vein usually pale. Wing yellow with black band and long spur. Hind tibia red to yellowish. Grassy hills and prairies. May to September. Often common.

23b **Pronotum with lateral lobes of about equal width at middle and bottom, or narrower below.................................24**

24a **Depression of fastigium (A) with no median ridge at rear; wing disc yellow; tegminal markings usually not of "leopard spot" type. Fig. 201...** *Sticthippus californicus* **Scudder Fastigial range grasshopper**

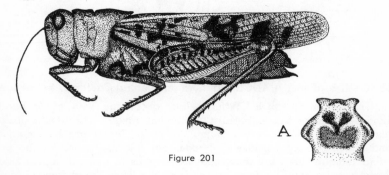

A

Figure 201

LENGTH: 27-35 mm. RANGE: California.

Gray or brown with darker markings and anal vein of tegmen light. Wing yellow with dark band and spur. Hind tibia reddish. Looks like a *Xanthippus*. Grasslands, June to August.

24b Depression of fastigium usually with a distinct median ridge at rear; wing disc yellow or red; tegminal markings often of "leopard spot" type. Fig. 202...
.......Xanthippus corallipes Haldeman Red-shanked grasshopper

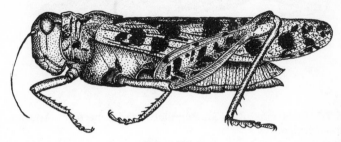

Figure 202

LENGTH: 45-52 mm. RANGE: British Columbia to Manitoba, Oregon, Texas, Minnesota, and Iowa.

Brown with darker markings. Hind tibia reddish. Wing yellow with black band. Destructively common on grasslands. An apparently plastic species which develops distinctive looking populations in different habitats.

X. c. buckelli Hebard, British Columbia to Oregon and Montana.

X. c. miniatus Strohecker, eastern California, is slender and smooth. A red-winged form near this occurs in the San Bernardino Mts. of southern California.

Orange-winged *X. olancha* Scudder, with streaky blackish tegminal markings, occurs in some of the desert mountain areas of southern California.

X. lateritus Saussure, Nevada red-winged grasshopper has red wing with black band and spur. It occurs commonly in the Nevada desert areas. Several other *Xanthippus* species are known but are difficult to separate, even for experts.

25a Size medium to medium large; antenna long, black, and heavy; tegmen with three dark cross bands; wing band narrow and near end; hind femur blue-black inside, on basal two-thirds; hind tibia red. Fig. 203...
...Hadrotettix trifasciatus (Say) Three-banded range grasshopper

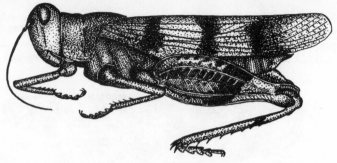

Figure 203

LENGTH: 25-44 mm. RANGE: Manitoba and Alberta to Arizona, Texas, and Mexico.

Brownish, pinkish, or blackish with dark bands. Wing disc yellow, spur short or absent. A handsome insect, found on rocky or sandy areas, along roads, or on open grassy plains.

25b Without the above combination of characters..................26

26a Pronotum with median ridge distinct and raised in profile, at least on prozona; body usually rather narrow at middle legs; wing often banded 27

26b Pronotum with median ridge obliterated or at most a raised hairline, not noticeable in profile; body often somewhat broadened at middle legs; wings seldom banded..........................59

27a Antenna (A) long, broad, and flattened from base; frontal costa narrower than antenna. Fig. 204...............................
Psinidia fenestralis (Serville) Long-horned band-winged grasshopper

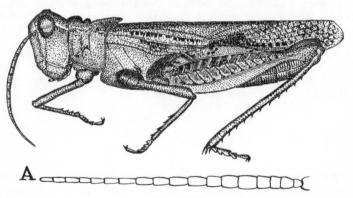

Figure 204

LENGTH: 15-25 mm. RANGE: Maine to Florida, Texas, and Nebraska.

Yellowish, brownish, reddish, or blackish with small markings, varying to match environment. Wing red, orange, or yellow with black band and spur. Hind tibia greenish-yellow, dark at ends and middle. Locally common. Sandy areas. Some adults even in winter in Florida.

P. amplicornis Caudell. Caudell's long-horned grasshopper, 21-28 mm., occurs in Texas. It is grayish with blackish mottlings; hind tibia blue, paler in females; antennae unusually broad.

27b Antenna not as described above..............................**28**

28a Tegmina and wings narrow and wing lacking a distinct band; pronotum with elevations on each side of midline. Fig. 205......
......*Trepidulus rosaceus* Scudder Shy rose-winged grasshopper

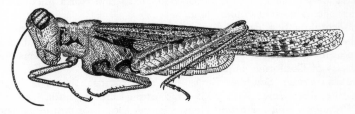

Figure 205

LENGTH: 22-28 mm. RANGE: California, Arizona, Nevada, and Utah.

Brownish with light and dark markings. Wing rose-red to clear with veins darker in usual band area. Hind tibia pale with dark areas. Sometimes common on desert flats and among desert growth. Quick and alert.

T. hyalinus (Scudder) Scudder's clear-winged grasshopper, is a clear-winged species which occurs in grassy areas in California. It has the pronotal elevations strongly developed.

28b Without this combination of characters.......................**29**

29a Pronotum with prozona and metazona about equal in length; eyes rather large, high, and protuberent; metazona rough with tubercles and short ridges, lateral prominences on each side near median ridge; hind femur slender; small. Fig. 206.....................
...........*Derotmema haydenii* (Thomas) Hayden's grasshopper

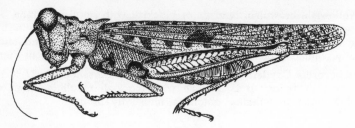

Figure 206

LENGTH: 20-30 mm. RANGE: Alberta and Saskatchewan to California, Arizona, Texas, and Mexico.

Brownish or gray, speckled with black. Wing red or yellow with broad band and long spur. Hind tibia yellowish-brown, mottled. Occurs on bare flats, in areas of sparse grass, and sandy-alkaline margins of wet spots. July to December. The Great Basin form is subspecies *rileyanum* Saussure. The West Texas and North Mexican form is subspecies *mesembrinum* Rehn.

D. *delicatulum* Scudder Delicate grasshopper, is small and pale with the wing almost colorless, the wing band not reaching front or hind margin, and ridges of pronotum weakly developed. Extreme desert areas of California and Arizona.

D. *saussureanum* Scudder Saussure's desert grasshopper, is a pretty California species with white and orange-brown markings.

29b Pronotum with metazona clearly longer than prozona; eyes usually smaller; metazona smooth or rough; hind femur slender or of normal breadth; small to rather large.......................30

30a Wing with some of dorsal anal veins swollen and heavily pigmented 58

30b Wing with anal veins normal, not swollen and heavily pigmented 31

31a Pronotum with median ridge rather low, pronotum slightly saddleshaped; slender and rather smooth. Fig. 207...................
........*Rehnita gracilipes* (Caudell) Rehn's slender grasshopper

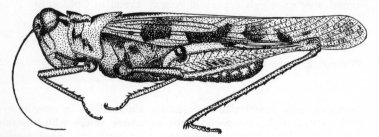

Figure 207

LENGTH: 22-29 mm. RANGE: Arizona and southern California.

Pale yellowish-brown with brown markings. Wing pale yellow, apex transparent. Slender and long-limbed. Hind tibia pale yellowish. Occurs on dry, bare, often rocky areas. Often comes to lights. May to October.

31b Pronotum with median ridge well elevated in part, pronotum not saddle-shaped; of average build, and usually with head and pronotum rather rough..**32**

32a Tegmen with intercalary vein rather straight and usually about midway between media and cubitus at its outer end; pronotum with metazona usually less than 1½ times as long as prozona, surface usually coarsely tuberculate; wing disc sometimes red.........**33**

32b Tegmen with intercalary vein usually curved and usually much closer to media than cubitus at its outer end; pronotum with metazona 1½ or more times as long as prozona, surface rather smooth to feebly tuberculate..**35**

33a Hind femur about 5 times as long as its greatest width. Fig. 208..
.................*Metator pardalinus* (Saussure) Pard grasshopper

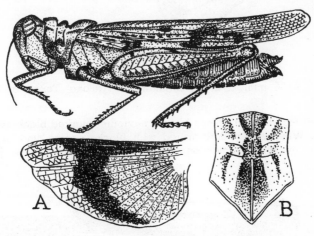

Figure 208

LENGTH: 28-37 mm. RANGE: Alberta and Manitoba to Arizona and Texas.

Grayish or brownish, mottled blackish. Tegmen with pale streak along anal vein. Wing (A) yellow, orange, or red; band with long spur. Hind tibia more or less bluish. June to September in grass and sedge areas. (B) shows the pronotum from above.

M. nevadensis (Bruner) is a Nevada species similar to above which occurs commonly in company with *Arphia pseudonietana* in well watered meadow bottoms. It tends to hide instead of taking flight when disturbed.

33b Hind femur about 4 times as long as its greatest width........**34**

127

34a Pronotum with hind angle of lateral lobe broadly rounded to nearly right-angled (see also *Trachyrhachis mexicana*). Fig. 209.......
..........*Mestobregma plattei* (Thomas) Platt range grasshopper

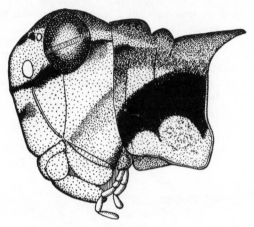

Figure 209

LENGTH: 25-35 mm. RANGE: Montana to Arizona, Texas, and Oklahoma.

Brown, tegmina with black bands, pronotum marked black obliquely at sides. Wing disc yellow or red with black border. Hind tibia yellowish or bluish. Common on rocky soil with sparse grass. June to October.

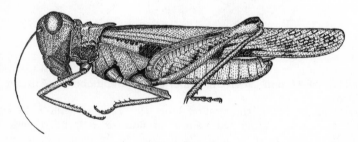

Figure 210

M. terricolor Rehn, (Fig. 210) Dirt-colored grasshopper, 25-38 mm., occurs in Arizona and Texas from July to September, on adobe flats. The wing is red with dark band. Hind tibia pale bluish.

M. impexum Rehn Narrow-fronted grasshopper, 28-32 mm., occurs from California to Idaho, Utah, and Arizona. Wing disc red or yellow, hind tibia buff; frontal costa decidedly constricted between antennal bases. Sandy or dry soil areas with scattered bunch grass. September.

M. thomasi Caudell Ash-brown grasshopper, 17-26 mm., occurs in central U.S. The wing is greenish or yellow with a faint band. Hind tibia with a whitish ring near base. Rocky areas, roadsides, and abandoned fields. May fly into trees to escape.

34b Pronotum with hind angle of lateral lobe acutely produced. Fig. 211......*Trachyrhachis kiowa* (Thomas) Kiowa range grasshopper

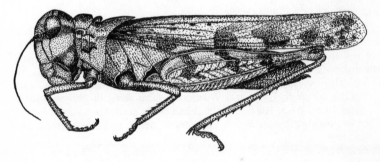

Figure 211

LENGTH: 18-26 mm. RANGE: British Columbia and Manitoba to Mexico. General except Michigan, Louisiana, and some of the Atlantic states.

Grayish, brownish, or greenish. Tegmen usually 3-banded; markings variable. Wing transparent, not banded, faintly yellowish toward base. Hind tibia blue to black, paler at base. Found commonly in grassy areas. Adults June to October.

T. mexicana Saussure Mexican band-winged grasshopper, averages larger than *kiowa* and has the wing yellow and banded, and the hind tibia blue. Sometimes destructively common in areas of sparse grass. Arizona to Mexico and New Mexico. The lateral lobes of the pronotum have the hind angles rounded.

T. coronata Scudder Crowned grasshopper, has the tegmen with 5 to 7 spots, the wing yellow and banded, and the hind tibia buff. Arizona to New Mexico and Colorado.

35a Pronotum with median ridge distinct on metazona; lateral lobe with lower edge nearly straight, usually angling down toward the rear, usually acute at rear; tegmen with dark markings usually confined to front half. Fig. 212..*Conozoa carinata* Rehn Ridged grasshopper

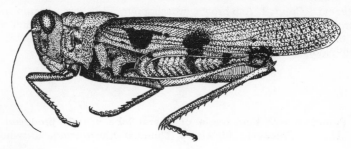

Figure 212

LENGTH: 28-35 mm. RANGE: Arizona.

Brownish. Median ridge of pronotum high. Wing yellow with black band and long spur. Hind tibia yellow. Cultivated areas and sandy washes in desert grassland at moderately high elevations. April to November.

C. wallula (Scudder) Wallula grasshopper, 25-35 mm., occurs from the Pacific states to Utah and Wyoming. The wing is yellow with black band and spur. Hind tibia reddish with pale ring and blackish at base, varying to yellowish. Occurs in areas of sparse grass, in river bottoms, etc.

C. sulcifrons Scudder Groove-headed grasshopper, 25-32 mm., occurs from Arizona to California and Utah. Brownish with yellow wing and black band with spur. Hind tibia faintly reddish, whitish toward base. The median ridge of the pronotum is low. Occurs in cultivated areas, low flats, and arroyos, at rather low elevations. March to November.

35b Pronotum with median ridge usually faint or obliterated on metazona; lower edge of lateral lobe broadly rounded at rear or with a tooth (see also *T. agrestis* and *T. albolineata*); tegmina with dark markings usually completely crossing them....................36

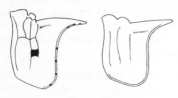

Figure 213

36a Pronotum with median ridge strongly elevated on prozona; hind tibia not reddish. Fig. 213. 37

36b Pronotum with median ridge scarcely to moderately elevated; hind tibia sometimes reddish..40

37a Head markedly elevated; head, thorax, and hind femur marked
with white. Fig. 214...
.....*Trimerotropis albolineata* (Brunner) White-lined grasshopper

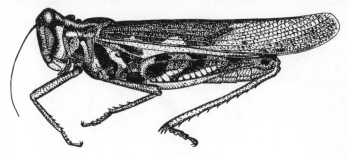

Figure 214

LENGTH: 29-33 mm. RANGE: California to southern Arizona.

Brownish, sometimes rusty. Wing yellow, band not intense. Occurs
on sandy areas about trees. Not a typical *Trimerotropis*. Shows some
relationship to *Derotmema* and *Conozoa*.

37b Head normal; not marked with white lines.....................38

38a Wing disc pale bluish to greenish-blue; tegmen banded; hind tibia
usually blue, whitish near base, varying to yellowish. Fig. 215....
Trimerotropis caeruleipennis Bruner Caerulean-winged grasshopper

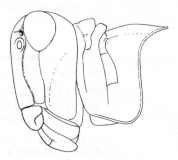

Figure 215

LENGTH: 21-30 mm. RANGE: Santa Catalina Island and California to
Washington, and the Rocky Mountains.

Brownish. Wing band and spur indicated as blackened veins or a
faint cloud. Wing twice as long as wide. A yellowish form occurs on
beach dunes about vegetation.

131

38b Wing disc yellow; tegmen banded to plain; hind tibia yellowish..**39**

39a Pronotum with tooth at hind angle of lateral lobe; western. Fig.
216..........*Trimerotropis cristata* McNeill Cristate grasshopper

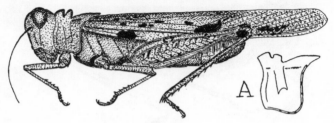

Figure 216

LENGTH: 25-29 mm. RANGE: California to Lower California, Arizona,
and Utah.

Pale brownish to reddish-brown. Wing disc faintly greenish-yellow,
band distinct but weak, spur short. Hind tibia yellowish. Occurs from
March to July in extreme desert areas.

T. bilobata Rehn and Hebard, 17-24 mm., (A) is a Great Basin species,
occurring from eastern Oregon, Washington, and California to Kansas. It is similar to *cristata* but darker and lacks the tooth on the
pronotal lobe. Sandy desert areas.

T. texana (Bruner) resembles the above but has the wing disc opaque
yellowish-green at base, a broad wing band, and hind tibia dull
orange with light subbasal ring. Bare spots in rocky areas of New
Mexico and western Texas. A slow flier.

39b Pronotum with hind angle of lateral lobe rounded. Fig. 217......
.........*Trimerotropis huroniana* Walker Great Lakes grasshopper

LENGTH: 19-28 mm. RANGE: East end of
Lake Superior, North end of Lake Michigan, and South shore of Lake Huron.

Pale brown with darker bands to rusty-
brown and unbanded. Wing pale yellow,
banded, spur reaching half-way to base.
Hind tibia dull yellow, base sometimes
paler. The pronotal profile easily separates
this from other species occurring with it.
Closely related to *T. saxatilis* and *T. pallidipennis*.

Figure 217

132

40a Wing disc and band area uniformly brown; wing often unusually wide and triangular in shape. Figs. 218, 219.............*Trimerotropis maculata* (Scudder) Brown-winged mountain grasshopper

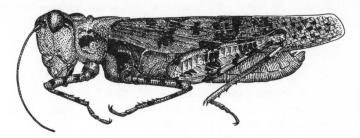

Figure 218

LENGTH: 27-30 mm. RANGE: California and Nevada.

Gray or brown with dark blotchy marks. Unusually fuzzy. Wing often clear near tip. Hind tibia light brownish, paler near base. Flies with a buzzing sound. Occurs in granite areas at high altitudes as along crest of Sierra Nevada mountains. A peculiar species which approaches *Circotettix* in some respects.

Figure 219

40b Wing disc not brown, band of a different color than disc, sometimes faint or absent; wing usually narrower or more rounded...41

41a Pronotum very broad, lateral lobes much wider at bottom than at middle, lobes flaring out conspicuously when viewed from above. Fig. 220....*Trimerotropis arenacea* Rehn Rehn's dune grasshopper

Figure 220

LENGTH: 30-38 mm. RANGE: California and Nevada.

Buffy-whitish with scattered brownish spots. Wing yellowish, band strong, spur short. Hind tibia pale yellowish. The unusual pronotum makes this an easily recognized species. On dunes.

41b Pronotum not as described above...........................**42**

42a Head marked with one or two black bands on front, above and below bases of antennae. Fig. 221...............................

...........*Trimerotropis koebelei* (Bruner) Koebele's grasshopper

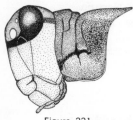

Figure 221

LENGTH: 25-28 mm. RANGE: California.

Reddish or brownish to white with dark markings, matching habitat. Wing disc yellowish, band color rather weak. Hind tibia blue or bluish, a white ring near base. The upper facial band is sometimes absent, the lower one almost always present. Rather closely allied to *T. fontana*. Moderate elevations on bare patches in grassy areas.

T. cincta (Thomas), 28-38 mm., occurs from Arizona and Oregon to the Dakotas. It is brown with dark bands on the tegmina. The face has black bands above and below the antennal bases. It occurs at moderate elevations on volcanic sand and gravel under yellow pines. Males fly with a distinct whirr. Closely allied to *fontana* and *koebelei*.

42b Head with front not marked as above........................**43**

43a Pronotum with tooth at hind angle of lateral lobe. Fig. 222......

............*Trimerotropis strenua* McNeill Strenuous grasshopper

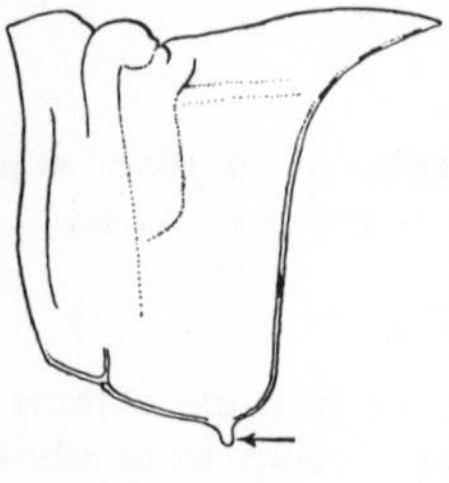

Figure 222

LENGTH: 32-42 mm. RANGE: Great Basin, Oregon, and California to Colorado and Texas. Whitish, gray, or brown with dark bands on tegmina. Wing yellow with strong band and spur. Hind tibia reddish with light ring near base. The pronotal tooth is occasionally absent but will be present on most specimens where a series is collected. Occurs on rocky soil in grassy areas. An active species which superficially resembles *T. pallidipennis*. June to October, commonest in August.

T. pacifica Bruner occurs in California and resembles *strenua* but has the hind tibia yellow.

43b Pronotum with no tooth on lower margin of lateral lobe........44

44a Wing with disc yellow and area from band to tip black; tegmina usually not distinctly banded. Fig. 223.........................
......*Trimerotropis suffusa* Scudder Crackling forest grasshopper

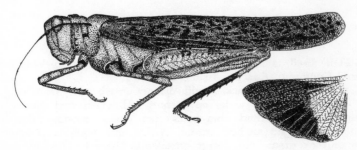

Figure 223

LENGTH: 33-40 mm. RANGE: British Columbia and Alberta to New Mexico, Arizona, and California.

Dark brown to black, tegmina without distinct contrasting bands. Wing sulphur-yellow with outer portion blackish. Hind tibia blue to greenish, mottled brown toward base. Forest and rocky areas. Occurs in a wide variety of habitats at high and low altitudes. Noisy in flight. This is a somewhat unusual species, classified at present in *Trimerotropis*.

"*Circotettix*" *verruculatus* (Kirby) the Cracker grasshopper of the Northeast closely resembles and is closely related to *T. suffusa*. It is a noisy and accomplished flier which occurs commonly in rocky areas. It is not very closely related to the western species of typical *Circotettix*.

44b Wing with area from band to tip clear to smoky; tegmina usually banded 45

45a Hind tibia reddish or orange in large part....................46

45b Hind tibia not colored reddish or orange.....................52

46a Wing band wider than disc. Fig. 224. . . . .

. . . . *Trimerotropis latifasciata* Scudder Broad-banded grasshopper

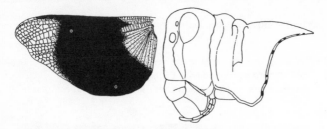

Figure 224

LENGTH: 29-46 mm. RANGE: Great Basin, Alberta to Washington and California, Arizona, Texas, and Iowa.

Gray or brown to blackish with distinct crossbands. Wing disc yellow to whitish, band wide, spur short. Abdomen and thorax with orange-red areas. Hind tibia red, often yellow outside near base. Fastigium with no median carina. Wary and vigorous. Occurs on bare or rock areas and desert grasslands. June to October.

T. melanoptera McNeill Black-winged grasshopper, occurs from Utah and Colorado to Mexico. Similar to *latifasciata* except wing band still wider and spur absent. In openings in areas of tall grass. June to September.

46b Wing band narrower than disc. **47**

47a Length 48 mm. or more; wing band with very short spur; antenna long and heavy. Fig. 225. . . . .

. . . . *Trimerotropis magnifica* Rehn Magnificent grasshopper

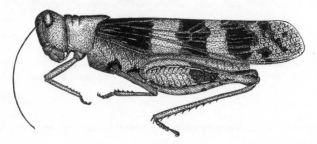

Figure 225

LENGTH: 48-56 mm. RANGE: Arizona to Texas, southwest Kansas, and Colorado.

Brownish, tegmina banded darker. Wing pale yellow, spur nearly obsolete. Antenna about 19 mm., long, heavy. Hind tibia red. Occasional on bare patches in grasslands. Resembles *Hadrotettix* to some extent but hind femur reddish-black inside. Related to *T. tolteca* and *pistrinaria.*

47b Length 45 mm. or less; wing band with spur reaching ½ way or more to base; antenna slender..............................**48**

48a Pronotum with hind angle of lateral lobe drawn down as a very large acute tooth. Fig. 226......................................
........*Trimerotropis agrestis* **McNeill Toothed field grasshopper**

LENGTH: 23-35 mm. RANGE: Great Basin, Alberta and Manitoba to Texas and Utah.

Figure 226

Plain brown with faint speckled indications of crossbars. Wing yellow, band entire, spur extending ½ way to base. Hind tibia red, yellowish near base. Found on sandy areas and bare patches among low weeds. Among cactus and sage in dry bottomland. Both sexes make crackling sounds just before landing. The specimen used for the drawing is from a population in which the tooth on the pronotal lobe is exceptionally large. Other populations referred to *agrestis* may have this tooth much less well developed.

48b Pronotum with hind angle of lateral lobe rounded to obtuse.....**49**

49a Species occurring in eastern U.S. Fig. 227......................
.............*Trimerotropis maritima* **(Harris) Seaside grasshopper**

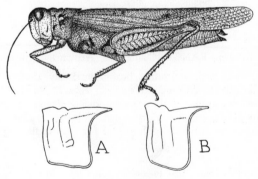

Figure 227

LENGTH: 19-35 mm. RANGE: Atlantic states to Great Lakes.
    Brown, tegmina sometimes faintly banded or mottled, usually rather plain. Wing pale yellow, band narrow, spur present. Hind tibia buff

137

to dull pink. Southern coastal specimens, (*acta* Hebard) tend to have whitish markings on head and pronotum. Great Lakes specimens (*interior* Walker) average a little smaller and more intensely colored. The pronotal profile readily separates *T. huroniana* (B) from interior (A) which may occur alongside.

T. citrina Scudder (A) Citrus-winged grasshopper, 20-32 mm., is similar to *maritima* except wing disc more strongly yellow to greenish-yellow. The hind tibia is pinkish, paler toward base. Gray, brown, or reddish with faint blackish marks. Occurs from Iowa and Pennsylvania to Florida, Texas, and eastern Arizona. A common species of wide distribution which has no striking distinguishing characteristics.

49b Species occurring in western U.S. (see also *T. citrina* above)....50

50a Wing narrow, twice as long as wide. Fig. 228..................
....*Trimerotropis inconspicua* Bruner Inconspicuous grasshopper

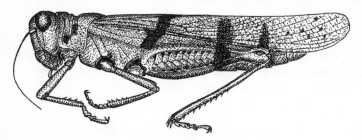

Figure 228

LENGTH: 25-32 mm. RANGE: California, Arizona, Utah, and Colorado.

Dark grayish-brown, tegminal bands variably distinct. Wing yellowish with band interrupted to entire. Hind tibia reddish. Occurs among yuccas, on rocky soil in exposed positions, in pinyon-juniper forest, and in river valleys of western Colorado. The narrow wing appears to be the most reliable character for distinguishing this species.

50b Wing broader, less than twice as long as wide................51

51a Tegmen (A) with first and second crossbands sharp, distinct, and separated by more than the width of one band. Fig. 229A.......
.....*Trimerotropis pistrinaria* Saussure Barren lands grasshopper

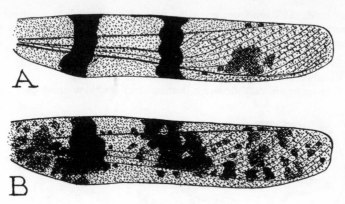

Figure 229

LENGTH: 30-36 mm. RANGE: Alberta, Montana, and the Dakotas to Mexico.

Brownish-gray with banded tegmina. Superficially resembles *Hadrotettrix*. Wing yellow with black band and broad spur which reaches about ½ way to base. The male eye is about equal to the fastigial width when viewed from above, narrower than fastigium in female. Hind tibia red. Hind femur reddish-yellow inside, a black band on apical ½ continuous with band on outer surface. Occurs on dry gravelly plains and hillsides and on eroded barren lands. June to October.

T. campestris McNeill Campestral grasshopper, is similar but with the tegminal bands irregular and broken. It occurs from British Columbia and Alberta to Arizona and Minnesota. August and September in grasslands of Upper Sonoran and Transitional zones.

T. humile (Morse) Morse's band-winged grasshopper, is similar to *pistrinaria* except that the male eye is wider than fastigium when viewed from above, that of the female about equal to fastigium in width. Occurs in Colorado at moderate elevations.

51b Tegmen (B) with first and second crossbands usually irregular and closer together than the width of one band. Fig. 229B.............
........*Trimerotropis laticincta* Saussure Great Plains grasshopper

LENGTH: 26-32 mm. RANGE: Alberta and the Dakotas to Mexico.

Brownish or gray with darker markings. Wing yellow with black band and spur. Hind tibia red.

T. tolteca subspecies *modesta* Bruner, Toltec band-winged grasshopper, 31-38 mm., Arizona to New Mexico, Colorado, and Mexico, has the tegmina distinctly or indistinctly banded. It resembles the above and is also related to *T. citrina*. The wing is nearly 2/3 as broad

139

as long. The hind angle of the lateral pronotal lobe is acute. Occurs on volcanic sand and gravel under yellow pines, and on grasslands. It crackles when alighting. June to August.

52a **Wing with band strong and entire, disc whitish to yellow, hind tibia yellow or yellowish. Fig. 230.............................**
Trimerotropis pallidipennis (Burmeister) Pallid-winged grasshopper

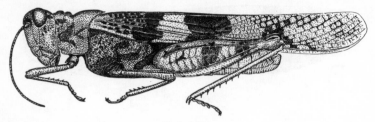

Figure 230

LENGTH: 31-42 mm. RANGE: British Columbia to Manitoba and south to Chile in South America.

Grayish, brownish, or reddish, usually with distinct crossbars on tegmina. Typically the wing band is beyond the middle of the wing and the spur reaches over ½ the distance to base. Occurs in a wide variety of habitats to 8,500 feet. The subspecies *salina* McNeill has the wing band in the middle and the spur reaches less than ½ the distance to base. Occurs in alkali areas, and is usually more reddish without strong bands on tegmina, and wing band weak. *Salina* occurs from Alberta, Saskatchewan, and Manitoba to Oklahoma and Colorado. It resembles *T. maritima interior*.

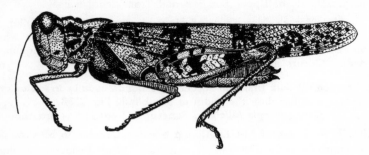

Figure 231

T. saxatilis McNeill, 23-33 mm., Rock-loving grasshopper, (Fig. 231) is a rock-frequenting eastern species with hind tibia greenish, paler at base. Colors vary to match lichen-covered rocks.

T. arizonensis Tinkham is somewhat similar to *pallidipennis* but with wing greenish, spur of band short, blunt, and poorly defined, and hind tibia greenish. It occurs sparingly in the Black Mountains of Arizona where it was taken on a gravelly knoll in a wash.

52b Without the above combination of characters..................53

53a Wing with band entire, disc usually blue; hind tibia blue in large
part, or brown. Fig. 232.......................................
......*Trimerotropis cyaneipennis* Bruner Blue-winged grasshopper

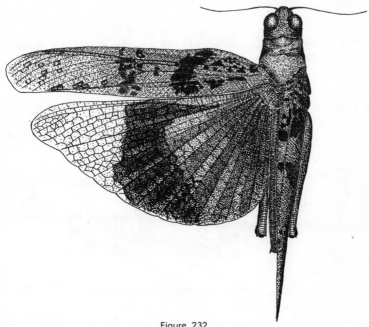

Figure 232

LENGTH: 26-38 mm. RANGE: California to Idaho, Utah, and Texas.

Brownish, tegmina banded. Wing usually blue varying to greenish-blue, yellow-green, silvery-blue, or purple. Wing band distinct, spur long. Hind tibia with pale ring near base. Occurs in canyons, on rocky slopes, and on gravelly soil in forested areas from 3,000 to 8,500 feet. A beautiful insect which is wary and vigorous. It crackles in flight.

T. occidentalis (Bruner) Occidental grasshopper, 21-30 mm., occurs in California west of the Sierra Nevada. The tegmina are brownish or grayish, more or less distinctly banded; the wing is feebly bluish, the band and long spur faint and the hind tibia blue, white basally. On rocky slopes with low or scanty grass. Often common.

53b Wing with band strong or weak, usually interrupted to dilute and indicated only as darkened veins and a smoky wingtip........54

54a Head, thorax, hind femur, and tegmina white or whitish or marked with white; wing band interrupted and weak, but traceable.....55

54b Not white or whitish or marked with white; wing-band sometimes clearly discernable, more often not............................56

55a Tegmen marked with narrow distinct crossbands; general appearance spotted. Fig. 233..
.....*Trimerotropis albescens* McNeill McNeill's white grasshopper

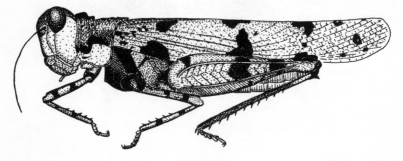

Figure 233

LENGTH: 22-28 mm. RANGE: California.

Whitish with black markings. Head and pronotum whiter. Wing pale yellow, band faint, broken. Hind tibia blue with white ring near base and base black. Mountain forest areas.

55b Tegmen marked with numerous black specks which are sometimes concentrated to form irregular and indistinct bands; general appearance speckled. Fig. 234...................................
.......*Trimerotropis helferi* Strohecker Helfer's dune grasshopper

142

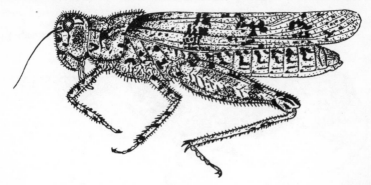

Figure 234

LENGTH: 19-30 mm. RANGE: Coast of northern California.

Brownish with black markings, white markings on head, pronotum, and hind femur. Hind tibia yellowish. Unusually pubescent. Wing almost clear with band weak and interrupted. Prozona often depressed. Occurs on beaches and dunes along the coast. Associated with *Artemesia pycnocephala*.

56a Tegmen distinctly banded; hind tibia blue. Fig. 235............
.............*Trimerotropis fontana* Thomas Fontana grasshopper

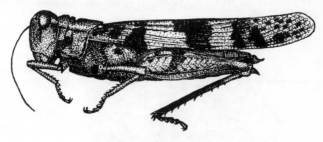

Figure 235

LENGTH: 23-35 mm. RANGE: California and Santa Catalina Island to Montana, Wyoming, Colorado, and Arizona.

Blackish, pinkish, brownish, or yellowish, tegmina with distinct bands. Wing yellow to pale greenish. Wing band weak to strong, area from band to wingtip sometimes clouded. Hind tibia blue, pale near base. Related to *koebelei* and *cincta*. Found on rocky slopes in grassy areas, on bare spots, in vacant lots, along roads, etc. June to October. Variable. Often varies to match environment.

143

56b Tegmen not distinctly banded; hind tibia not blue............57

57a Wing disc clear or pale bluish or greenish. Fig. 236............
..........*Trimerotropis sparsa* (Thomas) **Great Basin grasshopper**

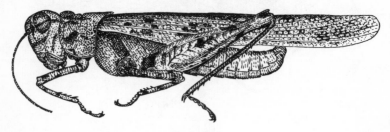

Figure 236

LENGTH: 27-37 mm. RANGE: Great Basin, Dakotas to Arizona, California, Oregon, and Washington.

Grayish-brown, speckled and mottled, tegminal bands poorly defined. Wing band narrow, pale, sometimes indicated only as blackened veins. Hind tibia yellow or brownish to greenish-buff. Occurs on bare eroded desert areas, alkaline flats, etc. They often whirr or crackle in flight, just before alighting.

57b Wing disc pale yellow or greenish-yellow. Fig. 237............
....*Trimerotropis gracilis* (Thomas) **Thomas' slender grasshopper**

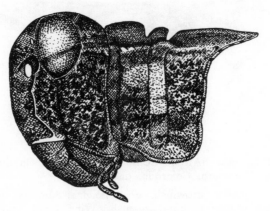

Figure 237

LENGTH: 28-35 mm. RANGE: Great Basin, British Columbia, Alberta, and Saskatchewan to California, Arizona, and New Mexico.

Dull grayish-brown, tegminal bands indistinct. Wing band indistinct, narrow, or absent; spur, when present, extending more than halfway to base. Hind tibia yellowish or brownish. Occurs in sagebrush areas where it is often almost impossible to see, so well does it match its surroundings. The more northerly populations are called subspecies *sordida* Walker. It occurs especially in sandy, alkaline spots.

T. thalassica Bruner California greenish-winged grasshopper, 23-32 mm., occurs in the coastal mountains of California and on Santa Catalina Island. It is rather granular appearing, with the tegminal bands mostly indistinct. The hind tibia is blue with a dull whitish ring near base. Wing pale greenish with band faint. Head unusually deep. They are rather fearless, fly only short distances, and often land in manzanita bushes. Locally fairly common.

58a Wing with all of anal veins swollen (Fig. 238); fastigium of male as wide as long. Fig. 239.....................................
***Aerochoreutes carlinianus* (Thomas) Carlinian snapper grasshopper**

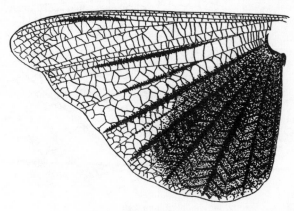

Figure 238

LENGTH: 32-45 mm. RANGE: Alberta and Manitoba to Nevada and Colorado.

Light gray-brown to reddish or purplish. Hind tibia dull yellowish. In the North more intensely colored specimens having the dark wing color more extensive, the wing tip longer, and the tegmen distinctly banded occur on sandy-alkaline eroded areas. A paler form, which is noisier in flight, occurs on dark mud outcrops and summer fallow fields. Intermediates are plentiful. A long-winged subspecies *strepitus* Rehn occurs from Nevada to British Columbia and Wyoming. In hot weather *Aerochoreutes* often hovers for many minutes at heights of 25 to 50 feet, whirring and clattering continuously.

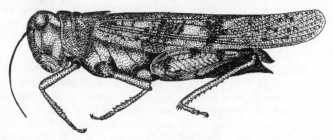

Figure 239

58b Wing with some but not all of anal veins swollen (Fig. 240); fastigium of male longer than wide. Fig. 241 ....
...... *Circotettix rabula* Rehn and Hebard Wrangler grasshopper

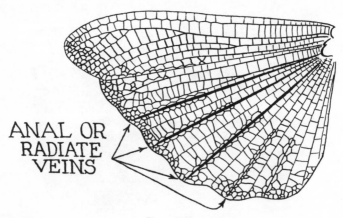

ANAL OR
RADIATE
VEINS

Figure 240

LENGTH: 38-42 mm. RANGE: British Columbia to Manitoba, Arizona, New Mexico, and Oklahoma.

Gray to brown, pinkish, or purplish, mottled darker. Wing yellow with fragmentary band. Hind tibia yellowish to brownish. Often found as "different looking populations." Steep rocky and eroded areas. Quick erratic flight and prolonged hovering accompanied by very loud sharp snapping and crackling sounds. The subspecies *nigrafasciatus* Beamer with stronger wing band occurs from Colorado to South Dakota and Kansas. The subspecies *altior* Rehn occurs at higher altitudes in Arizona, Utah, Colorado, and New Mexico.

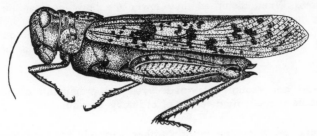

Figure 241

C. coconino Rehn Coconino grasshopper, common at higher altitudes in Arizona, is stockier, the tegmina and wings proportionally shorter, and the hind tibae blue.

C. crotalum Rehn Rattling grasshopper, occurs in Nevada and California. It is grayish or brownish and has a yellow wing with irregular band and two axillary veins. Hind tibia blue.

C. shastanus Bruner Shasta grasshopper, 31-33 mm., occurs in the mountains of California and Oregon. It has the wing yellow with outer half clouded with traces of a band. Hind tibia blue.

C. undulatus (Thomas) Undulant-winged grasshopper, 35-42 mm., occurs from British Columbia to California, Utah, and Wyoming. It often has the wing partly blue and partly green, sometimes bluish, or greenish, or yellowish. Hind tibia blue. It somersaults and hovers while producing loud snaps and crackling sounds. In rocky areas.

59a Head strongly elevated; eyes prominent; pronotum saddle-shaped; hind femur slender Fig. 242.....................................
.....*Spaniacris deserticola* (Bruner) Spanistic desert grasshopper

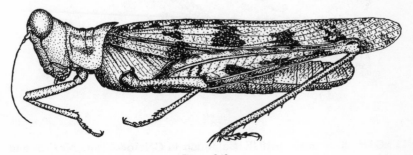

Figure 242

LENGTH: 19-34 mm. RANGE: California.
Whitish with brown markings. Wing faintly greenish. Flight low, direct, short. Occasional on dry sandy desert areas where vegetation

is sparse. When disturbed they lower the body against the ground, raising the legs in a spiderlike manner. This has recently been transferred to the subfamily ROMALEINAE. Because there is no outer spine at end of hind tibia this does not fall in that subfamily in the present key.

59b Head not strongly elevated; eyes not prominent; pronotum not saddle-shaped; hind femur of ordinary breadth.................60

60a Pronotum with hind margin rather narrowly rounded to angulate at middle as viewed from above.............................61

60b Pronotum with hind margin rather broadly evenly rounded as viewed from above..62

61a Fastigium with side ridges abruptly convergent ahead of compound eye and narrowly separated at apex (A); front margin of pronotum usually with a pair of short rounded projections (B) especially on the female; subgenital plate of female with median projection at apex; wing with no band. Fig. 243...........................
...............*Cibolacris parviceps* (Bruner) Cream grasshopper

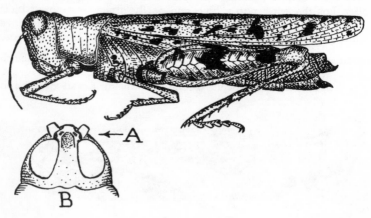

Figure 243

LENGTH: 20-32 mm. RANGE: California to Colorado, New Mexico, and Mexico.

Cream, gray, brown, or reddish, tegmina with blackish markings. Wing clear or bluish. Hind tibia white or blue. March to August on thin, rocky soils and overgrazed range, bare areas and gravelly washes in the desert.

61b **Fastigium with side ridges gradually converging and widely separated at apex (A); front margin of pronotum even; subgenital plate of female with no median projection at apex; wing band usually discernable. Fig. 244.** . . . .*Heliastus benjamini* Caudell Arroyo grasshopper

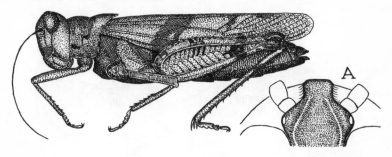

Figure 244

LENGTH: 21-32 mm. RANGE: Arizona, New Mexico, and Texas to Mexico.

Brown, tegmen with dark bands. Wing reddish with outer portion clouded. Hind tibia pale toward base, reddish toward apex, usually dark at middle. June to October on grasslands and in washes and arroyos.

62a **Pronotum with lateral lobes produced posteriorly. Fig. 245** . . . . . .
. . . .*Coniana snowi* Caudell Snow's desert grasshopper

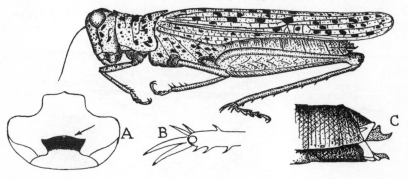

Figure 245

LENGTH: 19-25 mm. RANGE: Southern California, Nevada, and Utah.

Whitish with small dark spots. Wing clear. Hind tibia white. (A) shows the metasternum, (B) tip of hind tibia, and (C) the ovipositor. Compare with *Xeracris*. Sometimes common in sandy areas of the

149

Lower Sonoran zone in association with the low-growing plant *Coldenia palmeri*. Adults until October. Adults sometimes bury themselves in the sand overnight.

62b Pronotum with lateral lobes not produced posteriorly..........**63**
63a Hind femur very broad, about 3 times as long as greatest width.
    Fig. 246...*Shotwellia isleta* **Gurney Shotwell's range grasshopper**

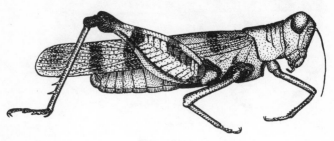

Figure 246

LENGTH: 21.5-30 mm. RANGE: Vicinity of Isleta Indian reservation, New Mexico.

Pale brownish with dark markings. Wing clear, faintly yellowish at base, faintly clouded in band area. Hind tibia yellow with a whitish ring and blackish base. The few known specimens were taken in short grass.

63b Hind femur narrow, about 5 times as long as greatest width....**64**
64a Metasternal interspace (A) about as long as wide in female, longer than wide in male. Fig. 247...................................
    ....*Xeracris minimus* **(Scudder) Least desert grasshopper**

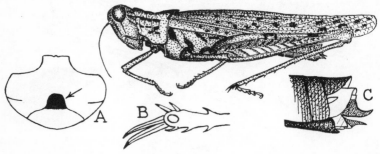

Figure 247

LENGTH: 12-20 mm. RANGE: California to Nevada and Arizona.

Tan with brown and white markings. Wing clear. Hind tibia yellowish. (A) shows the metasternum, (B) tip of hind tibia, and (C) the ovipositor. Compare with *Coniana*. Occasional from July to October in sandy areas, associated with such plants as *Dicoria canescens*, *Petalonyx thurberi*, and *Eriogonum* spp. Small males measure less than ½ inch in length and are our smallest acridids.

64b Metasternal interspace transverse in female, square or transverse in male. Fig. 248.....*Anconia integra* **Scudder Alkali grasshopper**

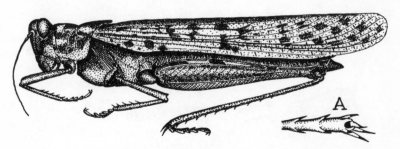

Figure 248

LENGTH: 22-42 mm. RANGE: California, Arizona, Nevada, and Utah.

Gray, brown or green, more or less distinctly spotted, often with small white markings, pronotum often with pale yellowish marks. Wing clear or bluish. Hind tibia yellowish, mottled with brownish. Occurs from March to August on alkali flats and bare adobe flats. Flies to lights. (A) shows tip of hind tibia.

A. hebardi Rehn Hebard's desert grasshopper, occurs in Texas. It is brownish with faint tegminal bands and mottling. The wing is blue with no band. Hind tibia faintly greenish-white, darker near base. An early spring form found in a small arroyo and on gravelly area of an adobe flat with scattered mesquite and *Atriplex*.

A. caeruleipennis Bruner Blue-winged desert grasshopper, is grayish, stouter than *integra*, with the wing bright blue. Found in Nevada.

SECTION 2—ACRIDIDAE

N this second artificial key section are included the remainder of the grasshoppers to be covered in this book. These are the forms usually classified as subfamilies *Acridinae* (slant-faced grasshopper), and *Cyrtacanthacridinae* (spur-throated grasshopper). About a dozen not very closely related elongate genera are grouped together for convenience at the start, followed by the slant-faced genera, with the spur-throats after.

KEY TO SECTION 2, ACRIDID GRASSHOPPERS

la Form decidedly slender and elongate; antenna more or less conspicuously sword-shaped, usually flattened and rather broad at

base, or triangular in cross-section; face varying from slanting to nearly horizontal 2

1b Form moderately slender to robust; antenna slender to moderately flattened and narrowly sword-shaped, or broadened at tip; face vertical to slanting 13

2a Tegmina reaching about to tip or past tip of abdomen........... 3

2b Tegmina short, not reaching to tip of abdomen.................. 9

3a Wing of male with front portion strongly fenestrate (A). Fig. 249...
..... *Metaleptea brevicornis* (Johannson) Short-horned grasshopper

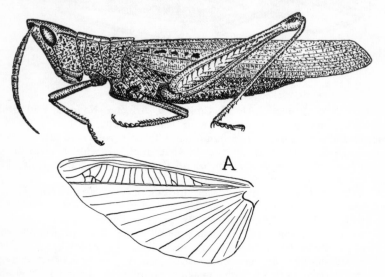

Figure 249

LENGTH: 19-35 mm. RANGE: Ontario and New England, Nebraska, and Arkansas, south to Florida and Argentina.

Green, brown, or both; brownish beneath. Hind tibia brownish. Locally common in sedges and rank grasses bordering fresh and salt water and in wet swales. Sometimes flies to light.

3b Wing of male not fenestrate................................... 4

4a Tegmen pointed at tip.. 5

4b Tegmen rounded at tip.. 7

5a Prosternum with an erect structure at middle, between front legs; eyes strongly converging in front as seen from above; head and pronotum lacking longitudinal ridges.......................... 6

5b Prosternum with no erect structure at middle; eyes subparallel as seen from above; head with a distinct median ridge, especially on anterior half; pronotum with distinct lateral ridges. Fig. 250......
Achurum sumichrasti Saussure Sumichrast's toothpick grasshopper

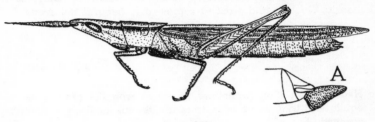

Figure 250

LENGTH: 38-45 mm. RANGE: Arizona and Texas to Guatemala.

Yellowish to greenish-brown, brown stripes on head and pronotum, brownish beneath. Hind tibia brownish. (A) shows tip of male abdomen. Found on coarse grasses with which they align upon alighting. Adults June and July.

A. hilliardi Gurney, Hilliard's toothpick grasshopper, is a similar looking species which is known thus far only from a bog located two miles south of Warren, Tyler County, Texas.

In this genus the hind femur is spined at tip, and the fastigium is flattened at sides.

6a Head as long as pronotum or longer; fastigium with the proportions of an isoceles triangle as seen from above, and with a median longitudinal groovelike depression. Fig. 251....................
...*Leptysma marginicollis* (Serville) Cattail toothpick grasshopper

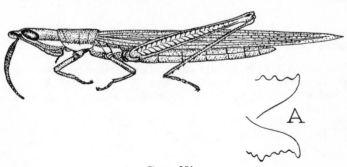

Figure 251

LENGTH: 28-38 mm. RANGE: Maryland to Kansas and Nebraska, Florida, and Texas.

Brownish or green, often suffused with pink, a yellowish stripe on side, brownish or greenish beneath. Hind tibia green or bluish. (A)

153

shows ovipositor. Found on sedges, grasses, and rushes bordering ponds and watercourses. Quick flight and clever dodging behind stems with which they align themselves make these hard to catch. Striking the vegetation as one walks slowly along often knocks them into the water from where they are easily taken. Specimens of *Leptysma* from California, Nevada and Arizona represent *L. hebardi* Rehn and Eades.

6b **Head shorter than pronotum; fastigium with the proportions of an equilateral triangle as seen from above, not medially longitudinally grooved. Fig. 252** ....*Stenacris vitreipennis* (Marschall) Glassy-winged toothpick grasshopper

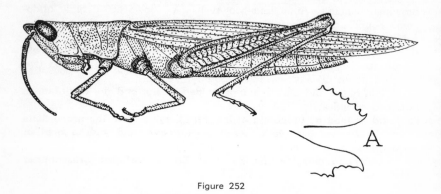

Figure 252

LENGTH: 24-29 mm. RANGE: Florida to North Carolina.

Green to yellowish, a faint stripe often present on side. Hind tibia green. (A) shows the ovipositor. A wary species found among cattails, sedges, etc., in bordering vegetation, especially about water.

7a **Tegmen with intercalary vein distinct; prosternum with no triangular elevation at middle; metasternal lobes distinctly separated; hind tibia orange with whitish ring near base. Fig. 253** ....*Acantherus piperatus* Scudder Slender range grasshopper

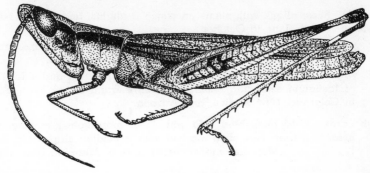

Figure 253

LENGTH: 19-29 mm. RANGE: Southeastern Arizona to Texas and Mexico.

Gray-brown with light markings, brown beneath. Hind tibia dull reddish. Occurs on rocky grasslands, especially in tall grasses under spiny shrubs up to lower edge of live oak zone. Adults June to October. Allied to *Horesidotes* but more elongate with sword-shaped antennae.

7b Tegmen with intercalary vein indistinct or absent; prosternum with a low triangular elevation at middle; metasternal lobes very close or touching at rear; hind tibia not ringed......................8

8a Smaller, 15-33 mm.; hind tibia with 14 or fewer spines in outer row; head and pronotum never marked with a median stripe. Fig. 254.. ...*Eremiacris acris* Rehn and Hebard Desert toothpick grasshopper

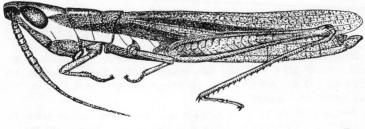

Figure 254

LENGTH: 22-32 mm. RANGE: Arizona and Nevada.

Light green to brown with pale stripe on side, brownish or greenish beneath. Hind tibia brown or green. Found on knee-high grass in grasslands. Flies, aligns with stems on which it alights, and dodges behind stems. Adults June to October.

E. *pallida* (Bruner) is similar but a little larger and with proportionally shorter head. It ranges to California and New Mexico.

E. *virgata* (Scudder) is similar but with longer tegmina and side ridges of fastigium extending behind the front margin of the eyes. Found in Colorado, New Mexico, and Arizona.

8b **Larger, 27-55 mm.; hind tibia with 15 or more spines in outer row; head and pronotum often marked with a median stripe. Fig. 255.**.
 . . . .*Mermiria maculipennis* Bruner **Mermiria grasshopper**

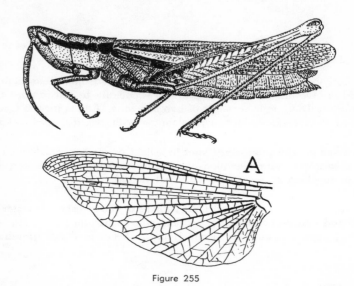

Figure 255

LENGTH: 38-51 mm. RANGE: Alberta and Saskatchewan south to Texas, Arizona, and Mexico.

Brownish to greenish with contrasting stripes, yellowish-brown beneath. Hind tibia reddish. Sometimes destructively common on the range and in cultivated areas. It jumps, dodges, and flies actively in rank grass and is hard to catch.

M. *bivittata* (Serville) is a similar species which occurs from Florida and South Carolina to Texas and Nebraska. Three additional rather similar looking U.S. species are known.

M. *texana* Bruner has sharply contrasting dark brown and yellow stripes on head and pronotum and a dark brown stripe along the midline above. It occurs from Arizona to Colorado, Texas, and Mexico.

9a Thorax roughly tuberculate; pronotum emarginate at middle of hind margin. Fig. 256...
.....*Clematodes larreae* Scudder Gray creosote bush grasshopper

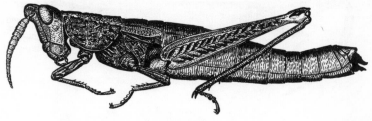

Figure 256

LENGTH: 20-28 mm. RANGE: Arizona to Mexico.

Mottled gray or brownish. The pronotum is rugose. Uncommon in collections. The excellent camouflage and secretive habits of this bush dweller make it hard to find. Reportedly commoner in the Chihuahua desert of Mexico. Adults May to July.

9b Thorax not roughly tuberculate; pronotum with hind margin truncate to rounded 10

10a Face nearly horizontal; antennae inserted in front of eye at a distance equal to the width of an eye. Fig. 257.................
.........*Prorocorypha snowi* Rehn Snow's toothpick grasshopper

Figure 257

LENGTH: 44-51 mm. RANGE: Arizona and Mexico.

Brownish with light stripe on side. This is the most elongate of our toothpick grasshoppers. It lives in tall grass at lower edge of live oak zone. It aligns with the stems, dodges, and hops actively.

10b Face strongly slanting; antennae inserted closer to eyes than maximum width of eye as seen in lateral view....................11

157

11a Head much longer than pronotum; hind femur terminating in prominent spines. Fig. 258.....................................*Radinotatum brevipenne* (Thomas) Long-headed toothpick grasshopper

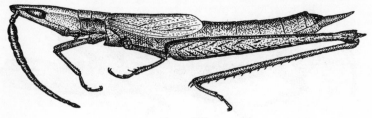

Figure 258

LENGTH: 31-48 mm. RANGE: Florida to South Carolina.

Brown or gray-brown, tegmina and legs sometimes partly green.
Found commonly on wire grass, tall grasses, and sedges in open pine
woods and bordering water. They are feeble jumpers and rely upon
protective mimicry for safety. They are scarcely noticeable when
aligned on dry grass. More elongate populations occur in southern
Florida and these have been called *R. b. peninsulare* Rehn and Hebard.
Adults may be found the year around. The antennae of *Radinotatum*
are strongly triangular in cross-section.

11b Head about the same length as pronotum or slightly longer; hind
femur not terminating in spines............................12

12a Pronotum with strong median and lateral longitudinal ridges; fastigium with strong median longitudinal ridge; foveolae of vertex
absent; hind femur of female moderately long. Fig. 259...*Pseudo-
pomala brachyptera* (Scudder) Short-winged toothpick grasshopper

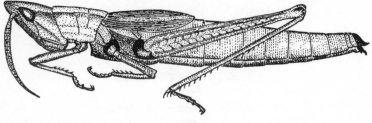

Figure 259

LENGTH: 25-35 mm. RANGE: New England to British Columbia and
south to Oregon, Nevada, Utah, Oklahoma, and Illinois.

Grayish or brown, yellowish-brown beneath. Hind tibia brownish.
Long-winged individuals occur. Found on coarse grasses, marsh elder

bordering salt marshes, and in various other situations. Locally common. Adults July and August.

12b Pronotum and fastigium with longitudinal ridge lines very feebly traceable; foveolae of vertex conspicuous, not visible to partly visible from above; hind femur of female small. Fig. 260......*Paropomala wyomingensis* (Thomas) **Wyoming toothpick grasshopper**

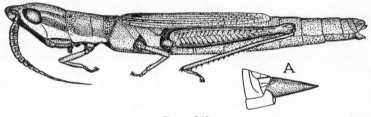

Figure 260

LENGTH: 20-29 mm. RANGE: Wyoming, Utah, Colorado, Nebraska, South Dakota, Kansas, and New Mexico.

Light green, brown, or both. (A) shows tip of male abdomen. Found on grass in moist places. This or a closely related form occurs in eastern California. Adults July to September.

13a Antenna with segments at end near apex widened and flattened, more strongly so in the male; prosternum with a distinct pyramid-like tubercle at middle, less developed in female; tegmen of male with veins enclosing large cells, many of them square, the costal marginal area fenestrate. Fig. 261..............................
........*Aeropedellus clavatus* (Thomas) **Club-horned grasshopper**

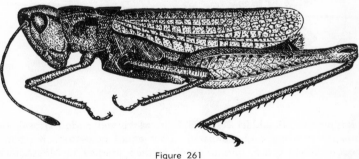

Figure 261

LENGTH: 17-19 mm. RANGE: Minnesota through southern Canada to Alaska, and from Montana and the Dakotas to Arizona and New Mexico.

Males usually greenish-black, females often conspicuously marked on head and pronotum with cream, green, and black. Sometimes destructively common on range grasses. Also found on sedges. Appears early in the season.

13b Without the above combination of characters..................**14**

14a Tegmen long and broad, that of male with intercalary vein strongly developed and equipped with stridulatory pegs which are readily visible at 20x; prosternum with a distinct conical tubercle at middle; last ventral abdominal segment of male conical, at least twice as long as wide..
.....*Stethophyma gracile* **(Scudder) Graceful sedge grasshopper**

LENGTH: 19-33 mm. RANGE: British Columbia to Newfoundland, south to Colorado, Nebraska, and New England.

Green to pale brown with faint yellowish stripes behind eyes, brownish beneath. Hind tibia yellowish, often with pale or dark ring near base. Found locally in rank grasses and sedges about ponds, marshes, meadows, and mountain tops. The males stridulate vigorously.

S. lineatum (Scudder) Striped sedge grasshopper, has a narrow yellow stripe running back from each eye, extending two-thirds the length of the tegmina. Occurs in sedge areas across southern Canada and the northern states.

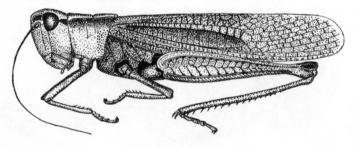

Figure 262

S. platypterum (Scudder) (Fig. 262) Broad-winged sedge grasshopper, has the prozona and metazona about equal in length. It occurs in sedge, dense grass, and tamarac swamp tangles in Massachusetts and Connecticut, Minnesota, Illinois, and Iowa, and South Carolina.

14b Without the above combination of characters..................**15**

15a Small southwestern desert species, living in bushes and stridulating loudly day and night; tegmen of male with discoidal vein
much thickened on ventral surface and, in conjunction with fenestrate marginal field, forming a powerful sound-producing mechan-
ism; prosternum with a low tubercle at middle................16

15b Without the above combination of characters.................17

16a Sexes similar in size; tegmen of male with fenestrate marginal
area largely divided by mediastinal vein. Fig. 263.............
............*Goniatron planum* Bruner Pecos clicker grasshopper

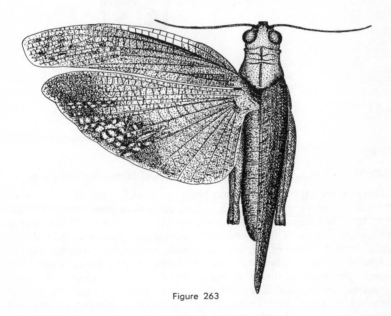

Figure 263

LENGTH: 18-27.5 mm. RANGE: Texas and Mexico.

Gray-brown or brown and speckled-looking, brownish beneath. Hind
tibia brownish-gray. Wing yellowish at base becoming brown toward
tip. Found on blackbrush, *Flourensia cernua* in what has been called
the Pecos Division of the Chihuahuan desert. These grasshoppers are
masters at "peek-a-boo" and their stridulations often have a ventriloquial quality.

16b Male decidedly smaller than female; tegmen of male with fenestrate marginal area not divided.............................
.......*Ligurotettix coquilletti* McNeill Desert clicker grasshopper

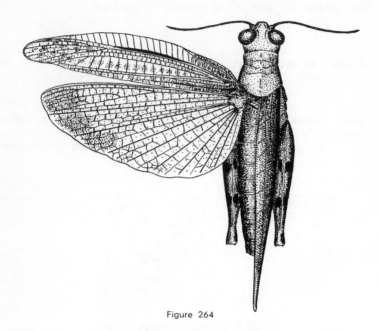

Figure 264

LENGTH: 11.5-26.5 mm. RANGE: Arizona, California, and Nevada.

Gray-brown with fine dark markings, yellowish beneath. Hind tibia brownish to feebly pale greenish. Wing clear or a little clouded blackish at tip. Common on stems of creosote bush. Males stridulate day or night when warm. Quick and elusive dodgers, jumpers, and flyers. Adults June to October. In Nevada small specimens representing the subspecies *cantator* Rhen occur on the scattered gray-green brush. The largest specimens occur in southern Arizona and represent the subspecies *kunzei* Caudell (Fig. 264). It prefers creosote bush. The typical subspecies *coquilletti* is characteristic of western Mojave desert and extreme western Colorado desert creosote bush areas in California. Many intermediates between races occur.

17a Prosternum with no spine or process at middle, between front legs 18

17b Prosternum with a prominent spine or process at middle, between front legs 47

18a Pronotum very broad, with hind margin undulant, surface rough, median longitudinal ridge sometimes arched up a little on prozona; face almost vertical; eye small; tegmina short. Fig. 265. . . . .
. . . .*Esselenia vanduzeei* Hebard   Vanduzee's grasshopper

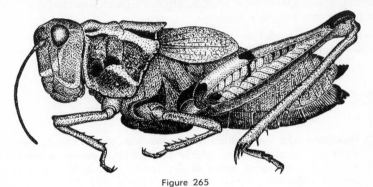

Figure 265

LENGTH: 13-23 mm. RANGE: California.

Brown with light and dark markings, brown beneath. Hind tibia brownish to dull reddish. Individuals which are boldly marked with yellow on pronotum and hind femora are especially fine for the collection. Found locally in grassy areas. Males are powerful leapers. This is a spring species.

18b Without the above combination of characters. 19

19a Green desert species with pearly markings; female antenna no longer than front femur; living in creosote bushes. Fig. 266. . . . . .
. . . .*Bootettix punctatus* Scudder   Creosote bush grasshopper

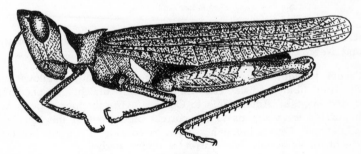

Figure 266

LENGTH: 20-26 mm. RANGE: Arizona and California to Mexico.

Green with pearly white, brown, and black markings, green beneath. Hind tibia green. Adults May to November.

B. argentatus Bruner is a very similar Texas and Mexican species. Adults are found throughout the year.

Found on creosote bush, *Larrea divaricata*. These peculiar and attractive grasshoppers show relationship to *Pedioscirtetes* and *Acrolophitus* (in section 1 of this key).

Bootettix males stridulate at night. The frontal costa is extremely narrow at upper end. Marginal area of male tegmen strongly fenestrate.

19b Without the above combination of characters..................20

20a Pronotum with longitudinal ridges obsolescent, front margin usually shallowly emarginate at middle in female; tegmina marked with scattered dark spots, some of the larger ones involving a reduction of underlying veins; wing pale bluish. Fig. 267............. ....*Heliaula rufa* (Scudder) Rufous grasshopper

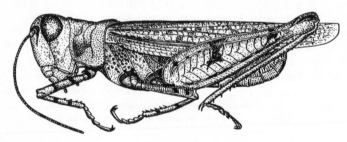

Figure 267

LENGTH: 19-25 mm. RANGE: Texas and Arizona to Utah, Colorado, and Nebraska.

Cream to light orange-brown with small markings, yellowish beneath. Hind tibia reddish. The wing is faintly bluish. An uncommon grassland species. Adults June to October. Grasshopper experts have been puzzled for years as to the correct placement of this species in classifications. One solution has been to consider it as not belonging in whichever subfamily was currently under study.

20b Pronotum with at least the median ridge distinct, front margin entire in female; tegminal spots, if present, not involving reduction of underlying veins..21

21a Fastigium with lateral foveolae rather distinct and visible from
  above; pronotum with lateral ridges (or markings in their stead)
  decidedly bent inward at middle.............................22

21b Fastigium with lateral foveolae indistinct or absent or not visible
  from above; pronotum with lateral ridges nearly straight, bent in
  at middle, or obsolete.......................................29

22a Hind tibia bluish; foveolae of head triangular.................23

22b Hind tibia not bluish; foveolae of head not triangular..........24

23a Subgenital plate of female strongly bisinuate at tip (Fig. 269A);
  male with inner spurs at tip of hind tibia strongly unequal (Fig.
  268A); tegmina leaving about one-third of abdomen exposed at
  end. Fig. 268...
  ...Drepanopterna femoratum (Scudder) White cross grasshopper

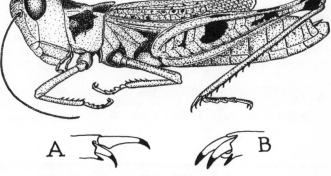

Figure 268

LENGTH: 16-25 mm. RANGE: Saskatchewan and Alberta south to
  Mexico.

Brownish with black markings, lighter beneath. Hind tibia blue.
Sometimes so common as to be destructive on range areas. Widely
distributed in the great plains. Adults June to October. Similar to
Aulocara elliotti (Thomas).

23b Subgenital plate of female weakly bisinuate at tip (Fig. 269B); male
  with inner spurs at tip of hind tibia moderately unequal (Fig. 268B);
  tegmina reaching nearly or quite to tip of abdomen. Fig. 269....
  ....Aulocara elliotti (Thomas) Elliott grasshopper

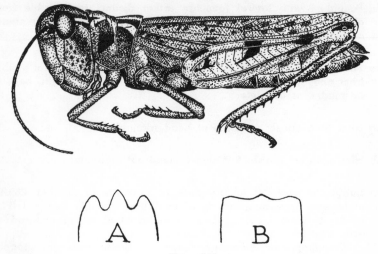

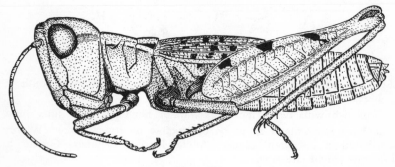

Figure 269

LENGTH: 20-27 mm. RANGE: British Columbia to Manitoba and south to Texas and California.

Gray-brown, a paler stripe commonly present along middle of back. Hind tibia blue, a pale ring near base. Sometimes destructively common, especially in short grass areas. Adults May through September.

24a Head disproportionally large; hind femora projecting far beyond end of body, hind tibia and antenna pale yellowish. Figs. 270, 271.
.....*Eupnigodes megocephala* (McNeill) Big-headed grasshopper

Figure 270

LENGTH: 12-15 mm. (Head to tip of abdomen). RANGE: California.

Light brownish with dark markings. Has been taken in numbers on salt-grass flats bordering a small stream feeding into San Joaquin

Valley, and at various other localities. The tegminal length of different populations may be different (see Fig. 271). This genus is close to *Ageneotettix*.

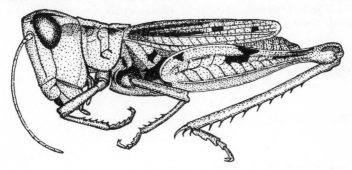

Figure 271

24b Head of normal or slightly large size; hind femora usually not projecting conspicuously past end of body; hind tibia and antenna not both pale yellowish.....................................25

25a Antenna whitish in life; hind tibia reddish; lateral ridges of pronotum obsolescent, usually replaced by light-colored markings. Fig. 272...*Ageneotettix deorum* (Scudder) White whiskers grasshopper

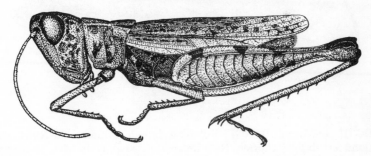

Figure 272

LENGTH: 10-22 mm. RANGE: Michigan to Alberta, California, Texas, and Mexico.

Brownish, commonly with a paler stripe along middle of back, yellowish beneath. Hind tibia red. Often common on grassland areas, especially where vegetation is scanty or the soil exposed and sandy. Adults June to November.

A. d. curtipennis Brunner is a short-winged form which occurs at somewhat higher altitudes, from California to Colorado.

A. sierranus Rehn and Hebard has a disproportionally long head, and is pale brownish with a few brown markings, antennae and hind tibiae pale brownish. Found in sparse grass areas of the southern Sierra Nevada mountains of California.

25b Without the above combination of characters..................26

26a Hind tibia with 12 or more spines in outer row..............27

26b Hind tibia with 10 or fewer spines in outer row..............28

27a Moderately slender; eye oblique; inner claws at tip of hind tibia subequal; pronotal disc proportionally more elongate. Fig. 273...
...*Chorthippus longicornis* (Latreille) Marsh meadow grasshopper

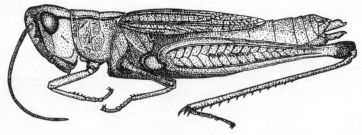

Figure 273

LENGTH: 13-24 mm. RANGE: Holarctic. British Columbia to Newfoundland, south to California, New Mexico, Arizona, Nebraska, Louisiana, and North Carolina.

Brown to green, sometimes contrastingly brown and green or marked with gray, pink, etc. Hind tibia brownish. Often common in damp grassy situations. Males draw attention by their stridulation. They make persistent small scale efforts to escape, especially on sunny days. Regional differences in appearance exist.

Recent studies indicate that more than one species is involved here, and that the European populations are different from ours.

27b Moderately robust; eye nearly vertical; inner claws at tip of hind tibia moderately unequal; pronotal disc proportionally shorter. Fig. 274.............*Bruneria brunnea* (Thomas) Bruner's grasshopper

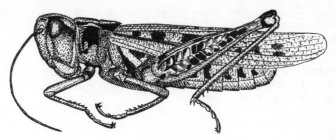

Figure 274

LENGTH: 18-25 mm. RANGE: British Columbia to Manitoba, and south to Utah and Colorado.

Head and pronotum brown or white or black with a yellow stripe along middle of top, tegmina shiny, spotted; brownish beneath. Hind tibia orange to red. Found on sedges and grass.

B. shastana (Scudder) is a brownish species found in California and Oregon. Females have the tegmina short. In males the tegmina reach pretty well back toward the tip of the abdomen. The tibia is red with black and white rings near base.

28a Pronotum with median ridge cut before middle; head rather broadly rounded at fastigium as seen in profile; antennal segments not flattened; lateral ridges of pronotum usually bordered by light-colored markings. Fig. 275......................................
..*Psoloessa delicatula* (Scudder) Brown-spotted range grasshopper

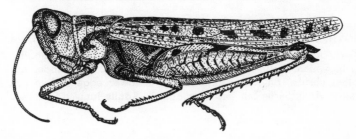

Figure 275

LENGTH: 16-22 mm. RANGE: Alberta to Manitoba, south to N.E. California, Arizona, and Texas.

Brown or dark gray to greenish with dark and light markings, yellowish beneath. Hind tibia yellow, reddish, bluish, or brown. A common grassland species. The subspecies *buckelli* Rehn occurs in British Columbia and Washington.

P. texana Scudder, with three subspecies, is a more slender species which occurs from the northern great plains to Mexico. It often has the lower half of the pronotal lobe light-colored. A common range species from April to September.

P. thamnogaea Rehn is a slender species in California and Lower California. Occasional individuals are somewhat reddish in color. Adults to January in south of range.

28b Pronotum with median ridge cut behind middle; head rather narrowly rounded at fastigium as seen in profile; antennal segments moderately flattened; lateral ridges of pronotum distinct but inconspicuous, usually not bordered by light-colored markings. Fig. 276 ....*Horesidotes cinereus* Scudder Ash-gray range grasshopper

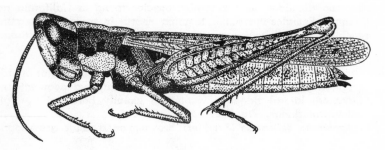

Figure 276

LENGTH: 19-25 mm. RANGE: Southern Arizona and southern California.

Gray-brown with light and dark markings, grayish beneath. Hind tibia brownish. Found on grass and other plants, often under mesquite or other shrubs, on rocky hillsides up to lower edge of live oak belt. Allied to *Acantherus* but less specialized. Adults June to October.

29a Frontal costa narrow with a narrow median groove; foveolae of head distinct beneath sides of fastigium; antenna distinctly flattened; lateral ridges of pronotum feeble. Fig. 277 ....*Cordillacris crenulata* (Bruner) Crenulated grasshopper

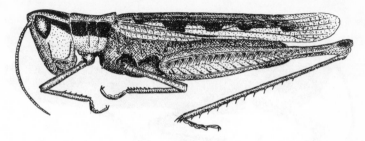

Figure 277

LENGTH: 17-21 mm. RANGE: Alberta to Texas and Arizona.

Light brownish, tegmen usually with a large dark brown crenulated central marking, cheeks often marked with gray; brownish beneath. Hind tibia brownish. Found especially in dry areas where the soil is thin and the grass sparse. When numerous it seriously hinders reseeding of range grasses. The subspecies *pima* Rehn occurs in Arizona and New Mexico. Adults May to September.

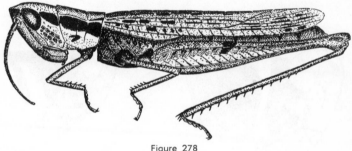

Figure 278

C. *occipitalis* (Thomas) (Fig. 278), 15-22 mm., occurs from Alberta to Manitoba, south to California, Arizona, New Mexico, and Texas. It is light brownish, tegmen spotted, sometimes whitish, cheeks often marked with gray, and brownish beneath. Hind tibia brownish. Often common on thin soil with scanty grass. Adults June to August.

29b Without the above combination of characters..................30

30a Male black; female usually green and brown with purplish hind tibia, sometimes entirely black; female head conspicuously large; male antenna longer than head and pronotum; wing bluish, often clouded at tip. Fig. 279...
..............*Boopedon nubilum* (Say) Black males grasshopper

171

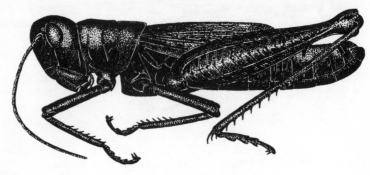

Figure 279

LENGTH: 25-39 mm. RANGE: Montana and South Dakota to Arizona and Texas.

Males and some females entirely black. Most females brown or partly gray or green. Common from August through October on grasslands.

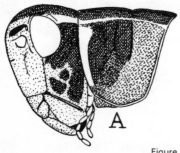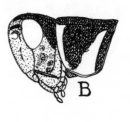

Figure 280

B. auriventris McNeill (Fig. 280B) is a brown species found from Texas to Iowa and Nebraska. The head and pronotum are shown in B.

B. gracile Rehn (Fig. 280A) is a brown species found from Texas to Kansas. The head and pronotum are shown in A.

30b Without the above combination of characters.................31

31a Hind tibia with 15-24 spines in outer row; sexes very different looking; male with tegmen strongly modified for stridulation and with
wing blackish or brown (A). Fig. 281...........................
Syrbula fuscovittata Thomas Brown-winged slant-faced grasshopper

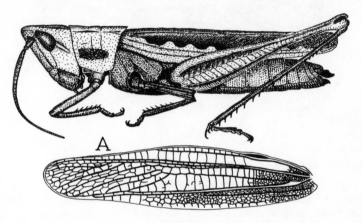

Figure 281

LENGTH: 25-39 mm. RANGE: Arizona to Texas and Colorado.

Female green, top of pronotum and large mark on tegmen brown.
Male dark brown with yellowish-white stripe along edge of tegmen
and lower edge of pronotum. Hind femur green with a blackish stripe
along middle. Greenish-brown beneath. Hind tibia brownish or blackish. Wing brown. Male tegmen as in A. The elegant elusive males
and the more easily captured females prefer taller range grasses. Males
stridulate conspicuously. Adults June to October.

S. *admirabilis* (Uhler) is similar and often common east of the Rocky
Mountains, north to Iowa, Nebraska, Indiana, Ohio, and Pennsylvania.

31b Hind tibia with 16 or fewer spines in outer row; sexes often much
alike in appearance; male wing not blackish or brown.........32

32a Pronotum with lateral ridges absent.........................33

32b Pronotum with lateral ridges present........................34

33a Hind tibia with 8 or 9 spines in outer row. Fig. 282..............
.......................*Zapata salutator* Rehn Zapata grasshopper

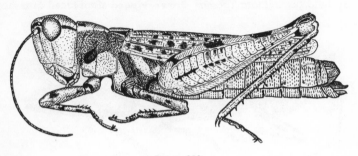

Figure 282

LENGTH: 12.5-16 mm. RANGE: Arizona.

Light brownish with darker markings, paler beneath. Hind tibia dull pink. Uncommon and hard to catch. Found among grasses on bare rocky slopes with saguaro and palo verde present. Catalina Mountains, Tucson Mountains at Tumamoc Hill, west to the Ajo and Sauceda Mountains. Adults August and September.

Z. brevipennis Bruner Short-winged zapata grasshopper, is a similar but short-winged Mexican form which occurs in the Chinati Mountains of Texas. It is small, uncommon, and a powerful leaper.

33b Hind tibia with 10 or more spines in outer row. Fig. 283.......
***Morseiella flaviventris* (Bruner) Yellow-bellied range grasshopper**

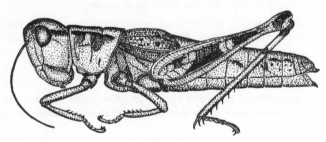

Figure 283

LENGTH: 22-35 mm. RANGE: Arizona and Mexico.

Brownish, the hind femora yellow with blackish marks, body yellow beneath. Hind tibia red. Sometimes destructively common on

174

range grasses. The red, yellow, and black hind legs enable immediate separation from structurally similar *Boopedon* with which *Morseiella* occurs.

34a Hind tibia with inner pair of spurs at tip about equal..........35

34b Hind tibia with inner pair of spurs at tip very unequal.......42

35a Male with tegmen strongly fenestrate........................36

35b Male with tegmen not strongly fenestrate....................37

36a Male tegmen (B) with middle (ulnar) portion strongly fenestrate; tegmina not reaching quite to end of abdomen; body not striped; pronotum with only one lateral ridge on each side. Fig. 284.....
........*Clinocephalus elegans* Morse Elegant marsh grasshopper

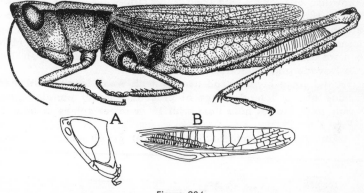

Figure 284

LENGTH: 17-28 mm. RANGE: New York to Texas and Florida.

Brown to olive, tegmina sometimes green, brownish beneath, Hind tibia brownish. Found in low moist areas bordering tidal marshes, especially on marsh spike grass *Distichlis, Scirpus,* and *Spartina.* Sometimes found in inland bog areas. "A" shows head of male.

36b Male tegmen (A) with marginal area strongly fenestrate; tegmina reaching past end of abdomen; body usually striped; pronotum often with paired lateral ridges. Fig. 285.......................
..*Amphitornus coloradus* (Thomas) Striped slant-faced grasshopper.

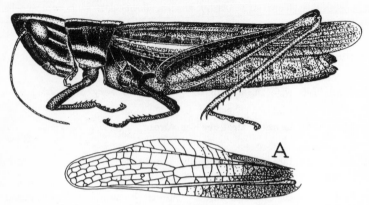

Figure 285

LENGTH: 17-24 mm. RANGE: Illinois to Texas, California, Oregon, Washington, and British Columbia.

Brownish or grayish with contrasting stripes, yellowish or brownish beneath. Hind tibia blue or purple. Often common in grassy areas. The subspecies *saltator* Hebard occurs at high altitudes in Nevada, Arizona, and Utah. It is short-winged. The subspecies *ornatus* McNeill is a more contrastingly colored form which ranges from British Columbia to Nevada and California.

37a Frontal costa broad; head usually with weak longitudinal median ridge above; lateral ridges of pronotum nearly parallel throughout; color brown; hind tibia with 16 or fewer spines in outer row. Fig. 286 ....
. . *Amblytropidia occidentalis* (Saussure) Brown winter grasshopper

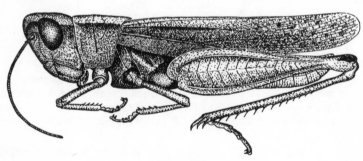

Figure 286

LENGTH: 19-32 mm. RANGE: Florida to Virginia, Oklahoma, and Texas.

Brown to gray, lighter beneath. Hind tibia brownish. The eye is large and the principal pronotal sulcus intersects but does not cut the median ridge. Found in old fields and open pine woods. Sometimes common. Adults in winter in Florida.

A. mysteca Saussure is a similar species which occurs in southern Arizona, Texas, and Mexico. Adults in winter.

37b Without the above combination of characters.................38

38a Tegmen of female reaching past end of abdomen; frontal costa narrow; head with no median ridge above; lateral ridges of pronotum usually divergent on metazona; color often green or grayish-brown. Fig. 287...
...........*Orphulella compta* Scudder Green desert grasshopper

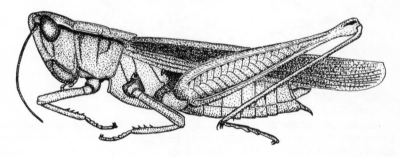

Figure 287

LENGTH: 15-25.5 mm. RANGE: California, Arizona, Nevada, and Utah.
Green, brown, or both, brownish beneath. Hind tibia brownish or greenish. Sometimes destructively common in alfalfa and barley, and in areas of green grass such as along water courses. The pronotum is usually somewhat elongate with lateral ridges parallel on prozona, divergent on metazona.

O. *speciosa* (Scudder) occurs from Manitoba and Ontario to North Carolina, Alabama, Louisiana, Texas, Colorado, Wyoming, and Montana. It usually has the pronotum proportionally shorter and its lateral ridges only moderately bent in. The tegmina often do not reach the tips of the hind femora or exceed them by no more than 1 mm. The foveolae of the head are not closed below.

O. *pelidna* (Burmeister) with its western subspecies *dasereta* Scudder, occurs from Canada to Mexico and from coast to coast except the extreme northeast. The tegmina of eastern specimens commonly extend 2 mm. or more past the tips of the hind femora. The foveolae of the head are usually closed below.

38b Tegmen of female not reaching to tip of abdomen.............39

39a Fastigium usually with a weak longitudinal median ridge; antenna distinctly flattened; colors mostly browns; upper valve of ovipositor often with prominent teeth in addition to the apical ones......40

39b Fastigium with no median ridge; antenna scarcely at all flattened; color often green; upper valve of ovipositor with a prominent tooth only at apex. Fig. 288...
..*Dichromorpha viridis* (Scudder) Short-winged green grasshopper

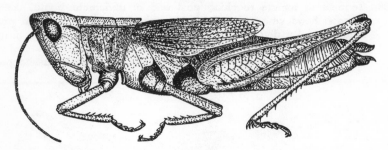

Figure 288

LENGTH: 15-27 mm. RANGE: Florida to New Mexico, Minnesota, Michigan, New York, and Massachusetts.

Green or brown or both, lighter beneath. Hind tibia greenish or brownish. Occurs in vegetation bordering fences, roads, lakes, ponds, ditches, etc. Adults are found all through winter in Florida. More seasonal northward.

40a Pronotum with hind margin cut squarely across as seen from above. Fig. 289......*Chloealtis conspersa* (Harris) Sprinkled grasshopper

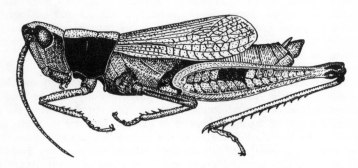

Figure 289

LENGTH: 15-28 mm. RANGE: British Columbia to Ontario, south to South Carolina, Oklahoma, and Colorado.

Brown to gray, male black on pronotal lobes, female tegmina commonly sprinkled with small black specks; yellowish beneath. Found in thickets, bordering vegetation, grassy areas, etc. Males stridulate conspicuously but are wary and jump rapidly and repeatedly. The eggs are laid in wood. Adults June to September.

40b Pronotum with hind margin obtusely angled as seen from above. . 41

41a Tegmen of male about 3 times as long as wide; fastigium bounded at front by narrow ridges with no trace of foveolae present. Fig. 290. . .*Neopodismopsis abdominalis* (Thomas) Thomas' grasshopper

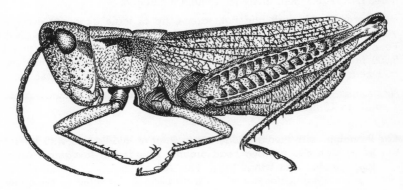

Figure 290

LENGTH: 18-28 mm. RANGE: British Columbia to Ontario, south to Arizona, New Mexico, and Louisiana.

Brown, paler beneath. Hind tibia brown, darker toward apex, or red. Found in hilly areas in openings in the forest, and on grasses and sedges, especially in low-lying areas. Males behave a lot like those of *Chloealtis*.

**41b Tegmen of male about 4 times as long as wide; fastigium bounded at front by sloping facets which often have their central portions a little depressed to form feeble foveolae. Fig. 291. . . . .
. . . .*Napaia aspasma* Rehn and Hebard Welcome grasshopper**

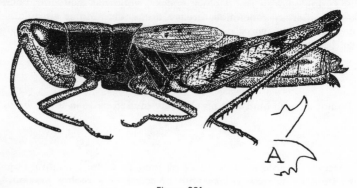

Figure 291

LENGTH: 17-23.5 mm. RANGE: Southern Oregon.

Brownish with dark and light areas, tip of male abdomen orange; yellowish beneath. Hind tibia reddish. (A) shows the ovipositor. Found in grassy spots in open forest and on a treeless summit at about 5,600 feet in the Siskiyou Mountains, in grass at Woodruff Meadow, and near Corvallis. Males stridulate much like males of *Chloealtis*.

N. gracilis McNeill is a similar but paler form which occurs farther south in California.

**42a Pronotum with median ridge cut in front of middle and with lateral lobes high and narrow; head broadly rounded at fastigium in profile; tegmina and wings long. Fig. 292..........................
........*Rhammatocerus viatoria* (Saussure) Traveller grasshopper**

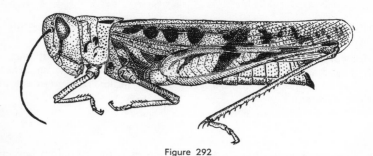

Figure 292

LENGTH: 25-38 mm. RANGE: Arizona to Texas, Mexico, Honduras, Guatemala, and Costa Rica.

Light and dark brown, often with green areas, brownish beneath. Hind tibia brownish, often darker toward tip. Found among grasses on grasslands and rocky slopes. Adults October to August of the following year.

42b Pronotum with median ridge usually cut behind middle or not cut at all, and usually with lateral lobes about as long as high or longer than high; head broadly or narrowly rounded at fastigium in profile; tegmina and wings short to long.................**43**

43a Head large, broadly rounded at fastigium in profile; face not very strongly slanting; green with distinctive light and dark markings. Fig. 293 ....
Phlibostroma quadrimaculatum (Thomas) Four-spotted grasshopper

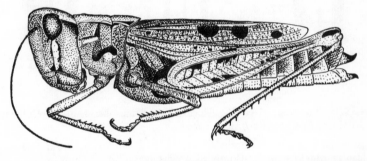

Figure 293

LENGTH: 14-25 mm. RANGE: Manitoba and Alberta south to Arizona and Texas.

Green or brownish with black and yellow markings; light brownish beneath. Hind tibia brownish. Sometimes numerous on dry short-grass range areas. Adults July to September. Selected specimens rank among our most attractive grasshoppers.

43b Head of normal size, rather narrowly rounded at fastigium in profile; face more or less strongly slanting; green or brown but differently marked **44**

44a Pronotum about equally wide in front and rear as seen from above and with lateral ridges about parallel, supplementary ridges (between median and lateral ridges) absent; head with only a median ridge at fastigium. Fig. 294...................................
.................*Opeia obscura* (Thomas) Obscure grasshopper

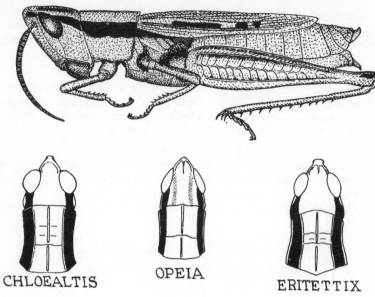

CHLOEALTIS   OPEIA   ERITETTIX

Figure 294

LENGTH: 13-25 mm. RANGE: Alberta and Manitoba, south to California Arizona, New Mexico, and Texas.

Brownish, green, or both; brownish beneath. Hind tibia brownish, or faintly blue-greenish. Sometimes destructively common in grain and on the range. The head and pronotum of *Opeia, Chloealtis,* and *Eritettix* are shown for easy comparison (Fig. 294). Adults April to October.

O. *atascosa* Hebard is an uncommon southern Arizona species in which the spurs (calcaria) at the tip of the hind tibia are nearly equal in length. These are very unequal in O. *obscura.* Adults May to October.

44b Pronotum usually wider at rear as seen from above and with lateral ridges usually bent inward at middle, supplementary ridges (between median and lateral ridges) often present, and a corresponding pair of weak ridges often present on top of head......45

45a Tegmen usually long, reaching beyond tip of abdomen; antenna often a little flattened at tip; head usually with supplementary ridges on top...
............*Eritettix simplex* (Scudder) Velvet-striped grasshopper

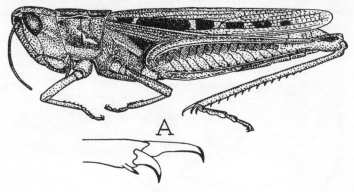

Figure 295

LENGTH: 16-24 mm. RANGE: Alberta and Saskatchewan south to Texas, and eastward from Connecticut to Florida.

Gray, brown, or green or combinations of these; paler beneath. Individuals occur with a light-colored stripe along the middle of the pronotum, usually accompanied by supplementary lateral ridges. Hind tibia mottled brownish. (A) shows calcaria at tip of hind tibia. Often fairly common on grassy areas, old fields, etc. Adults April to October. Males stridulate but rather quietly. *E. variabilis* Bruner (Fig. 295) is a similar brownish species which is often common on grasslands of Arizona, New Mexico, and southwestern Texas.

45b **Tegmen short, not reaching to tip of abdomen; antenna narrowly sword-shaped with several segments beginning with segment 3 flattened and widened** **46**

MESOCHLOA

MACNEILLIA

Figure 296

46a Pronotum with lateral ridges strongly bent in at middle and with hind margin strongly to weakly obtusely angulate at middle behind, lateral lobes with strong relief pattern. Figs. 296, 297......
....*Meso-chloa abortiva* (Bruner) Texas short-winged slant-faced grasshopper

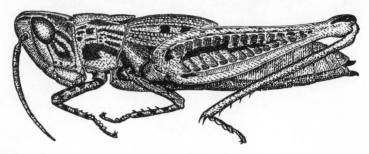

Figure 297

LENGTH: 9-16 mm. RANGE: Texas.

Green to brown, yellow lines on pronotum, brownish beneath. Rather common in April in closely grazed pastures of central Texas. Males have the hind femora reaching far past the tip of the abdomen.

46b Pronotum with lateral ridges moderately bent in at middle and with hind margin weakly obtusely angulate with a small feeble emargination at middle behind, lateral lobes with no strong relief design. Figs. 296, 298..
...........*Macneillia obscurum* (Scudder) McNeill's grasshopper

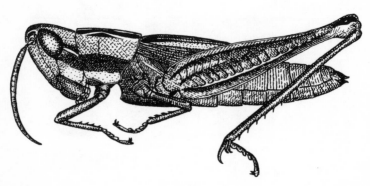

Figure 298

LENGTH: 13.5-24 mm. RANGE: Florida.

184

Brown or brown and green, a light stripe bordered by dark ones accompanied by supplementary ridges sometimes present along midline above, brownish beneath. Hind tibia brownish. Found especially in open pine and oak woods and in wire grass clumps. Often occurs locally in colonies of limited extent. Adults present through winter from October to April.

47a Mesosternum with lateral lobes longer than wide (A). Fig. 299..48

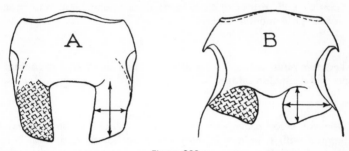

Figure 299

47b Mesosternum with lateral lobes as wide as long or wider than long (B). Fig. 299...56

48a Male with tegmen narrow, length about 9 times width at middle; restricted to "rosemary" *Ceratiola ericoides* Michx. in sand scrub areas of central Florida; nocturnal. Fig. 300............*Schistocerca ceratiola* Hubbell and Walker Rosemary bird grasshopper

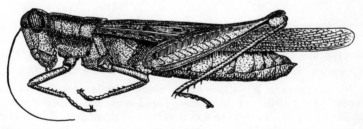

Figure 300

LENGTH: 24.4-36 mm. RANGE: North central Florida.

Gray-brown, finely mottled greenish with a faint pale stripe along middle of head and pronotum; yellowish to whitish beneath. Hind tibia reddish or brownish. A slender nocturnal species occurring only in areas of white very sandy soil. Though hard to locate in daytime, they are easily collected in the early hours of night when they move to the outer portions of the bushes to feed and mate.

48b Male with tegmen proportionally broader, length about 5 to 8 times width at middle; on various host plants; diurnal...............49

49a Tegmen with rather distinct large dark spots; head and pronotum with a pale median stripe....................................50

49b Tegmen plain colored or, if spotted, then head and pronotum with no pale median stripe.......................................51

50a General color brownish; hind femur without distinct crossbands; tegmen with a pale subcostal stripe on basal third. Fig. 301.....
..........*Schistocerca americana* (Drury) American grasshopper

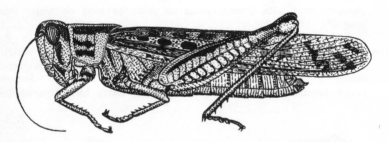

Figure 301

LENGTH: 39-55 mm. RANGE: Ontario to West Indies, Mexico, Central America, Columbia, and Argentina, west to the Great Plains.

Various browns, a yellow stripe along middle of back; yellowish beneath. Hind tibia red. A common and sometimes very destructive migratory species which occurs in a variety of situations. Adults present the year around in Florida, seasonal farther north. The northernmost records are based upon migrants, resident populations occurring mostly south of the 40th parallel.

50b General color grayish; hind femur with distinct crossbands. Fig. 302............*Schistocerca vaga* Scudder Gray bird grasshopper

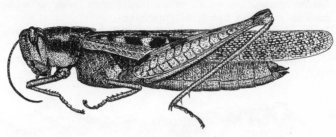

Figure 302

LENGTH: 40-70 mm. RANGE: California to Texas, Mexico, and Nicaragua.

Gray or brownish, a pale stripe along middle of top of head and pronotum; brownish beneath. Hind tibia brown to black. A large powerful flier which is sometimes destructively common. It occurs north to Lake County in California.

Schistocerca gregaria of Africa and *S. paranensis* of South America are two of the most destructive grasshoppers in the world.

51a Foliage green with red hind tibia; head and pronotum commonly with a median yellow stripe. Fig. 303..........................
.........*Schistocerca shoshone* (Thomas) Green bird grasshopper

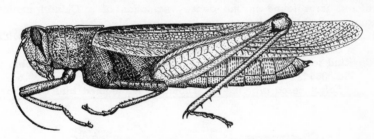

Figure 303

LENGTH: 37-64 mm. RANGE: California to Mexico, Colorado, and Texas.

Green, a yellow stripe commonly present along middle of top of head and pronotum; light brownish beneath. Hind tibia red. Tergites of abdomen without small black rows of dots commonly found on members of this genus. Sometimes destructively common. Often found in rank vegetation along streams and ditches, as well as in fields, gardens, hillside brush, and other situations. Careful handling is needed to preserve the bright green color—but it can be done.

51b Darker green, brownish, or purplish-brown, with or without pale
median stripe on head and pronotum.........................52
52a Dark, almost blackish, with bright yellow mark on lateral lobe of
pronotum. Fig. 304..
......*Schistocerca chinatiensis* Tinkham Chinati bird grasshopper

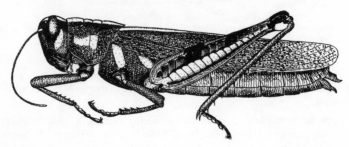

Figure 304

LENGTH: 51.5-52.5 mm. RANGE: Texas, Chinati Mountains, and Carls-
bad, New Mexico.

Black with yellow marks on head and pronotum, a yellow stripe
along middle of back, tegmina becoming brownish toward tips, hind
femur yellowish and white with black crossbars on top. Hind tibia
black with black-tipped yellow spines. A large uncommon strikingly
colored form found in the dense vegetation of a Chinati mountain
canyon. Probably also occurs in northern Mexico.

52b Greenish, brownish, or purplish-brown; pronotum usually without
a bright yellow mark on lateral lobe.........................53
53a Hind femur with very distinct blackish crossbands; hind tibia red.
Fig. 305 ....
..*Schistocerca albolineata* (Thomas) White-lined bird grasshopper

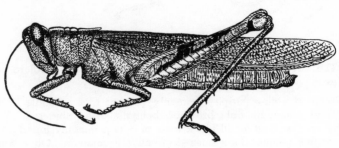

Figure 305

LENGTH: 36-52 mm. RANGE: Southeastern Arizona to Mexico.

Brownish with yellow stripe along middle of back, hind femur yellow with black cross bands above. Hind tibia red. Usually in hilly areas on various shrubby plants. Adults, August through October. Occasional specimens have a yellow spot on pronotal lobe, about as in *chinatiensis*.

53b Hind femur without distinct crossbands, or with weak brownish or pink crossbands; hind tibia usually brownish..................54

54a Larger species, proportionally rather elongate; female usually 45 mm. or more in length; pronotum not much narrowed as seen from above, the median ridge moderately raised...................55

54b Smaller species, proportionally rather short and stocky; female usually under 42 mm. in length; pronotum rather narrow as seen from above with the median ridge sharply raised. Fig. 306........ *Schistocerca damnifica* (Saussure) Mischievous bird grasshopper

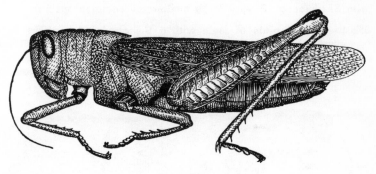

Figure 306

LENGTH: 25-42 mm. RANGE: Pennsylvania to Illinois and south to the Gulf of Mexico.

Reddish-brown, a pale stripe along middle of head and pronotum; yellowish beneath. Hind tibia brownish. Specimens from Florida to South Carolina are more compressed and slender and usually thickly sprinkled with tiny dark specks and represent the subspecies *calidior* Rehn and Hebard (Fig. 306). Often common along roads, in old fields, on hilltops, in open places in oak and pine woods, etc.

55a Subgenital plate of male with deep V-shaped notch at tip; tegmina usually purplish-brown; females very large, 50-60 mm. in length. Fig. 307 ....*Schistocerca obscura* (Fabricius) Obscure bird grasshopper

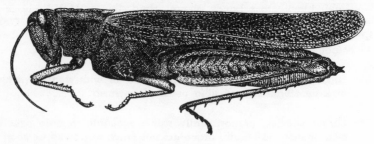

Figure 307

LENGTH: 34-61 mm. RANGE: Maryland to Florida, Texas, and Mexico.

Dark olive green to purplish-brown, a yellow stripe sometimes present along middle of back, unstriped females sometimes faintly spotted; brownish beneath. Hind tibia blackish-purple with black-tipped yellow spines. Found in a variety of situations, often together with *S. alutacea.* A very large moderately common species.

55b Subgenital plate of male with a U-shaped notch at tip; tegmina usually brownish to greenish; females usually less than 50 mm. in length. Fig. 308..
.........*Schistocerca lineata* Scudder Spotted bird grasshopper

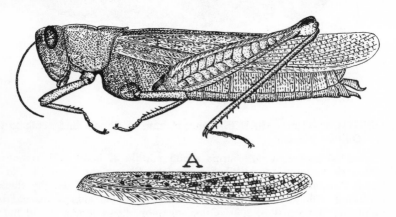

Figure 308

LENGTH: 23-50 mm. RANGE: Alberta to Arizona, New Mexico, Texas, Tennessee, North Carolina and north to Connecticut.

Reddish-brown, a yellow stripe along middle of back, yellow spots on hind portions of pronotum; brownish beneath. Hind tibia brownish,

190

pink, or blackish. The hind femora vary from uniformly brown to banded above. In the region from Iowa to New Mexico green individuals with red hind tibiae closely resemble *S. shoshone*, but have black specks on the abdominal tergites. The yellow dorsal stripe is sometimes weak or absent.

S. alutacea (Harris) Leather-colored bird grasshopper, yellowish-brown to olive, dorsal yellowish stripe always present; brownish beneath, hind tibia yellowish, brownish, reddish, or black. Occurs from Massachusetts to Florida and Texas, in southern Great Lakes region, and locally in northern Alabama, Tennessee, Arkansas, and Oklahoma. Prefers moist habitats.

S. rubiginosa (Harris) Rusty bird grasshopper, is very similar to both *alutacea* and *lineata* except eyes a little more protuberant and male pronotum widened at front to receive head, as viewed from above. it occurs from New Jersey to Florida and west to Texas with local populations in northeastern Alabama, and on the Piedmont of Virginia and the Carolinas. It generally prefers drier situations than *alutacea*. The dorsal stripe is often feeble or absent. "A" shows the tegmen of the spotted variety. *S. lineata*, *alutacea*, and *rubiginosa* are considered to be sibling species.

56a Face strongly oblique, making an angle of 35° to 55° with the back; tegmina and wings much reduced; eyes about twice as long as wide; hind tibia blue or greenish. Fig. 309...................
..*Aptenopedes sphenarioides* Scudder Linear-winged grasshopper

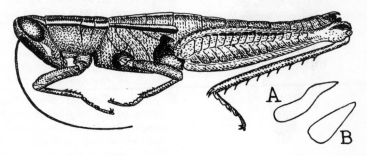

Figure 309

LENGTH: 16-34.9 mm. RANGE: Florida to Georgia and Alabama.

Green or brown, sometimes with back reddish, yellow stripes from eyes to tegmina and down middle of back; dull yellowish beneath. Hind tibia blue-green or pink. At least five distinctive races are known. Found on low bordering vegetation such as wire grass and huckleberry in open pine woods. Favors lush weedy spots. Adults March to November. (A) and (B) show two forms of male cerci.

A. aptera Scudder is a related Florida species in which the tegmina are so minute as to be easily overlooked. Green or brown, males often with broad reddish stripes on pronotum. Five races are known of this species. Selected males easily rank among the most colorful of our grasshoppers.

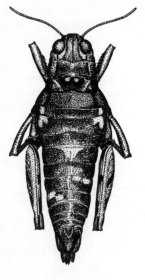

Figure 310

LENGTH: 18-23 mm. RANGE: Oregon to California.

Brownish with light and dark markings, fastigium with small red spots, hind femur barred with black, marked with red beneath; body brownish beneath. Hind tibia brown, marked with red and black. Taken in mountain meadows, for example around the rim of Crater Lake. Like other members of the genus it is slow-moving and not difficult to capture once located.

B. pinguis Scudder occurs commonly in the Sagebrush country around Reno, Nevada. *B. kaibab* Hebard occurs in Arizona and Utah. Several species are found in the mountains of California.

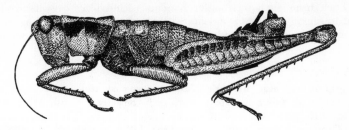

Figure 311

LENGTH: 14-25 mm. RANGE: Northeastern U.S. to Ontario.

Olive or brownish above, male with broad dull dark stripes; yellow beneath. Hind tibia bluish or brownish. Occurs on high peaks from Quebec to eastern Pennsylvania. Subspecies *canadensis* (Walker) with longer antennae and longer cerci than the typical form occurs from Ontario to Michigan. Subspecies *variegata* (Scudder) has the hind femora marked with black, male antenna one-fourth or more longer than hind femur (longest of three forms), and male cerci long and strongly narrowed at middle. The eastern *Zubovskya* occur in weedy and shrubby places and on trees. *Z. polita* (Scudder) is similar but with hind tibia yellowish. Occurs principally on lily-leafed false Solomon seal on Mary's Peak and a few other Oregon hilltops. The abdomens of *Zubovskya* females are distinctively pointed looking.

60b Male with cercus conical to tip and supraanal plate with no large teeth at sides; form broader. Fig. 312...........................
.....*Buckellacris nuda* (Walker) Buckell's timberline grasshopper

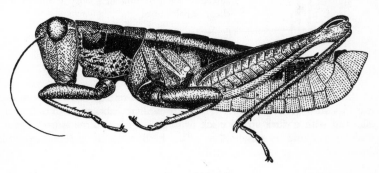

Figure 312

LENGTH: 15-24 mm. RANGE: Alberta and British Columbia to Washington, Idaho, and Montana.

Greenish-black to brownish above with a yellow dorsal stripe running back from each eye; paler beneath. Hind tibia greenish-yellow. Found in alpine meadows and above timberline. The subspecies *relicta* Rehn and Rehn occurs in Idaho.

61a Form rather elongate and slender; eyes of male very large and prominent; metazona very short, only one-third length of prozona. Fig. 313 . . . .
. . *Gymnoscirtetes pusillus* Scudder Little wingless grasshopper

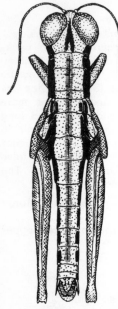

LENGTH: 12.5-22 mm. RANGE: Georgia and Florida.

Dull greenish-yellow with black stripes. Hind tibia dull green. Common in certain marshy portions of pine barrens among sedges, etc., and in undergrowth of low-lying areas of long-leaf pine forests. Alert and agile. Only the sharp-eyed collector who handles his net with skill can expect to secure a series of this form.

G. morsei Hebard was found in a wire grass and bog plant area at De Funiac Springs, Florida. The male subgenital plate has a large median projection as well as a smaller one at each side on the upper margin. *G. pusillus* has only a small median projection.

Figure 313

Netrosoma nigropleura Scudder occurs in Texas and Mexico. The males are tiny and great jumpers. They are whitish, abdomen tinged pinkish, and with a dark stripe back from eye. Females measure 22 mm., violet-gray, and are secretive. The hind tibia is reddish in both sexes.

61b Form not elongate or very slender; eyes not large or prominent; metazona proportionally longer **62**

62a Eyes close together above, separated by about width of basal antennal segment; marked with broad blackish bands on sides; hind
   tibia greenish or bluish; male cercus usually more than twice as
   long as greatest width. Fig. 314...............................
   ....*Paraidemona mimica* (Scudder) Mimic grasshopper

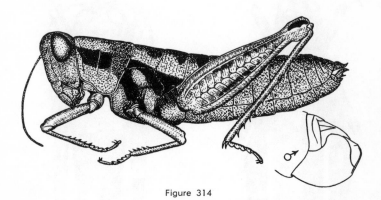

Figure 314

LENGTH: 13-20 mm. RANGE: Texas to Mexico.

Yellowish-brown, paler beneath. Hind tibia pale greenish. This
variable form has the black band of the head and pronotum from
strong to absent in the female. Reported common in June and July
in cotton fields near Victoria, Texas.

62b Eyes well separated above by more than width of basal antennal
   segment; not marked with broad blackish bands on sides; hind
   tibia reddish or brownish; male cercus only about twice as long
   as wide or shorter...63

63a Fastigium with weak ridges at sides; furculae absent; rather weakly marked; ovipositor with tooth near base of lower valve. Fig.
   315.............*Nisquallia olympica* Rehn Olympic grasshopper

LENGTH: 15.6-25.2 mm. RANGE: Mt. Ellinor, Mason Co., Washington.

Brownish mottled above, brown to orange-cinnamon beneath. Hind tibia reddish. Thus far found only at the type locality. Mt. Ellinor is 5940 feet high. The habits and food plants are unknown.

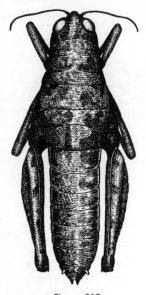

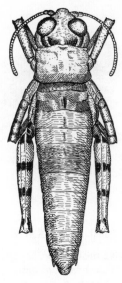

Figure 315   Figure 316

63b Fastigium with no ridges at sides; furculae feebly present; conspicuously marked; ovipositor with no tooth near base of lower valve. Fig. 316..
......*Hebardacris albida* (Hebard) **Mount Whitney grasshopper**

LENGTH: 15-26 mm. RANGE: 10,000-12,500 feet in Mt. Whitney area of Sierra Nevada Mts. of California.

Whitish-buff with dark markings, yellowish beneath. Hind tibia brownish, tinged pinkish, darker at base. Found about granite debris with few plants present. Protective coloration is highly developed in this rather inactive species.

64a Head disproportionally large and quite broad as viewed from above, especially in the female. Figs. 317 and 318............
...*Phoetaliotes nebrascensis* (Thomas) **Large-headed grasshopper**

LENGTH: 21-30 mm. RANGE: Canada to Mexico, west to California and British Columbia, east to Indiana, Illinois, and Oklahoma.

Brown, head and pronotum usually pale on top. Hind tibia bluish or purple. The short-winged form is far commoner than the long-winged. Found on grasslands and prairies. The male cercus narrows from base to tip.

Chloroplus cactocaetes Hebard Cactus grasshopper, is a big-headed, large-eyed, very active Texas species which lives in joint cactus *Opuntia* sp. It is brownish and green above, yellowish or greenish beneath, with the tibia blue. Especially noted in July and August about Corpus Christi. Somewhat related to *Campylacantha*.

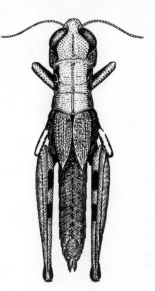

Figure 317

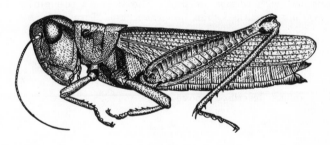

Figure 318

64b Head not disproportionally large or especially broad as viewed from above..**65**

65a Color bluish with bold red and yellow marks. Fig. 319....*Dactylotum bicolor* subspecies *variegetum* (Scudder) Rainbow grasshopper

197

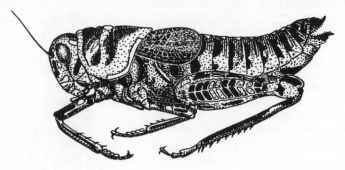

Figure 319

LENGTH: 20-35 mm. RANGE: Arizona to Texas and northern Mexico.

Bluish with red, white, and yellow markings. An active brilliant species which makes a splendid addition to the collection. Found in desert grasslands, especially on gravelly soil areas with sparse vegetation. Sometimes numerous in alfalfa fields but usually only moderately common. Adults June to October.

D. bicolor subspecies *pictum* (Thomas) Pictured grasshopper, occurs from northern Texas and northeastern New Mexico to Montana. It is strikingly marked with bands of black and yellow, the latter usually ornamented with orange or pink. The tegmina are narrower and more widely separated than in *variegatum*. ˉTypical *D. bicolor* are found in Mexico.

65b Colors not as described above..............................66

66a Hind margin of pronotum broadly emarginate Fig. 321 (A) (see also *Melanoplus gracilis* p. 247); cercus of male often somewhat downcurved at tip..67

66b Hind margin of pronotum straight to rounded or angulate (narrowly notched at middle in 2 spp. of *Dendrotettix* and occasional specimens of *Appalachia)* cercus of male variable..................69

**67a Northern mountain species having pronotum rather weakly emarginate behind. Fig. 320...
.............*Asemoplus montanus* (Bruner) Montana grasshopper**

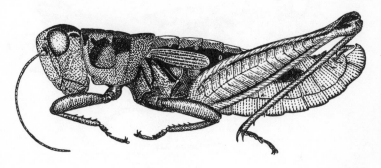

Figure 320

LENGTH: 15-18 mm. RANGE: British Columbia and Alberta to Montana.

Brownish with white to yellowish stripes above, yellow beneath. Hind tibia yellowish. Taken at moderate elevations among junipers on north mountain slopes.

Prumnacris rainierensis (Caudell) Cascade timberline grasshopper, is similar except male cerci not more than twice as long as basal width, and not downcurved at tip. The lateral ridges of the pronotum are evident though rounded. Found near timberline in alpine meadows of the Washington and northern Oregon Cascades, where it prefers lupine.

The tegmina of both of these species are small. The colors are hard to preserve in cabinet specimens.

67b Southwestern desert species having pronotum more deeply emarginate behind (A) or only feebly emarginate. Fig. 321...........................68

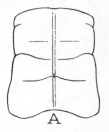

Figure 321

68a Tegmen longitudinally divided in color, darker in lower half; antenna brown. Fig. 322...
.............*Conalcea huachucana* Rehn Huachuca grasshopper

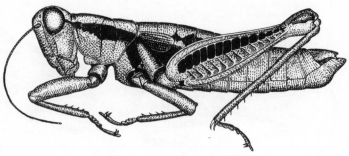

Figure 322

LENGTH: 21-29 mm. RANGE: Arizona to New Mexico and Mexico.

Grayish-brown with a light brownish stripe down middle of abdomen; pale brownish beneath. Hind tibia reddish. On grasses and low plants on slopes with scattered trees, among leaves under oak trees, etc. Subspecies *coyotero* Hebard of central Arizona has the male cercus much enlarged in the apical third, and usually has no black stripe on the upper half of the hind femur. Found at 5,400 to 6,500 feet on low plants in the chaparral and oak zone. Adults July to October.

Phaedrotettix dumicola palmeri (Scudder) from Texas and Mexico is a small brown species with green hind tibia. The male subgenital plate is not conical. It is related to *Conalcea*.

68b Tegmen uniformly blackish with pale veins; antenna orange. Fig. 323.....*Barytettix humphreysii* (Thomas) Humphrey's grasshopper

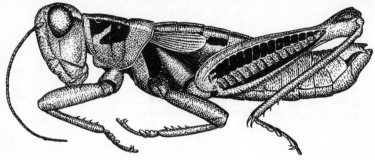

Figure 323

LENGTH: 19.5-36 mm. RANGE: Arizona to New Mexico and Mexico.

Yellow-brownish above and beneath with extensive grayish areas. A narrow yellowish stripe down middle of back. Hind tibia usually yellowish, sometimes red. A handsome, rather large grassland species found adult from April to November.

B. *cochisei* Gurney, Cochise grasshopper, is a similar southern Arizona species which has the hind tibia and usually tip of hind femur and tip of abdomen reddish.

Phaulotettix eurycercus Hebard and *P. compressus* Scudder have small narrow lateral tegmina covering the tympana. The hind margin of the pronotum is feebly emarginate. They occur in Texas. They have red hind tibiae and the distance between the compound eyes is about equal to width of first antennal segment (in *Prumnacris* and *Asemoplus* the distance between compound eyes is usually more than width of first antennal segment).

69a Fastigium and face forming a rather sharp, nearly 90° angle as seen in profile; tegmina short and broad; lateral ridges of pronotum conspicuous; tips of ovipositor valves minutely notched. Fig. 324 ....
Paratylotropidia beutenmuelleri Morse Beutenmueller's grasshopper

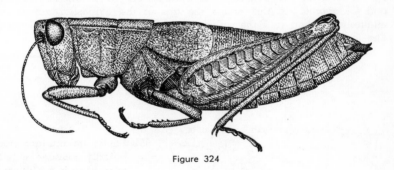

Figure 324

LENGTH: 21-30 mm. RANGE: South Carolina.

Brownish above, abdomen marked with yellow; yellowish beneath. Hind tibia red. *P. brunneri* Scudder (Fig. 325) is a striped species in Texas to Arkansas and Dakota. It is usually short-winged, but sometimes (A) long-winged. *P. moresi* Rehn and Rehn resembles *brunneri*

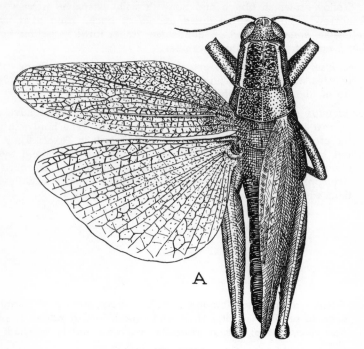

Figure 325

except tegmina rounded instead of lanceolate. It occurs in Arkansas and Oklahoma. In this genus the tips of the ovipositor valves are minutely notched and the valves are not strongly excavate beneath. The lower valve has no tooth near base.

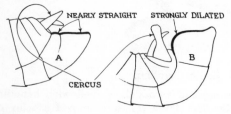

Figure 325½

69b Fastigium and face more broadly rounded together as seen in profile; tegmina and lateral ridges of pronotum variable. Fig. 325½..........70

70a Male subgenital plate with side margins (viewed from side) straight to feebly curving (Fig. 325½A), not strongly dilated or widened at base 71

70b Male subgenital plate with side margins (viewed from side) strongly dilated or widened at base (Fig. 325½B)..................77

71a Prosternal spine very wide (A); eye large; hind femur very broad. Fig. 326...*Aidemona azteca* subspecies *amrami* Roberts Brown aztec grasshopper

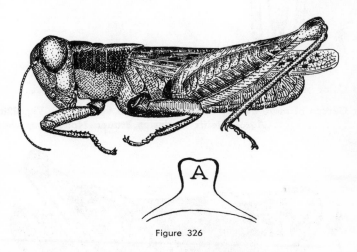

Figure 326

LENGTH: 17-25 mm. RANGE: Southern Arizona to Mexico.
Brownish above, pale beneath. Hind tibia dull pale bluish-green, yellowish toward base. Found mostly on grasses and bushes under live oak trees. A plain-looking species. Adults October through the winter.

71b Prosternal spine not very wide; eye and hind femur variable...72

72a Color green with a bright red stripe down middle of head and pronotum; legs red or bordered red. Fig. 327................
........*Aztecacris gloriosus* (Hebard) Atascosa gem grasshopper

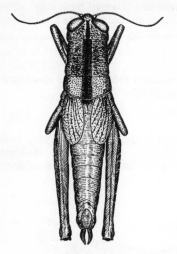

LENGTH: 16-25 mm. RANGE: Atascosa Peak to Ruby, Arizona.

Green, red stripe down middle of head and pronotum, front and middle legs red, hind femur red above and beneath. A gaudy bush-dwelling species which was found on *Baccharis* and *Encelia*. No specimens have been found since the severe drouth of the 1940's.

Figure 327

72b Color not green and red....................................73

73a Cercus of male deeply forked at tip; eye very large. Fig. 328....
............*Agroecotettix modestus* Bruner Modest grasshopper

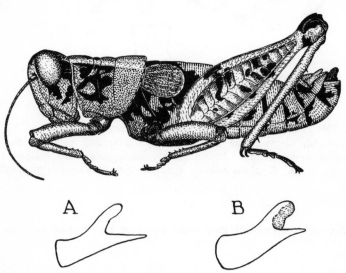

Figure 328

LENGTH: 16-30 mm. RANGE: Texas to Mexico.

Brownish, more or less yellowish above, more yellowish beneath. Hind tibia red and brownish, often black near base. An active species which is found in various types of desert vegetation, especially thorny bushes. Adults August and September. Two subspecies of this occur in Texas. "A" shows the male cercus of *A. m. aristus* Hebard, and "B" the male cercus of *A. m. crypsidomus* Hebard.

73b Cercus of male not forked at tip; eye normal in size...........**74**

74a Tegmina widely separated on back. Fig. 329.................
...*Appalachia hebardi* **Rehn and Rehn Appalachian grasshopper**

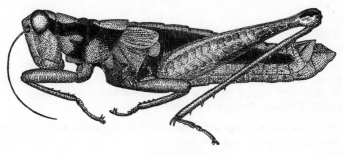

Figure 329

LENGTH: 15-31 mm. RANGE: Pennsylvania, Virginia, and West Virginia.

Brownish or greenish-gray with black markings, yellow beneath. Hind tibia yellowish. Found on Appalachian ridges and uplifts along the east flank of the Alleghany Plateau from Moosic Lake to Bald Knob, Bath Co., Virginia, and near White Sulphur Springs, West Virginia. Mostly on vegetation in scrub forest and huckleberry barrens. On sweet fern, bracken, oak, alder, etc.

A. arcana Hubbell and Cantrall is a Michigan species. It is found on trunks of pines, on blueberry, sweet fern, leatherleaf, and other vegetation in sunny openings as in bogs and pine barrens. The hind femur is red below and next to the body. In *A. hebardi* those areas are dull yellowish-green.

74b Tegmina meeting or nearly meeting on back.................**75**

75a Male cercus distinctly flattened at tip; male with furculae very weakly developed; body rather fuzzy. Fig. 330...............
Campylacantha olivacea (Scudder) **Fuzzy olive-green grasshopper**

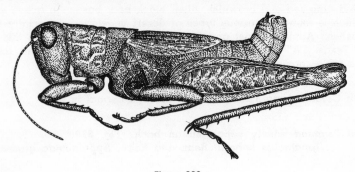

Figure 330

LENGTH: 19-31 mm. RANGE: Illinois to Georgia, Nebraska, Colorado, and Texas.

Green, brown, or blackish. Hind tibia variable in color, orange, greenish, etc. Found in dry weedy fields. The southern subspecies *vivax* (Scudder) occurs in New Mexico and Texas to southeastern Colorado and Kansas. Prefers *Flourensia cernua*.

75b Male cercus not distinctly flattened at tip; male with furculae well developed; body not notably fuzzy...........................76

76a Male cercus bent inward; male with furculae rather long projecting conical fingers about one-fifth as long as supra-anal plate; no conspicuous blackish band running back from eye; tegmina long or short. Fig. 331..
...........*Hypochlora alba* (Dodge) Greenish-white grasshopper

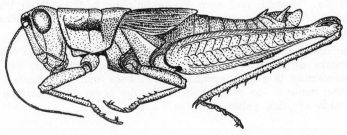

Figure 331

LENGTH: 15-24 mm. RANGE: Alberta to Manitoba and south to Texas.

Grayish to greenish-yellow. Hind tibia faintly bluish-green. A bush-dwelling species whose coloration affords good camouflage against grayish foliage. Usually short-winged. Common in sagebrush. Adults July to October.

76b Male cercus straight; male with furculae short diverging structures which lie close to the supraanal plate; a conspicuous blackish band running back from eye; tegmina short. Fig. 332.......
........*Eotettix signatus* Scudder Handsome Florida grasshopper

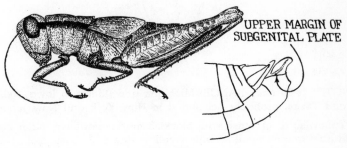

UPPER MARGIN OF
SUBGENITAL PLATE

Figure 332

LENGTH: 18-30.6 mm. RANGE: Florida.

Pale bluish-green and brownish above, pale beneath. Hind tibia pale red. A handsome species occasionally found in moist grassy areas, e.g. in pine woods, along edges of hummocks, etc.

E. pusillus Morse is a much smaller species with greenish-yellow hind tibiae, found in Florida, Georgia, and the Carolinas.

The species of genus *Phaulotettix*, found mostly on sotol in Texas and Mexico, might run here if the feeble emargination of the hind edge of the pronotum were overlooked. They are mentioned briefly under couplet 68b.

77a Head rather large as seen in profile, with eyes proportionally rather small and unusually protuberant; male supraanal plate with low conspicuous angular prominences at about middle on each side (A); tree-inhabiting species. Fig. 333.....................
.............*Dendrotettix quercus* Packard Post oak grasshopper

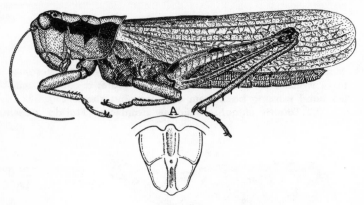

Figure 333

LENGTH: 24-30 mm. RANGE: Michigan and Illinois to Iowa, Nebraska, and Texas, probably accidental in New York and New Jersey.

Yellowish or greenish with blackish markings above, paler beneath. Hind tibia greenish-yellow with a yellow ring near base. Both long and short-winged individuals occur. The mesosternal interspace is as broad or broader than one of the mesosternal lobes. Found mostly on oaks. The nymphs are fast runners.

D. australis (Morse) from Alabama, Tennessee, and North Carolina, (mostly on *Pinus virginiana*), and *D. zimmermanni* (Saussure) from the Carolinas (on *Quercus rubra borealis*) are both short-winged species with pronotum notched in middle at rear. *D. australis* is larger, darker, and has cherry-red on the hind femur. *D. zimmermanni* has the hind femur yellowish-green below and on the side next to the body.

77b Without the above combination of characters.................78

78a Cercus of male broadest at base, tapering to and terminating in a narrowly rounded or pointed tip.........................79

78b Cercus of male distinctly broad in form, or distinctly widened past middle, or with a side branch, not tapering from base to a point at tip...83

79a Body usually rather deep through metathorax with head and pronotum proportionally a little small as seen from side; hind femur
rather short and stout; head and pronotum often with a distinctive
dark pattern above (shown); male subgenital plate with a distinct
subapical tubercle. Fig. 334.................................*Aeoloplides tenuipennis* (Scudder) Narrow-winged bush grasshopper

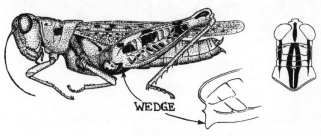

Figure 334

LENGTH: 14-28 mm. RANGE: Southern California to New Mexico, Utah,
and Idaho.

Brownish, pale beneath. Hind tibia purplish, blue, or reddish . A
common bush-dwelling species. The hind femur has a projecting wedge-
like structure below (Fig. 334), at the base. Seven additional western
U.S. species are known, living on bushes, especially of the family
Chenopodiaceae (such as saltbush *Atriplex*, Russian thistle *Salsola*, etc.).
These neat little grasshoppers make an interesting special group to
study and they are fun to collect. Some are short-winged.

79b Without the above combination of characters.................80

80a Pronotum with a red or white stripe down midline, general color
of head, pronotum, tegmina, and outer portions of hind femora
green to greenish-brown with red or white markings, or lacking
the red or white stripe but speckled with blue, black and white
dots 81

80b Not colored in either of two ways described above...........82

81a Tegmina long or short; pronotum often marked with a blackish
spot on side; tegmina often marked with red or white stripes;
transverse sulci of pronotum shallowly impressed. Fig. 335......
........*Hesperotettix viridis* (Thomas) Green striped grasshopper

209

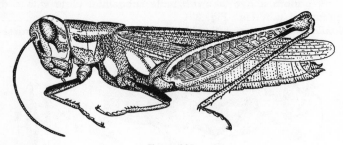

Figure 335

LENGTH: 17-30 mm. RANGE: Widely distributed from Canada to Mexico and from Atlantic to Pacific.

Green to brown with white or yellowish stripes, black marks, and pink areas on legs. Greenish beneath. Hind tibia bluish-green. A common pretty inhabitant of bushy plants. A smaller short-winged but otherwise similar form, subspecies *nevadensis* Morse occurs in Arizona and Nevada. *H. v. pratensis* Scudder occurs from Manitoba to British Columbia and south to Oklahoma. Several additional forms of *Hesperotettix* are known.

81b **Tegmina long; pronotum with no large black spot on side; tegmina not marked with red or white stripes; transverse sulci of pronotum usually deeply impressed. Fig. 336**..........................
....*Poecilotettix pantherina* (Walker) **Panther-spotted grasshopper**

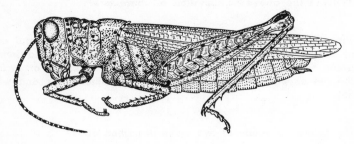

Figure 336

LENGTH: 25-29 mm. RANGE: Arizona to Sonora, Mexico.

Greenish-yellow, head and pronotum with small black and white spots, antennae black with white rings on alternate segments, legs with rows of black spots; hind tibiae pale blue-green. Found on sunflower, *Baccharis*, etc. A beautiful species in which the colors are hard to preserve. Adults April to November.

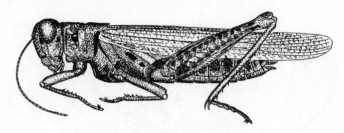

Figure 337

P. longipennis (Townsend) (Fig. 337) is greenish with red stripes on middle of head and pronotum, and on sides of pronotum. On *Baccharis* and other shrubs in California, Arizona, and Nevada.

82a Body stout and heavy in short-winged forms (Fig. 338); male with all femora heavy; pronotum with lateral ridges evident and with a distinct angulation along lateral ridges, prozona often somewhat swollen; lower lobe of distal end of hind femur without conspicuous black marks. Long-winged form much like *Melanoplus* except cerci pointed in male (A) and lower half of distal end of hind femur pale and unmarked. Fig. 339...................................
............*Oedaleonotus enigma* (Scudder) Valley grasshopper

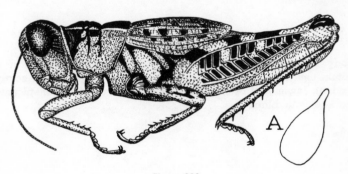

Figure 338

LENGTH: 17-27 mm. RANGE: California to Washington, Idaho, Nevada, and Arizona.

Brownish with darker markings; paler beneath. Hind tibia bluish. The long and short-winged forms of this species are very different in general appearance. Often common on grasslands of inner coast ranges of California.

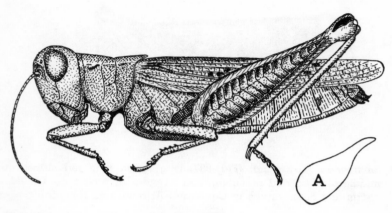

Figure 339

O. *borckii* (Stal) is a stout variably colored but usually brownish short-winged species with bluish hind tibia which occurs in California, Oregon, Nevada, and Arizona. Distinctive looking local populations are often found. Boldly marked individuals are especially fine for the collection. Usually in grass.

82b Body usually less stout; male femora variable; prozona of pronotum usually not at all swollen, and lateral ridges not or scarcely evident; lower half of distal end of hind femur often conspicuously marked with black..83

83a Body stout and heavy; pronotum with disc distinctly set off from lateral lobes but with no evident lateral ridges; eyes small; vertex broad; dull colored except red hind tibia and red lower edge of hind femur. Fig. 340...
...............*Argiacris rehni* Hebard Rehn's slow grasshopper

LENGTH: 16.9-29.4 mm.
RANGE: Livingston, Park County, Montana (5,000').

Brownish above, clay-brown beneath. H i n d tibia and lower face of hind femur red. Taken July 29 on the ridge of a rocky hogback with scanty vegetation. A stout species known only from the type locality. At least one subsequent attempt to locate the species at the type locality late in July failed.

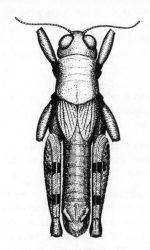

Figure 340

83b Without the above described combination of characters.......84

84a Face slanting about 50° to 60°; form subcylindrical, slender; male antenna rather long; male eyes large and rather protuberant; fastigium with foveolae evident though feeble. Fig. 341.............
....Paroxya clavuliger (Serville) Olive-green swamp grasshopper

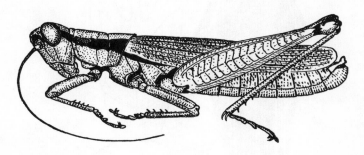

Figure 341

LENGTH: 22-40 mm. RANGE: Ontario and southern New England to Texas and Florida.

Green and brown marked with black and yellowish or white; greenish beneath. Hind tibia bluish-green. Locally common in swampy areas on *Spartina, Scripus,* and assorted rank vegetation. *P. atlantica* Scudder is a smaller long-winged brownish species found in Indiana and Illinois, and from New Jersey to Florida, mostly in bogs, grassy places among inkberry shrubs, and salt marshes. Two additional races or subspecies of *Paroxya* are known.

The short-winged *Paroxya* never have short, rounded, lobe-shaped tegmina such as are found on many species of *Melanoplus.* Two types of supra-anal plates occur, one wider and with very short furculae in male *P. atlantica,* and one longer and proportionally narrower with furculae nearly one-third as long as supra-anal plate in *P. clavuliger.*

84b **Face not as strongly slanting, varying to vertical; form usually less slender; male antennae variable but usually shorter; eyes of male variable; fastigium with foveolae usually not evident..........85**

85a **Male cercus short, heavy, and conical; female appearing as shown with structures at tip of abdomen as shown; space broad between eyes; pronotum truncate in front, with hind margin truncate except very feebly bilobate; lateral lobes of pronotum about one and one-quarter times as long as high; legs rather slender. Fig. 342......**
..............*Podisma hesperus* (Hebard) Hesperus grasshopper

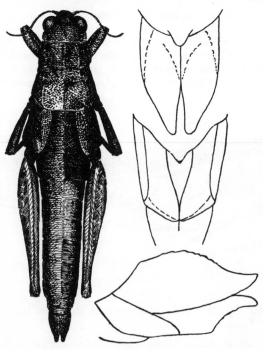

Figure 342

LENGTH: 27.7 mm. RANGE: McKenzie Pass area, Cascade Mts., Oregon.

Dark brown above, brownish-buff beneath. Hind tibia yellow-buff with black-tipped spines. Known only from the unique type female. The Alder Springs area is densely forested and few grasshoppers are present there. McKenzie Pass itself is an area of nearly barren lava flows. Between the pass and Alder Springs there are some likely spots, however, and further search in those places might produce additional specimens of this species which is the only species of *Podisma* known to occur in North America. Those forms which used to be called *Podisma* have been transferred to other genera.

85b Without the above described combination of characters.....*Genus Melanoplus*, treated in a separate key which follows immediately

GENUS MELANOPLUS

ELANOPLUS is a large genus containing mostly brownish species, some of which are among the most important agricultural pests in America. The tegmina are commonly spotted, occasionally striped, sometimes plain. The tegmina are either long with the wings fully developed, or reduced, sometimes to short rounded lobes, with the wings correspondingly more or less reduced or rudimentary. In a few cases both long-winged and short-winged individuals of the same species occur in the same area. In such cases the long-winged form usually has the tegmen proportionally broader with the veins more widely separated than is usual in long-winged forms. A diagonal whitish mark is commonly present on the side (episternum) of the metathorax. The underside of the hind femur is usually colored reddish or yellow. There is often a black band extending back from the eye onto the pronotum on each side. The hind tibia is often variable in color.

Long-winged forms tend to be widespread in their occurrence while short-winged forms tend to occur in restricted areas. Individuals of a single species are sometimes very different in "general appearance" and figures may not be particularly helpful in such cases.

The most convenient diagnostic characters are found in the male terminal abdominal structures, the external ones of which are relied upon rather heavily in the following key. Females of closely related species are very hard to tell apart, even for specialists. These are usually easily associated with the corresponding males in the field.

KEY TO MELANOPLUS

1a Mesosternum of male as viewed from the side with a conspicuous swelling or hump..2

1b Mesosternum of male as viewed from the side with no conspicuous swelling or hump..5

2a Furculae of male large, heavy, and usually reaching to middle of supra-anal plate (B); distribution northerly or at very high altitudes farther south. Figs. 343, 344....................................
....*Melanoplus bruneri* Scudder. Bruner's spur-throat grasshopper

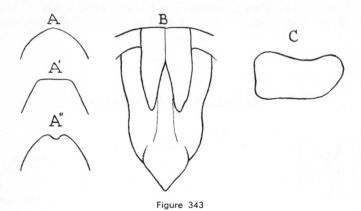

Figure 343

LENGTH: 19-28 mm. RANGE: Alaska to Alberta, and south to Arizona, New Mexico, and Iowa.

Brownish to blackish; greenish-yellow beneath. Hind tibia reddish to pale greenish-yellow. Length of tegmen variable. Similar in general

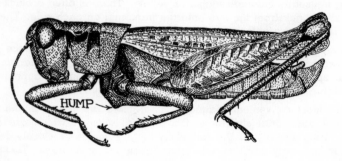

Figure 344

appearance to *M. bilituratus* and a member of the same species group (the "Mexicanus group"). Often an important pest on rangeland. Also found in bushy undergrowth. "A" shows variable subgenital plate and "C" the cercus of male.

Of the eleven forms in the "Mexicanus group" eight are of economic importance.

2b Furculae of male smaller and usually reaching no more than one-third of length of supra-anal plate; distribution general...........**3**

3a Subgenital plate of male with margin entire as viewed from rear. Fig. 345 ....
...*Melanoplus arizonae* Scudder Arizona spur-throat grasshopper

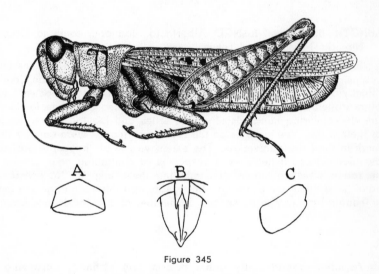

Figure 345

LENGTH: 25-29 mm. RANGE: Arizona to Utah, Colorado, Kansas, Texas, and Mexico.

Brownish with darker markings; pale beneath. Hind tibia usually blue. Resembles *M. bilituratus* but usually darker and more heavily marked. The male subgenital plate is entire here, notched in *bilituratus*. Found on grasslands. Adults May to October. Considered to be a member of the "Angustipennis group," consisting of three species, all more or less destructive.

3b Subgenital plate of male with margin notched or bilobed as viewed from rear..**4**

4a Tegmina proportionally rather broad and subequal in width to tip. Fig. 346. . . . .
. . . . *Melanoplus spretus* (Walsh) **Rocky Mountain grasshopper**

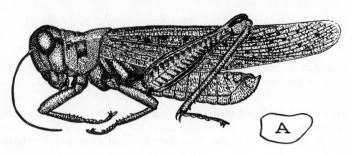

Figure 346

LENGTH: 30-36 mm. RANGE: Alberta to Manitoba, south to Oregon, Nevada, Missouri, and Texas.

Brownish above with dark markings; lighter beneath. (A) is the male cercus. Hind tibia blue or red. Before 1900 this species, then called "Rocky Mountain Locust," "Hateful Locust," "Migratory Locust," etc., often appeared over farming areas in swarms so dense as to darken the sky, covering hundreds of square miles and leaving barren wastes in their wake. The nymphs on the breeding grounds were equally thorough in their destructiveness. The extensive use of "hopperdozers" and the plowing of all fields even suspected of containing eggs proved to be rather effective means of combating these insects. No specimens have been taken for more than fifty years and this plague grasshopper is thought by many to be extinct. A member of the "Mexicanus group."

4b Tegmina proportionally rather narrow and distinctly narrowing to tip. Fig. 347. . . . .
. . . . *Melanoplus bilituratus* (Walker) **Migratory grasshopper**

LENGTH: 23-34 mm. RANGE: Alaska, Canada, and United States except peninsular Florida.

Brownish to yellowish with spotting above; pale beneath. Hind tibia red to buff or grayish. An important pest of grasslands and crops. Populations of this species were formerly usually called *M. mexicanus* or *M. atlanis*. Concentrations of up to 300 individuals per square yard have been recorded, and they sometimes migrate in tremendous swarms. Adults from May to Christmas in California. A subspecies *vulturnus* Gurney and Brooks occurs in southeastern U.S., and a subspecies *defectus* Scudder occurs from southern California to Texas.

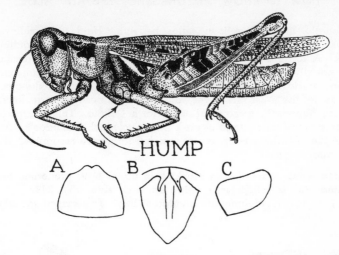

Figure 347

(A) male subgenital plate, (B) male supraanal plate, and (C) male cercus.

M. mexicanus (Saussure) is now considered to be mostly a Mexican species which enters southern Texas. It is much like *bilituratus*.

5a Very large species; male cercus with a prominent projection at the side; wings and tegmina well developed........................6

5b Mostly smaller species; male cercus variable; wings and tegmina variable 7

6a Hind femur marked with a black herringbone pattern; pronotum and tegmina not striped; very large. Fig. 348...................
.......*Melanoplus differentialis* (Thomas) Differential grasshopper

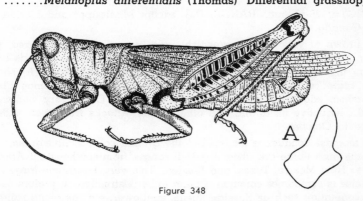

Figure 348

LENGTH: 28-44 mm. RANGE: California and Oregon to Louisiana, North Carolina, New Jersey, Michigan, Minnesota, North Dakota, and Montana.

Usually brownish-yellow; paler beneath. Hind tibia yellow. (A) shows the male cercus. The pronotal sutures are usually outlined in black. A large common, non-migratory very destructive grasshopper. Occasionally yellow individuals make striking cabinet specimens. Subspecies *nigricans* Cockerell occurs from eastern Texas, Oklahoma, and Kansas to the Missouri River, and through northwestern Iowa and western Minnesota to southwestern North Dakota. This subspecies includes a small percentage of dark brown to black individuals. A member of the "Ponderosus group" of which 6 forms are recognized, 3 being economic species.

6b Hind femur marked with blackish in upper half; pronotum and tegmina with a conspicuous stripe on each side. Fig. 349...........
..............*Melanoplus bivittatus* (Say) Two-striped grasshopper

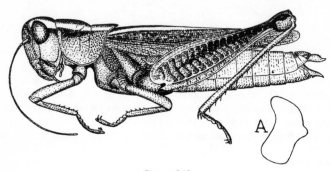

Figure 349

LENGTH: 26-40 mm. RANGE: U.S. except Mississippi and Florida, to Canada.

Brown to yellowish or greenish; pale beneath. Hind tibia red, yellow, blue, bluish-black, or purplish-brown. A pale stripe extends back from the eye to near the tip of the tegmen on each side. (A) shows the male cercus. Prefers lush vegetation such as is common about marshes, edges of fields, and forest margins. Often very numerous and destructive on alfalfa and other crops. Attacks fruit trees. Adults June to October.

M. thomasi Scudder is similar but the ground color is blue-green, and the hind tibiae are always red. It ranges from southeastern Arizona to New Mexico, Texas, and Mexico. This very handsome large species is sometimes common enough to be destructive. It prefers dense vegetation such as Russian thistle, sunflower, etc., as along railroad tracks, ditches, fences, etc.

M. bivittatus, thomasi, and *yarrowii* (Thomas) comprise the "Bivittatus group."

7a Male subgenital plate roughly as high as wide as viewed from rear
and shaped as in "A"; furculae very large, about ½ as long as
supra-anal plate "B"; cercus shaped as shown "C"; tegmina either
short (shown) with wings rudimentary, or tegmina and wings fully
developed for flight. Fig. 350...................................
..*Melanoplus dawsoni* (Scudder) Dawson's spur-throat grasshopper

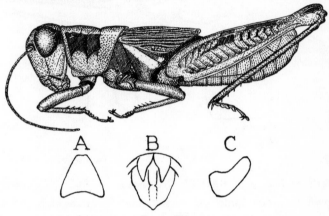

Figure 350

LENGTH: 15-20 mm. RANGE: Alberta to Manitoba and Great Lakes
south to New Mexico, and Maine to Pennsylvania.

Brownish to gray; pale beneath. Hind tibia red. Tegmina long or
short. Generally found on dry sandy soil areas with or without plant
cover. Adults July and August.

This species and *M. gladstoni* Scudder comprise the "Dawsoni
group."

7b Male without above combination of characters..................8

8a Male subgenital plate with a strong tubercle "A"; furculae small
and supra-anal plate as in "B," cercus shaped as shown in "C";
sides of abdomen marked with black; tegmina either short (shown)
and wings rudimentary, or tegmina and wings fully developed for
flying. Fig. 351.......................................
Melanoplus marginatus (Scudder) Margined spur-throat grasshopper

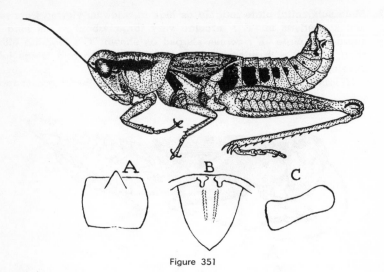

Figure 351

LENGTH: 14.5-22 mm. RANGE: California.

Brown to green; pale yellowish beneath. Hind tibia brownish to olive. Occasional green individuals have the tegmina and pronotum reddish. Destructively common on grasslands, in weedy areas, in gardens, and on crops. Several other non-economic species are placed with this to form the "Marginatus group." Included is *M. sonomaensis* Caudell which occurs on Pringle's bird's beak (*Cordylanthus pringlei* Gray) at Mt. St. Helena, California.

8b Male without above combination of characters.................9

9a Male subgenital plate wider than high and elevated at middle as viewed from rear (A); furculae absent (B); cercus strongly widened at apex (C); tegmina and wings short or long. Fig. 352............
Melanoplus ponderosus Scudder Ponderous spur-throat grasshopper
LENGTH: 25-35 mm. RANGE: New Mexico and Texas to Iowa, Illinois, Tennessee, and Mississippi.

Brownish to greenish or gray; grayish beneath. Hind tibia reddish or orange with light and dark rings toward base.

A Mississippi valley "race" which prefers undergrowth in woods is called *viola* (Thomas). It ranges north to Iowa and Illinois and west to Oklahoma. Adults August and September.

M. eumera Hebard is a highly colored related species from about 5,000 to 7,000 feet in certain valleys of the Chinati, Chisos, and Blue Mts. of Texas.

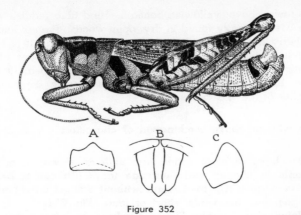

Figure 352

M. tunicae Hebard and the widespread *M. differentialis* (Thomas) also belong to the "Ponderosus group."

9b Male without above combination of characters.................10

10α Male subgenital plate about as high as wide and shaped about as shown (A); furculae small and supra-anal plate with little transverse ridges beyond middle (B); cercus large, long, and straplike (C); tegmina reaching just beyond middle of hind femur, or sometimes past end of hind femur. Fig. 353.........................
Melanoplus fasciatus (Walker) Huckleberry spur-throat grasshopper

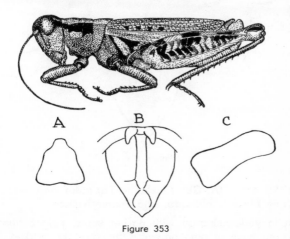

Figure 353

LENGTH: 19-27 mm. RANGE: Newfoundland and Labrador to British Columbia, south to Alabama, Arkansas, and New Mexico.

Gray-brown above; yellowish beneath. Hind tibia reddish with pale ring near base. Usually found in dry, open woods. Prefers huckleberry and blueberry bushes, especially in sunlit spots. Difficult to flush and persistent trampling may be required to locate specimens. Easier to take by night collecting. Found in modest numbers at altitudes up to 10,600 feet in the Colorado Rockies. Adults June to September. The sole member of the "Fasciatus group."

10b Male without above combination of characters................11

11a Male subgenital plate wider than high as viewed from rear (A) (variable in shape); male furculae large (B); cercus broader at base than apex (C); hind femur without distinct cross-band markings; tegmina and wings short or long. Fig. 354................
...*Melanoplus borealis* Fieber Northern spur-throat grasshopper

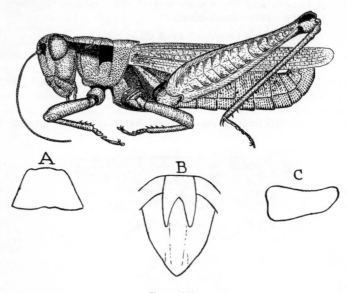

Figure 354

LENGTH: 17-28 mm. RANGE: Alaska to Labrador and south to California, New Mexico, Missouri, and Pennsylvania.

Brownish to yellowish-gray with darker spots; pale beneath. Hind tibia red to yellowish or pale brown. Often prettily marked. Destructive to range and crops alike. Generally prefers cool damp situations but occurs elsewhere. A short-winged subspecies *stupefactus* (Scudder) occurs in Arctic Alpine and Hudsonian life zones in northern New

Mexico and southwestern Colorado. Two other subspecies are recognized; *palaceus* Fulton from California to Montana and Wyoming, and *utahensis* Scudder from Utah. "Mexicanus group."

11b Male without above combination of characters...............12

12a Male with tegmina and wings well developed and reaching about to end of abdomen or beyond..............................13

12b Male with tegmina and wings much reduced.................35

13a Male cercus with a conspicuous protuberance from the side, the cercus often "boot-shaped"; furculae small....................14

13b Male cercus not with a conspicuous protuberance from the side, sometimes expanded, usually simple or with only a small irregularity of outline; furculae large or small......................18

14a Male with furculae extending down a little way over the supra-anal plate as distinct pointed horns which are longer than wide (B); subgenital plate transverse with subparallel upper and lower margins as viewed from the rear (A); cercus with a broad prominent tooth at side but not "boot-shaped" (C). Fig. 355.............
Melanoplus confusus Scudder Little pasture spur-throat grasshopper

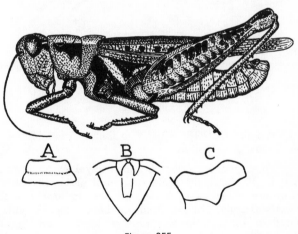

Figure 355

LENGTH: 16-25 mm. RANGE: New England to British Columbia, south to North Carolina, Oklahoma, and Arizona.

Brownish to yellowish with darker spots; pale beneath. Hind tibia reddish to greenish-blue. One of the earliest grasshoppers to appear. Often common in old fields, pastures overrun with coarse grasses, sedges, etc., and on grass in open woods, especially in areas of sandy or gravelly soil. Adults from June to August. While superficially looking like several other species this is nevertheless considered to be distinct enough to be placed by itself in the "Confusus group."

14b Male with furculae reduced, blunt; subgenital plate not as above; cercus often "boot-shaped"......................................15

15a Male cercus with a prominent long acute tooth projecting from the side (C) but not "boot-shaped"; subgenital plate as seen from the rear shaped as in (A). Fig. 356..................................
....*Melanoplus keeleri* (Thomas) Keeler's spur-throat grasshopper

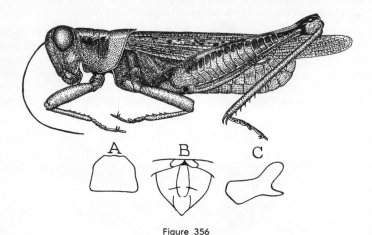

Figure 356

LENGTH: 17-35 mm. RANGE: Alberta to Ontario and Maine, south to Nevada, Texas, and Florida.

Brown, often tinged purplish-red; greenish-yellow to olive beneath. Hind tibia red. (B) shows the male supraanal plate. Prefers dry open woodlands where it occurs in grass and low undergrowth. The subspecies *luridus* (Dodge) ranges from southern Canada and northern New England to Utah, Colorado, Kansas, Idaho, and Arkansas, on prairies, in sandy or blow-out areas, pastures, sometimes on sagebrush, and on sparsely wooded slopes. Destructive to alfalfa, cabbage, and apple and plum trees. Adults June to November. No other species are placed in the "Keeleri group."

15b Male cercus with a prominent short rounded protuberance projecting from the side, forming the "heel" of the "boot-shaped" structure; subgenital plate as seen from the rear variously shaped....16

16a Male subgenital plate as viewed from rear with a rectangular elevated median portion (A); cercus shaped as shown (C). Fig. 357..
.....*Melanoplus alpinus* Scudder Alpine spur-throat grasshopper

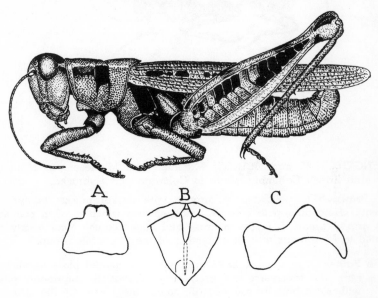

Figure 357

LENGTH: 18-25 mm. RANGE: Colorado to Alberta, British Columbia, and California.

Brownish to grayish with dark markings; pale beneath. (B) shows the male supraanal plate. Hind tibia brownish, bluish or reddish. Occurs in grassy areas. As is the case with many boreal species, *M. alpinus* is found at progressively higher altitudes the farther south one goes. One of two species in the "Infantilis group."

16b Male subgenital plate as viewed from rear and male cercus differently shaped..17

17a Small species, 15-20 mm.; male subgenital plate as viewed from rear roughly triangular in form and narrowly notched at apex (A); supra-anal plate with sides nearly straight (B); cercus as shown (C). Fig. 358..
....*Melanoplus infantilis* Scudder Tiny spur-throated grasshopper

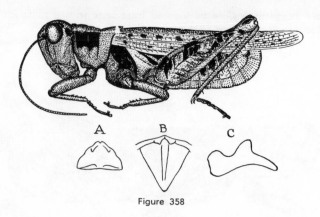

Figure 358

LENGTH: 15-20 mm. RANGE: Manitoba and Minnesota to Montana and British Columbia, south to Colorado and Nebraska.

Brownish to yellowish or grayish with darker marks; lighter beneath. Hind tibia pale blue. A small species which is often common in grassy areas. It feeds on grass and other plants. Most nearly related to *M. alpinus* the other member of the "Infantilis group."

17b Rather large species, 28-36 mm.; male subgenital plate as viewed from rear transverse and irregularly suboval (A); supra-anal plate with sides broadly rounded (B); cercus as shown (C). Fig. 359.... *Melanoplus clypeatus* Scudder Shield-tailed spur-throat grasshopper

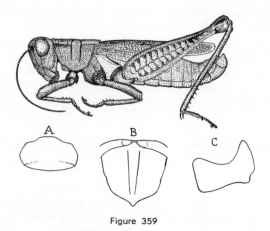

Figure 359

LENGTH: 28.5-36 mm. RANGE: Georgia and Florida.

228

Brownish, tegmina yellowish in part, with darker marks; pale beneath. Hind tibia dull red, paler toward base. Uncommon. Found in dense undergrowth of gray-bark pine woods where somewhat swampy. The Florida form, living in grassy swamp areas, has the tegmina longer. It has been called *M. clypeatus symmetricus* Morse. One of four species in the "Clypeatus group."

18a Male cercus tapering evenly from near base to sharp point (A); often prettily colored with brown, red, and green. Fig. 360 . . . .
. . . .*Melanoplus regalis* (Dodge) Regal spur-throat grasshopper

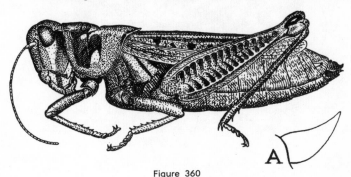

Figure 360

LENGTH: 22-30 mm. RANGE: Nebraska to Arizona, Texas, and Mexico.
Brown with light and dark markings, pale beneath. Hind tibia blue. Many specimens are very handsomely marked with red and green on head, pronotum and hind femora. Other specimens have none of the pretty colors at all. Common on grasslands, especially near mesquite and grama grass.

18b Male cercus variable, not terminating in a sharp point; variously colored, usually plainer than above 19

19a Male furculae large, reaching about one-fourth to more than one-half length of supra-anal plate; cercus not wider at apex than at base 20

19b Male furculae absent or small, reaching less than one-fifth length of supra-anal plate; cercus often much wider at middle or at apex than at base 27

20a Male subgenital plate more or less deeply notched or emarginate on upper edge at middle as viewed from rear 21

20b Male subgenital plate entire, not notched at middle as viewed from rear 25

21a Form rather slender and elongate; male furculae very wide and with tips broad (B); supra-anal plate angulate on sides at apical third (B); subgenital plate with a weak emargination at middle (A); cercus as in "C". Fig. 361................................
Melanoplus herbaceus Bruner Arrowweed spur-throat grasshopper

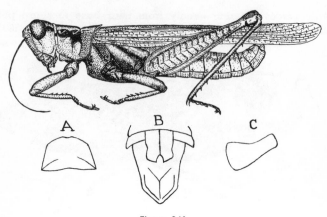

Figure 361

LENGTH: 23-28.5 mm. RANGE: Texas to California and Mexico.

Greenish; pale beneath. Hind tibia pale greenish-blue. Found mostly on arrowweed *Pluchea sericea* along watercourses in Lower Sonoran life zone areas. Adults March to October. A distinctive species which stands alone in the "Herbaceus group."

21b Form average, not notably elongate; male furculae slender and terminating as slender points; supra-anal plate not angulate as above; notch of subgenital plate variable......................22

22a Male subgenital plate with a broad emargination on upper edge at middle (A); supra-anal plate becoming wider past middle before narrowing to apex (B); cercus as in "C". Fig. 362...........
......*Melanoplus femurrubrum* (De Geer) Red-legged grasshopper

LENGTH: 19-26 mm. RANGE: U.S. and Canada.

Brownish, yellowish, or reddish. Hind tibia red to yellowish. In arid areas it is found in irrigated places. Common in fields, pastures, meadows, on lawns, and in open woods. A widespread destructive pest. Adults June to December. The subspecies *propinquus* Scudder occurs in Florida, north to southern North Carolina and west to Mississippi. This form has the furculae longer in the male, is generally paler in color, and has the tegminal spots larger and more numerous. Adults persist through the winter. "Femurrubrum group."

This species is an intermediate host to the poultry tapeworm *Choanotaenia infundibulum*. It and *M. differentialis* are intermediate hosts to

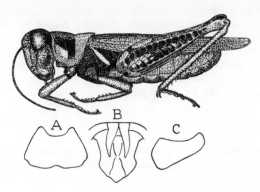

Figure 362

globular stomach worm *Tetrameres americana* which affects chickens, turkeys and quail. Various species of *Melanoplus* as well as *Chorthippus longicornis*, and *Paroxya clavuliger* are intermediate hosts to the tapeworm *Metroliasth lucida*, which occurs in the intestine of turkeys and guinea fowl.

I do not eat grasshoppers!

22b Male subgenital plate notched to moderately emarginate at middle; supra-anal plate narrowing from middle to apex; cercus variable **23**

23a Furculae strongly divergent (B); supra-anal plate with sides strongly turned up basally (B); markings inconspicuous. Fig. 363. . *Melanoplus angustipennis* (Dodge) Narrow-winged spur-throat grasshopper

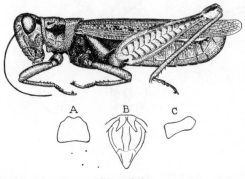

Figure 363

LENGTH: 17-22 mm. RANGE: Alberta and Manitoba to Arizona, Texas, North Carolina, and Georgia.

Brownish to gray; pale beneath. Hind tibia red, gray, or pale bluish-green, sometimes paler near base. Usually found in areas of sandy soil, especially on grasslands. Adults June to October. Looks much like *bilituratus*. The subspecies *impiger* Scudder occurs from Kansas and Iowa to Texas, Georgia, and South Carolina. It occurs in open forest areas where the soil is sandy. It is usually larger than the typical form, with the furculae longer.

23b Furculae weakly divergent and longer; supra-anal plate with sides not strongly turned up basally; dark markings usually conspicuous **24**

24a Male supra-anal plate abruptly constricted past middle (B); cercus narrowed at middle (C); subgenital plate notched as in "A." Fig. 364 ....*Melanoplus bispinosus* **Scudder Two spined spur-throat grasshopper**

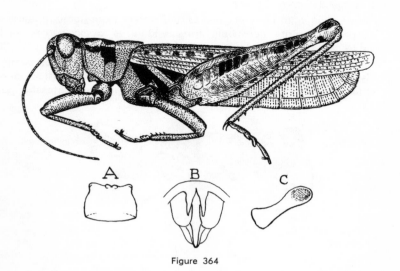

Figure 364

LENGTH: 24-32 mm. RANGE: Texas to Kansas and Arkansas.

Grayish to reddish above; pale beneath. Hind tibia greenish, yellowish at end. The prominent furculae suggested the name of this insect. Specimens from the southern end of the range average somewhat smaller and darker. Common along roadsides, in stubble and pastures.

Sometimes destructive in cotton and alfalfa. One of the three species in the "Angustipennis group."

24b Male supra-anal plate rather evenly narrowed from middle to apex (B); cercus not narrowed at middle (C); subgenital plate notched as in "A." Fig. 365.....................................
.........*Melanoplus devastator* Scudder Devastating grasshopper

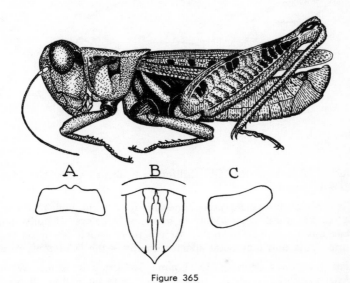

A   B   C

Figure 365

LENGTH: 21-24 mm. RANGE: California to Washington and Nevada.

Brownish or yellowish above, usually with rather pretty contrasting colored markings; pale beneath. Hind tibia red to grayish. Occurs in spring as nymphs on hills. Later in season, as adults, migrates to agricultural areas lower down and is a major pest. While many economic pests among the grasshoppers begin laying eggs as early as 10 days after becoming adults, this species, interestingly, has a waiting period of from 90 to 176 days until cool fall weather and the germination of annual plant seeds, before starting egg-laying. Adults May to December. A member of the "Mexicanus group." The mesosternum may be slightly swollen, but not enough to be confused with *bilituratus*.

25a Male furculae long and slender (B); cercus narrowed at middle (C, E). Fig. 366...
......*Melanoplus cinereus* Scudder Ashy spur-throat grasshopper

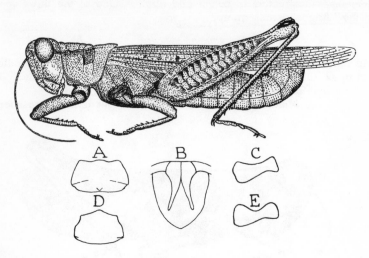

Figure 366

LENGTH: 23-26 mm. RANGE: California to British Columbia, Montana, and Wyoming.

Grayish or brownish; pale beneath. Hind tibia bluish. Specimens from various areas vary widely in intensity of colors. Usually found in bushes but sometimes in grass. Active fliers which are good sport to capture. This and four other species comprise the "Cinereus group."

M. complanatipes Scudder, 15-23 mm., California to Idaho, Wyoming, Arizona, and Mexico is brownish with blue hind tibia. It occurs in sagebrush areas of the Great Basin Desert. In the eastern part of its range darker, grayer, proportionally shorter specimens represent subspecies *canonicus* Scudder. Related to *cinereus*. "D" & "E" show structures of *complanatipes*.

25b Male furculae broad; cercus not narrowed at middle.........26

26a Tips of furculae turned in a little toward each other (B); coloration rather rich with markings distinct and varied; form a little more slender than next species; cercus shorter, broader at base, and less slender (C). Fig. 367......................................
......*Melanoplus pictus* Scudder Pictured spur-throat grasshopper

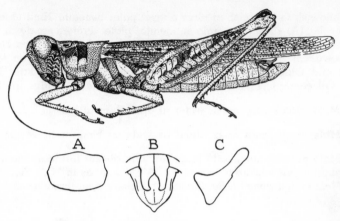

Figure 367

LENGTH: 25-32 mm. RANGE: Arizona.

Brown with brown markings; pale beneath. Hind tibia blue. (A) shows the male subgenital plate. Sometimes destructive to small plantings of alfalfa, cotton, soybeans, and other crops. Common in weedy spots and in various bushes. Member of "Flavidus group."

26b Tips of furculae not turned in toward each other (B); coloration rather plain with simple markings; form less slender than preceding species, and cercus longer, less broad at base, and more slender (C). Fig. 368 . . . .
Melanoplus flavidus Scudder Yellowish spur-throat grasshopper

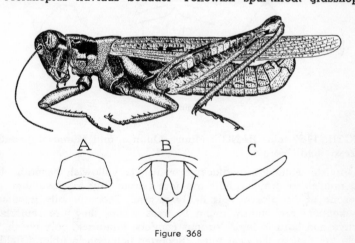

Figure 368

LENGTH: 19-26 mm. RANGE: Alberta to Manitoba, south to Arizona, Texas, and Illinois.

Yellowish to brownish or olive above; paler beneath. Hind tibia blue or purple. (A) shows the male subgenital plate. Prefers sandy or blow-out areas where it occurs on grass. Found in and about yucca clumps. *M. bowditchi* Scudder occurs from Alberta and Saskatchewan to Arizona and Oklahoma. It is similar to *flavidus* except a little larger and dull colored. Five forms are assigned to the "Flavidus group."

27a Male cercus very much wider at apex than at base............**28**

27b Male cercus with apex about as wide as base or narrower....**32**

28a Male antenna unusually long; furculae absent (B); male subgenital plate as viewed from rear as in "A"; cercus as in "C." Fig. 369...
Melanoplus punctulatus (Scudder) **Grizzly spur-throat grasshopper**

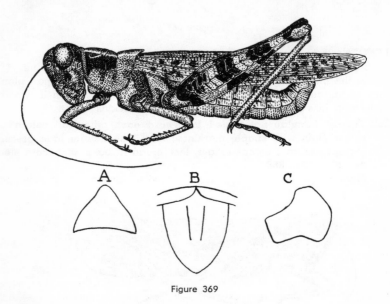

Figure 369

LENGTH: 19-29 mm. RANGE: Maine, Ontario, and Minnesota, south to Texas and Georgia.

Grayish, mottled with black; brownish to yellowish beneath. Hind tibia reddish to gray. Adults are found from July to November. The metazona of the pronotum is finely rugose. These usually uncommon grasshoppers are mainly found in trees where they are remarkably inactive and hard to find. Various conifers, tamarack, oak, beech, and maple are among the host trees. Reported common in upland fields in northern Georgia. Four other species are included in the "Punctulatus group."

28b Male antenna of normal length; furculae usually present though small; cercus variable...29

29a Male subgenital plate with the proportions of an equilateral triangle as seen from rear (A); cercus rather abruptly, equally widened above and below at apex (C). Fig. 370.....................
..*Melanoplus yarrowii* (Thomas) Yarrow's spur-throat grasshopper

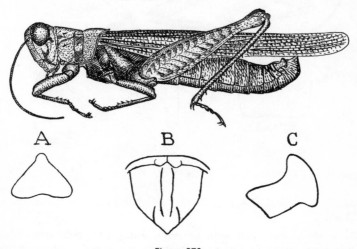

Figure 370

LENGTH: 30-39 mm. RANGE: Colorado to California, Arizona, and New Mexico.

Greenish-brown; pale yellowish beneath. Hind tibia red. (B) shows the male supraanal plate. Common in weedy areas in washes. Sometimes destructive to alfalfa, clover, and cotton. Placed with *M. bivattatus* and *M. thomasi* to form the "Bivittatus group." Years ago when a species was dedicated to someone the specific name was often formed by adding a double "i" to the person's name. These old spellings are preserved today. Nowadays when such a name is formed only a single "i" is added to the person's name, or "ae" if the person is female.

29b Male subgenital plate not triangular as viewed from rear; cercus more broadly and gradually widened........................30

30a Furculae short but distinct, slender (B); male subgenital plate nearly rectangular as seen from rear (A); cercus as in "C." Fig. 371...
....*Melanoplus*
glaucipes (Scudder) Glaucous-legged spur-throat grasshopper

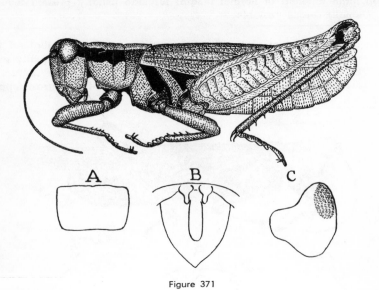

Figure 371

LENGTH: 22-28 mm. RANGE: Texas to Colorado, Kansas, and Durango, Mexico.

Brownish above; yellowish beneath. Hind tibia pale greenish-blue, whitish near base. Fairly common in grassy areas. Often commoner along streams. A distinctive species which stands as the sole member of the "Glaucipes group."

30b Furculae reduced to blunt knobs; male subgenital plate nearly trapezoidal as seen from rear; cercus a little different from above species **31**

31a Species in which both solitary and (longer-winged) migratory phases occur; distribution extending to California, Nevada, and Oregon; solitary phase grayish in general ground coloration, migratory phase usually with orange-reddish tinges on pronotum and hind femur. Fig. 372 ....
.... *Melanopus rugglesi* Gurney Nevada sage grasshopper

LENGTH: 17-33.5 mm. RANGE: Nevada to California, Idaho, Montana, Utah, and Wyoming.

Reddish-brown, grayish, or blackish, with contrasting pale areas. Hind tibia lavender, paler at base. This species is of particular interest as distinct "solitary" (or stationary) and migratory phases are developed. Some individuals are more or less intermediate between the

238

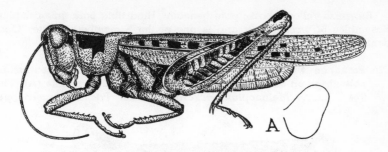

Figure 372

two phases. This is one of the 5 members of the "Occidentalis group," all of which are of economic importance. "A" shows the male cercus. *M. occidentalis* (Thomas) occurs from British Columbia to Saskatchewan and south to Arizona and Texas. It is much like the above but has no migratory phase. The hind tibia is blue. Usually not common, but widely distributed in grassland areas. Often found on mallows. Occurs sparingly to 10,500 feet (above timberline) in New Mexico.

31b Species in which no migratory phase is developed; distribution not including California, Nevada, or Oregon; general ground color yellowish-brown. Fig. 373.............................*Melanoplus cuneatus* Scudder. Wedge-shaped spur-throat grasshopper

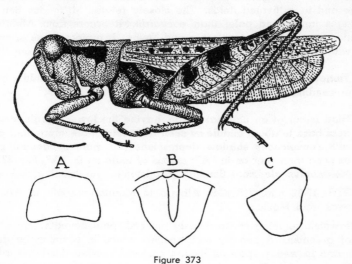

Figure 373

LENGTH: 21-28 mm. RANGE: Arizona and New Mexico.

Brownish-yellow above; pale beneath. Hind tibia pale greenish-blue. Resembles *M. occidentalis* and is one of the 5 members of the "Occidentalis group."

32a Pronotum with a rather distinct though not strongly contrasting pale stripe on each side; male cercus narrowed at middle (A). Fig. 374..........*Melanoplus packardii* Scudder Packard grasshopper

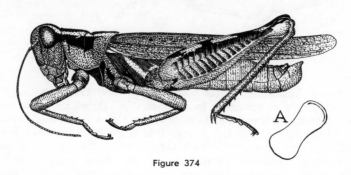

Figure 374

LENGTH: 21-32 mm. RANGE: West of Mississippi River, north to Saskatchewan, Alberta, and British Columbia.

Brownish, head and pronotum usually appearing striped; pale beneath. Hind tibia greenish or red. Sometimes a serious pest on the range and in cultivated fields. The closely related *M. foedus* Scudder averages larger and paler than *packardii*. It occurs from Alberta to Manitoba and south to California and Texas. It prefers areas of sandy soil with a scanty grass cover. Belongs in the "Packardii group."

32b Pronotum not striped; male cercus not narrowed at middle as in preceeding species...33

33a Hind femur of an unusual shape, having the lower margin straight from base to about middle as seen from side; male supra-anal plate with conspicuous shallow depressions (B); male subgenital plate as seen from rear as in "A"; cercus of male as in "C." Fig. 375... *Melanoplus gladstoni* Scudder Gladston's spur-throat grasshopper

LENGTH: 17-22 mm. RANGE: Alberta to Manitoba, south to Arizona, Texas, and Mexico.

Brownish, tegmina conspicuously marked; pale beneath. Hind tibia red or greenish. A heavily built species which is common on grasslands and in weedy spots on bushes such as Russian thistle. Northern specimens tend to be smaller and darker, and Mexican ones tend to be larger and proportionally more robust. This and *M. dawsoni* comprise the "Dawsoni group."

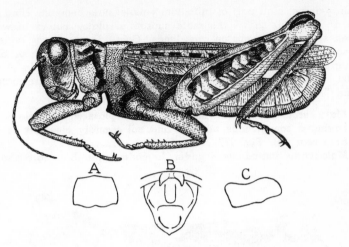

Figure 375

33b Hind femur of normal shape; male supra-anal plate without conspicuous depressions of preceeding species; male subgenital plate
and cercus unlike those of preceeding species................34

34a Male cercus broad (C); male subgenital plate with middle portion
of upper margin strongly elevated as seen from rear (A), and with
no tubercle. Fig. 376...
Melanoplus kennicotti Scudder Kennicott's spur-throat grasshopper

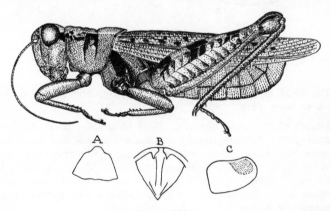

Figure 376

LENGTH: 17-21 mm. RANGE: Alaska to Saskatchewan, south to New
Mexico.

Gray-green, hind part of pronotum yellow; pale beneath. Hind tibia blue or buff. (B) shows the male supraanal plate. Found in weedy places, sedge areas, and on grasslands. Colorado specimens represent the subspecies *nubicola* (Scudder). This is a darker grayish or blackish form with reddish hind tibia which occurs on Mt. Lincoln at from 11,000 to 13,000 feet, above timberline. No other species are included in the "Kennicotti group."

34b Male cercus narrow (C); male subgenital plate with middle portion having a conspicuous tubercle and not strongly elevated as seen from rear (A). Fig. 377 . . . .
Melanoplus impudicus Scudder Immodest spur-throat grasshopper

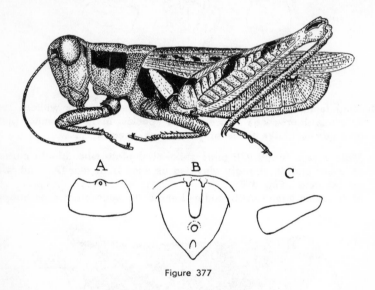

Figure 377

LENGTH: 16-27 mm. RANGE: Kansas and Oklahoma east to Atlantic, north to New York.

Brownish above; pale beneath. Hind tibia red. (B) shows the male supraanal plate. Occurs mostly on shale barrens and pine barrens. Specimens from the southern states are more yellowish with markings more contrasting. A closely related species is *M. tuberculatus* Morse, a small, inconspicuous, feebly marked species with pale yellowish-green hind tibia, described from Texas. These two species make up the "Impudicus group."

35a Male subgenital plate with upper edge broadly angularly or arcuately emarginate as seen from rear, sometimes with a tubercle at middle **36**

35b Male subgenital plate with upper edge sometimes bisinuate but more often highest at middle, not emarginate..................41

36a Male subgenital plate with upper edge arcuately emarginate as seen from rear...37

36b Male subgenital plate with upper edge angularly emarginate as seen from rear...38

37a Male cercus ending in a downcurved point (C); male supra-anal plate as shown in "B"; abdomen marked with black. Fig. 378....
......*Melanoplus tribulus* Morse Tribulus spur-throat grasshopper

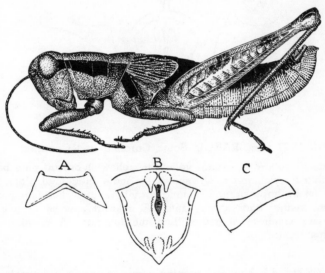

Figure 378

LENGTH: 18-26 mm. RANGE: New York, New Jersey, and Pennsylvania south to Georgia and Alabama.

Reddish-brown; pale yellowish beneath. Hind tibia pale greenish-blue. (A) shows male subgenital plate. Found in undergrowth of deciduous woods on hillsides and mountainsides. There are eight short-winged species in the "Tribulus group" to which this belongs.

37b Male cercus rounded at end (C); male supra-anal plate as shown in "B"; abdomen not marked with black. Fig. 379...............
....*Melanoplus australis* Morse Southern spur-throat grasshopper

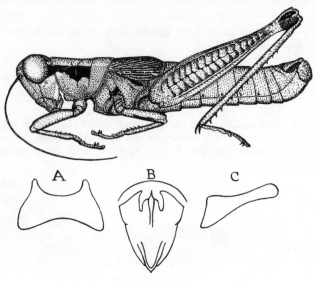

Figure 379

LENGTH: 16-27 mm. RANGE: South Carolina and Georgia.

Greenish-yellow or orange-yellow to yellowish-brown; pale beneath. Hind tibia grayish-green. (A) shows the male subgenital plate. Found mostly on swampy ground, among gray-bark and short-leaf pines, on bracken, sedge, and other plants. A colorful species in which the males are much more active than the females. A member of the "Decorus group."

38a Black stripe behind eye running across metazona of pronotum. . .39

38b Black stripe behind eye not crossing metazona of pronotum. 40

39a Male cercus blunt at tip (C); furculae rather long and slender (B); male subgenital plate with a large tubercle at middle (A); black stripe behind eye narrowing across metazona of pronotum; abdomen and hind femur not conspicuously marked with black. Fig. 380 . . .*Melanoplus decorus* Scudder Decorated spur-throat grasshopper

LENGTH: 9.5-13 mm. RANGE: North Carolina.

Brownish to blackish above; greenish-yellow beneath. Hind tibia pale greenish. Found in vegetation bordering swampy areas. The "Decorus group," to which this belongs, has four species.

244

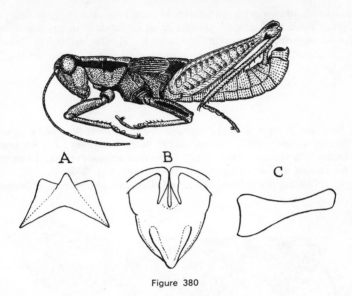

Figure 380

39b **Male cercus with a downcurved point at tip (C); furculae minute (B); subgenital plate with a small tubercle at middle (A); black stripe behind eye continuing wide across metazona of pronotum; abdomen and hind femur conspicuously marked with black. Fig. 381** . . . .*Mela-noplus viridipes* **Scudder Green-legged spur-throat grasshopper**

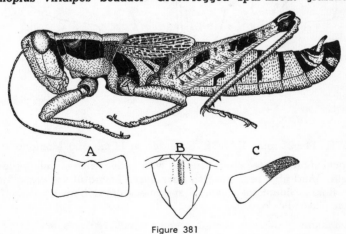

Figure 381

LENGTH: 16-23 mm. RANGE: New England to Nebraska.

Brownish above with extensive blackish markings; greenish-yellow beneath. Hind tibia green. Occurs most commonly in growth at edges of fields and woods, and in low woods. Adults mostly in June and July. Ten additional species are placed with this to make up the "Viridipes group."

40a Tegmina longer than pronotum, meeting over the back, and distinctly striped; male cercus about three times as long as greatest width (C); furculae very small (B); male subgenital plate appearing as shown in "A" when seen from rear. Fig. 382 . . . .
. . . .*Melanoplus dodgei* (Thomas) Dodge's spur-throat grasshopper

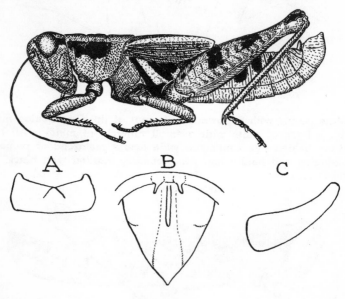

Figure 382

LENGTH: 14.5-21 mm. RANGE: Colorado to Idaho and Montana.

Blackish-brown, tegmina usually with pale stripes; dull yellowish beneath. Hind tibia red, blackish near base. Found at various altitudes in the Rocky Mountains. Typical specimens occur from 8,200 to 12,000 feet on Pike's Peak.

M. bohemani (Stal) is a similar species which replaces *dodgei* at altitudes of 7,000 to 12,000 feet in southern Colorado and northern New Mexico. Often found commonly in grass and mountain plants.

246

M. huroni Blatchley is again similar but with the tegmina spotted black. Found in Michigan in an old clearing with wild strawberry, wire grass, and dewberry present.

These three forms comprise the "Dodgei group."

40b Tegmina shorter than pronotum, separated over the back, and not striped; male cercus about two and one-half times as long as greatest width (C); furculae well developed (B); male subgenital plate appearing as shown in "A" when seen from rear. Fig. 383 . . . .
. . . *Melanoplus militaris* Scudder Military spur-throat grasshopper

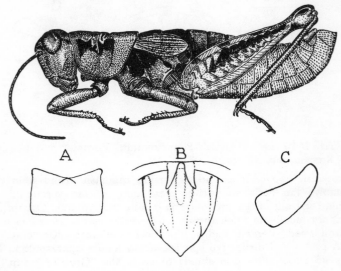

A   B   C

Figure 383

LENGTH: 17-22 mm. RANGE: Idaho.

Dark brown, sometimes with reddish tinges; pale beneath. Hind tibia red. This structurally distinctive species stands alone in the "Militaris group."

41a Hind femur and hind tibia green in life; male tegmina narrow and separated by more than the width of one tegmen; male cercus as shown (C). Fig. 384 . . . .
. . . . *Melanoplus gracilis* (Bruner) Graceful spur-throat grasshopper

247

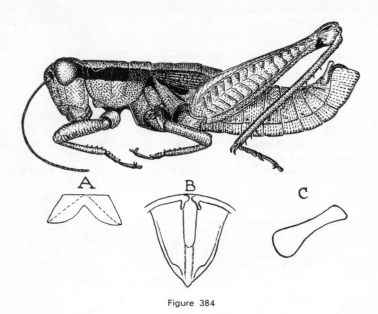

Figure 384

LENGTH: 14-20 mm. RANGE: Pennsylvania, Virginia, and Mississippi to Kansas and Nebraska.

Brownish above, legs and underside greenish. Hind tibia green. (A) shows the male subgenital plate and (B) the supraanal plate. The hind margin of the pronotum is a little emarginate. Occurs rather commonly locally in thick grassy and weedy spots. Noted especially on "Iron weed" *Veronia* and in blackberry undergrowth of elder thickets. A pretty and distinctive species, noted for its somersaulting leaps. It has no close allies and stands alone in the "Gracilis group."

41b Hind femur and hind tibia not bright green; male tegmina varying from separated to touching on back; male cercus variable......42

42a Male with furculae short and blunt (B); cercus about twice as long as greatest width and narrowed in middle (C); subgenital plate as seen from rear as in "A." Fig. 385............................
....*Melanoplus texanus* (Scudder) **Texas spur-throat grasshopper**

LENGTH: 23-32 mm. RANGE: Texas to Kansas, Oklahoma, and Missouri.

Grayish-brown; pale greenish-brown beneath. Hind tibia pink. Found on the prairie from Labette and Cowley Counties in southeastern Kansas to Waxahatchie and Comanche Counties in northeastern Texas. This and four other species make up the "Texanus group."

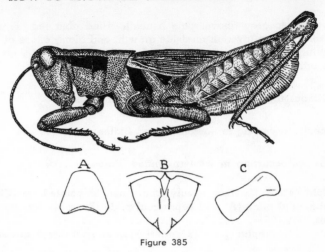

Figure 385

42b Without the above combination of characters..................**43**

43a Male cercus twice as long as greatest width (C); male subgenital plate as seen from rear as in "A"; furculae and supra-anal plate as in "B." Fig. 386...
...*Melanoplus scudderi* (Uhler) Scudder's spur-throat grasshopper

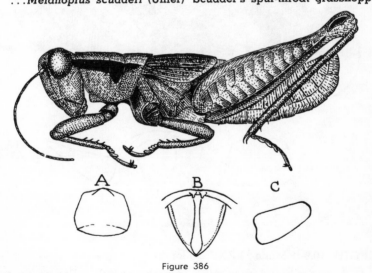

Figure 386

LENGTH: 16-24 mm. RANGE: South Dakota to Atlantic and Gulf states, Massachusetts to Texas.

Brownish to gray above; pale beneath. Hind tibia red. Frequently found along fence rows, in roadside growth, and along edges of woods. Adults July to October. Six additional species are placed with this in the "Scudderi group."

43b Without the above combination of characters.................44

44a Species occurring in eastern United States....................45

44b Species occurring in western United States...................50

45a Male cercus tapering evenly from base to pointed tip (C); male subgenital plate (A) and supra-anal plate (B) as shown; small species. Fig. 387...
......*Melanoplus puer* (Scudder) Florida spur-throat grasshopper

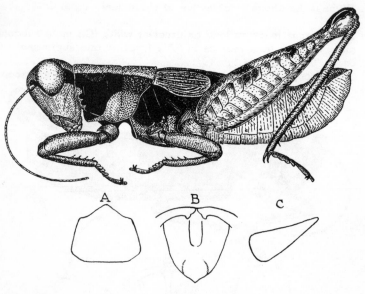

Figure 387

LENGTH: 10.9-18.5 mm. RANGE: Florida.

Dull reddish-brown to purplish-gray above; dull yellowish beneath. Hind tibia purplish-green. This species divides into 3 subspecies, the typical form occurring in north-central Florida, subspecies *seminole* Hubbell about De Soto and Manatee Counties, and subspecies *pennin-*

sularis Hubbell in southern Florida. Six additional closely related species from Florida are assigned to the "Puer group." All of these occur in scrub or undergrowth.

45b Male cercus not tapering evenly from base to pointed tip......46

46a Male with pallium strongly raised above margin of subgenital plate (A); supra-anal plate (B), and cercus (C) as shown. Fig. 388..
.... *Melanoplus rotundipennis* Scudder Round-winged spur-throat grasshopper

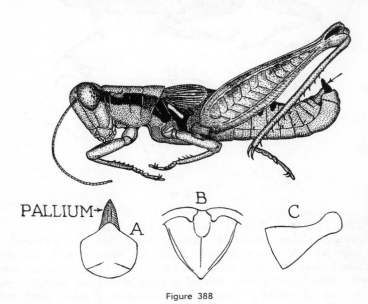

PALLIUM→   **B**
A   **C**

Figure 388

LENGTH: 13-23 mm. RANGE: Georgia and Florida.

Brownish above; yellowish beneath. Hind tibia dull pale greenish or yellowish. It varies in color according to the surroundings and is common and widespread in northern Florida. Adults may be found the year around in Alachua County. One other species, *M. pygmaeus* Davis is assigned to the "Rotundipennis group." *M. pygmaeus* has the prosternal spine wider and more sharply truncate and is a little smaller and proportionally more slender. It occurs in undergrowth near De Funiac Springs, Walton County, Florida.

46b Male pallium not raised above margin of subgenital plate.....47

47a Male cercus very much widened toward apex (C). Fig. 389..*Melanoplus scapularis* Rehn and Hebard Scapular spur-throat grasshopper

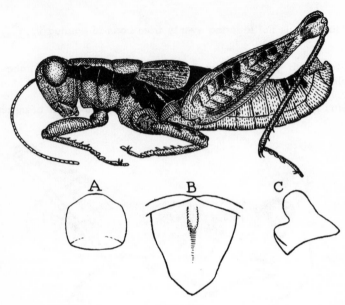

Figure 389

LENGTH: 15-22 mm. RANGE: Georgia and Florida.

Brownish above; yellowish beneath. Hind tibia dull yellowish to dull greenish. (A) shows the male subgenital plate, and (B) the male supraanal plate. Found in turkey oak scrub and other scrub or undergrowth. Three other closely related species have been assigned with this to the "Scapularis group": *M. tumidicerus* Hubbell from near Uvalda, Georgia, *M. mirus* R. & H., from Weldon, North Carolina, and *M. stegocercus* R. & H., from near Groveland, Georgia. All of these species occur in brushy areas.

47b Male cercus not as in preceeding species.....................48

48a Male furculae rather large and supra-anal plate abruptly narrowed near apex (B); male cercus strongly narrowed at middle (C); male subgenital plate as in "A" when seen from rear. Fig. 390........
....*Melanoplus strumosus* Morse Swollen spur-throat grasshopper

LENGTH: 15-26 mm. RANGE: North Carolina to Alabama.

Brownish above; whitish or yellowish beneath. Hind tibia pale greenish. Found in undergrowth in rather open forests. This and the following species make up the "Strumosus group." *M. foxi* Hebard oc-

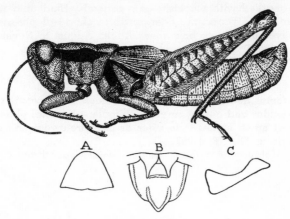

Figure 390

curs in Georgia and is distinguished by having the transverse ridge extending clear across the male supra-anal plate, and the furculae subcylindrical instead of flattened.

48b Male furculae small and supra-anal plate with sides evenly narrowing to apex; male cercus not strongly narrowed at middle; subgenital plate of a different shape when seen from rear........**49**

49a Hind femur heavily marked with black; male cercus appearing distinctly bent (C); male subgenital plate with upper edge bisinuate as seen from rear (A); supra-anal plate as in "B." Fig. 391....
Melanoplus nigrescens Scudder Black-sided spur-throat grasshopper

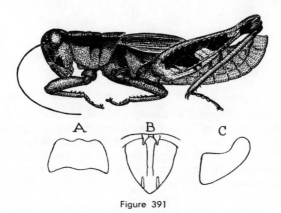

Figure 391

LENGTH: 23-26.5 mm. RANGE: Georgia, North Carolina.

Brown marked with blackish; pale beneath. Hind tibia red, a little blackish at base. Found in undergrowth in short-leaf pine woods, and among leaves under live oak trees. Adults August to November. This and four related species are placed in the "Nigrescens group" (also called "Querneus group" after *M. querneus* R. & H.).

49b Hind femur not heavily marked with black; male cercus rather long and slender and gently curved (C); male subgenital plate with middle part much higher than sides as seen from rear (A); supra-anal plate as in "B." Fig. 392.....................................
......*Melanoplus mancus* (Smith) Smith's spur-throat grasshopper

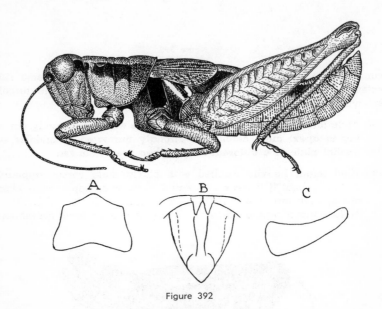

Figure 392

LENGTH: 14-25 mm. RANGE: Quebec and Maine to Virginia.

Brown above; clay-yellow beneath. Hind tibia pink. Common on Speckled Mt., Maine on high bare areas among *Vaccinium* (huckleberry) plants. Otherwise on hilltops and high bare ledges (Hammonasset River, Connecticut). Adults of this active species are found from July to September. Three other Appalachian species are included in the "Mancus group."

50a Male subgenital plate with a distinct tubercle at middle on upper edge 51

50b Male subgenital plate with no distinct tubercle at middle on upper
edge, sometimes with a vague swelling in that area............53

51a Male tegmina a trifle prolonged and narrowly rounded at apices;
male cercus broad (C); male subgenital plate about as high as
wide as seen from rear (A); male supra-anal plate as in "B." Fig.
393 ....
Melanoplus artemesiae (Bruner) Sagebrush spur-throat grasshopper

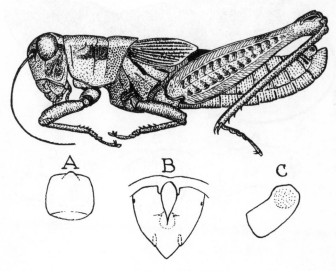

Figure 393

LENGTH: 16-21 mm. RANGE: Idaho.

Grayish with black markings; pale beneath. Hind tibia dull pale
greenish-blue. A little-known species collected on sagebrush in August
at Salmon City, Idaho. Taken in foothills of the Salmon River Mountains just west of town, and in Upper Canyon, Morgan Creek, Salmon
River Mountains at 6,650 feet.

M. lemhiensis Hebard is a very similar species which was taken from
4,300 to 4,400 feet along Cow Creek, Lemhi Mts., Idaho. No other
species are included in the "Artemesiae group."

51b Male tegmina broadly rounded at apices; male cercus proportionally longer than in preceding species; male subgenital plate wider
than high as seen from rear.................................52

52a Antenna of male unusually long; hind femur marked with black;
   male supra-anal plate a little interrupted at middle on each side
   (B); and furcula projecting well out over basal portion; male cercus
   as in "C." Fig. 394 . . . .
      . . *Melanoplus indigens* Scudder Indigene spur-throat grasshopper

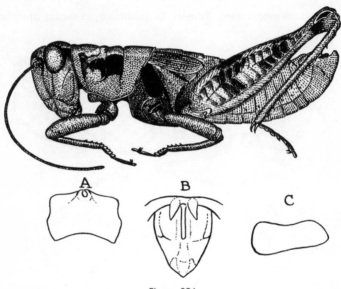

Figure 394

LENGTH: 20-25 mm. RANGE: Idaho to Montana.

   Blackish-brown above; dull yellowish-brown beneath. Hind tibia
dull greenish. (A) shows the male subgenital plate. Found in scanty
undergrowth of lodge-pole and fir forest, on open hillside covered with
low mountain plants and some sage brush, in or near thickets of wild
rose and *Spirea* in conifer forest, etc. 3,600 to 9,225 feet. Several additional closely related species belong with this in the "Indigens group."

52b Antenna of male of normal length; hind femur without black markings; male supra-anal plate unmodified at middle on sides (B) and
   furculae very tiny; male cercus as in "C." Fig. 395 . . . .
      . . . *Melanoplus immunis* Scudder Immunis spur-throat grasshopper

LENGTH: 14-21 mm. RANGE: Oregon.

   Brownish above, females often largely green; pale beneath. Hind
tibia brownish. (A) shows the male subgenital plate.   Common on

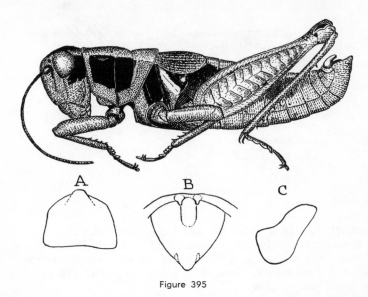

A   B   C

Figure 395

top of Mary's Peak (the type locality) and on Jackson's hill, near Philomath, Oregon. On Mary's Peak it occurs with the larger *M. saltator* Scudder in a large grassy meadow area.

M. caroli Gurney and Helfer, Alexander's spur-throat grasshopper, occurs in grassy areas and among scattered huckleberry, manzanita, and salal clumps along the northern California coast.

More than a dozen other similar western short-winged species are placed with these to form the "Immunis group."

53a Male subgenital plate with middle part of upper edge rounded and much higher than sides......................................54

53b Male subgenital plate with middle portion and side angles of upper edge all at about the same height.........................56

54a Tegmina longer than pronotum; male cercus as in "C"; furculae represented by two blunt swellings at base of supra-anal plate (B). Fig. 396 ....
.....*Melanoplus plebejus* (Stal) Plebeian spur-throat grasshopper

257

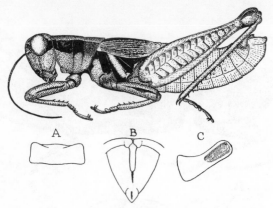

Figure 396

LENGTH: 21-24 mm. RANGE: Texas and Oklahoma.

Gray-brown; yellowish beneath. Hind tibia pale blue-greenish, pale at base, with a black ring. (A) shows the male subgenital plate. Uncommon in collections. Three other forms are placed with this to make up the "Plebejus group."

54b Tegmina shorter than pronotum; male cercus not as in preceeding species; furculae short but distinct processes..................55

55a Male cercus very broad at base, narrowing abruptly to a slender, tapering apical process (C). Fig. 397...........................
        ...*Melanoplus rileyanus* Scudder Riley's spur-throat grasshopper

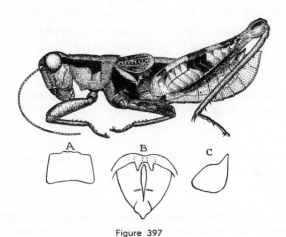

Figure 397

LENGTH: 17-20 mm. RANGE: California (Sierran).

Brown; pale beneath. Hind tibia pale greenish-blue, often yellowish toward the base. (A) shows the male subgenital plate. (B) shows the male supraanal plate. This species, divided into two subspecies, stands alone to make up the "Rileyanus group."

55b Male cercus very long and slender and narrowed near middle (C).
Fig. 398 ....
..*Melanoplus aridus* (Scudder) Arid lands spur-throat grasshopper

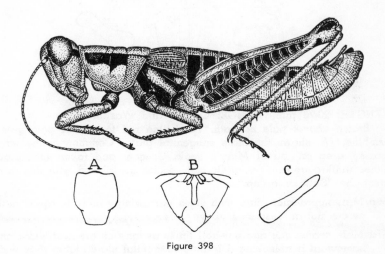

Figure 398

LENGTH: 13-20 mm. RANGE: Texas to California.

Bluish-gray; yellowish beneath. Hind tibia greenish-blue. (A) shows the male subgenital plate and (B) shows the male supraanal plate. Occurs from lower sonoran desert to 9,400 feet. Widespread and common in the Southwest. On *Dalea, Eriogonum, Baccharis,* and other plants. Sometimes numerous enough to be destructive in fields. Only one other described species is now placed with this in the "Aridus group."

56a Male supra-anal plate abruptly narrowed at apical third with conspicuous ridges at sides in that area (B); male cercus two and one-half times as long as greatest width and narrowed at middle (C).
Fig. 399 ....
....*Melanoplus saltator* Scudder Leaping spur-throat grasshopper

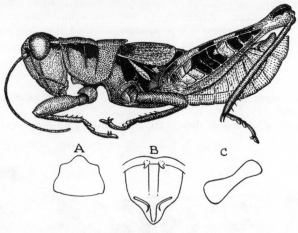

Figure 399

LENGTH: 20-26 mm. RANGE: Oregon and Washington.

Brown above; pale beneath. Hind tibia red to buff or pale green-ish-blue. (A) shows the male subgenital plate. Common in the large grassy area on top of Mary's Peak, Oregon, and taken in various other similar areas. Five additional species are placed with this in or near the "Saltator group."

56b Male supra-anal plate with sides narrowing evenly to apex; male cercus not as described above.................................57

57a Male cercus one and one-half times as long as greatest width and somewhat bent-looking (C); male subgenital plate higher than wide as seen from rear (A). Fig. 400.................................
Melanoplus discolor (Scudder) Contrasting spur-throat grasshopper

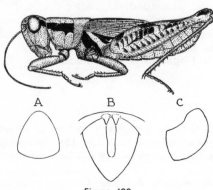

Figure 400

LENGTH: 19-25 mm. RANGE: Colorado and Kansas to Texas and Arizona.

Yellowish to ashy-brown above; pale brownish-yellow beneath. Hind tibia red. (B) shows the male supraanal plate. Found locally among low grasses and other plains plants. Placed as the sole member of the "Discolor group."

57b Male cercus of more slender proportions, twice as long as greatest width and gently curved (C); male subgenital plate wider than high as seen from rear (A). Fig. 401.............................
Melanoplus montanus (Thomas) Montana spur-throat grasshopper

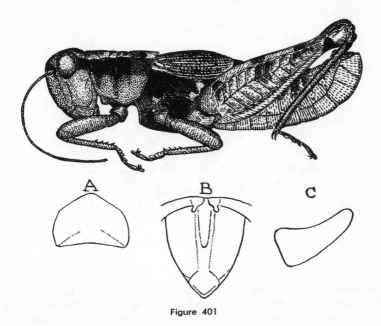

Figure 401

LENGTH: 19-26 mm. RANGE: Montana, Alberta, Wyoming, and British Columbia.

Blackish-brown with reddish tinge. Pale beneath. Hind tibia red. (B) shows the male supraanal plate. Taken in long grass and in scant vegetation at edge of conifer forest. Found on nearly bare west-facing slopes at Bozeman Mountain, and on gravelly soil in openings in lodge-pole pine forest at West Yellowstone. Northern specimens are darker in color. This and five other related species make up the "Montanus group."

KATYDIDS

Here are found some of our largest and most interesting Orthoptera including numerous species that look like leaves, prettily marked forms, and many insect musicians. They are mostly nocturnal and easily overlooked in casual collecting. A few decticids are destructive as well as a few of the leaf-shaped ones belonging to the genera *Scudderia* and *Microcentrum*. Most are leaf-feeders, but a few capture and eat grasshoppers and other insects. Quite a few are scavengers and they commonly vary their diets by eating their dead brethren. The eggs of the destructive leaf-shaped forms are flat, shaped like flaxseeds, and are laid slightly overlapping in a neat row along the edge of a leaf or along a twig.

KEY TO KATYDIDS

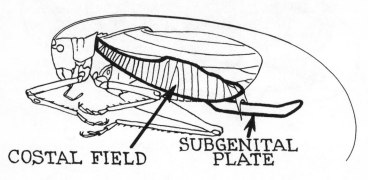

COSTAL FIELD   SUBGENITAL PLATE

Figure 402

1a Tegmina broad, ovate, convex, enclosing the abdomen, and with the costal field broad and crossed by numerous conspicuous parallel veins; male subgenital plate narrow and projecting about 10 mm. past tip of abdomen; fastigium acute—(*Pterophyllinae*).....2

1b Tegmina usually not at all as described above; male subgenital plate shorter; fastigium variable................................4

2a Pronotum with hind margin broadly rounded; Texas. Fig. 403....
..*Paracyrtophyllus excelsus* (Rehn and Hebard) Chisos leaf katydid

LENGTH: 39-42 mm. RANGE: Chisos Mts., Texas.

Green. Common in low scattered oaks, *Quercus emoryi*. Males call in endless series of "*quonk-quonk-quonk*" sounds. Rather fearless and easily taken when located.

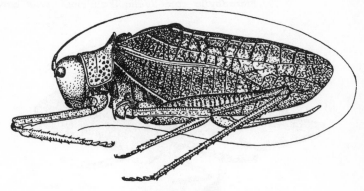

Figure 403

P. robustus Caudell, from south-central Texas has the head and pronotum proportionally larger and tegmina and legs proportionally shorter. In addition the male has a large stout erect knob on the third abdominal tergite.

2b Pronotum with hind margin less strongly rounded or bluntly angulate; eastern U.S. to eastern Texas.............................3

3a Pronotum with lateral lobes longer than high; female cercus forked at tip. Fig. 404.....*Lea floridensis* (Beutenmuller) Florida katydid

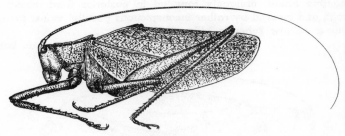

Figure 404

LENGTH: 44-48 mm. RANGE: Florida.

Green, pinkish-brown, or yellowish-green. Fairly common in palmettos and bushes, sometimes high in trees. Adults from June 1 to end of August. The subspecies *divergens* Hebard averages smaller and is found farther north, in Volusia County, in oaks, in hammocks and in cabbage palmettos and bushes.

3b Pronotum with lateral lobes not longer than high; female cercus not forked at tip. Fig. 405...................................... ....*Pterophylla camellifolia* (Fabricius) True katydid

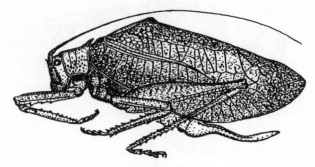

Figure 405

LENGTH: 46-55 mm. RANGE: Ontario to Florida, west to Texas, Arkansas, and Kansas.

Green. Commonly heard in tops of trees, delivering a loud two-part "xr" sound. Occasionally individuals produce the three-part "Katy-she-did" sound which is usually mentioned. Both sexes can stridulate. Eggs are laid in bark and probably also in the soft stems of woody plants.

Southwestern Arkansas specimens represent the subspecies *dentifera* Hebard, and Mississippi Gulf Coast specimens are of the subspecies *intermedia* (Caudell).

4a Tegmina broad, obliquely rounded in posterior third, costal field broad and crossed by rather inconspicuous parallel veins; fastigium with a narrow tubercle. Fig. 406............................... ....*Phrixa maya* Saussure and Pictet Yucatan katydid

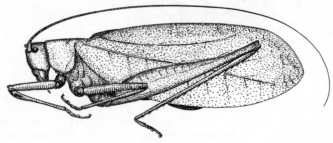

Figure 406

LENGTH: 38 mm. RANGE: Mexico and Florida.

Green. This is thought to be an adventive now established in Florida. It is uncommon. A specimen was taken in Monroe County, August 17, 1960 by T. J. Walker.

4b Tegmina not as described above; fastigium variable............5

5a Fastigium produced forward as a rounded tubercle, usually with concave sides, or as a distinct cone..........................6

5b Head more or less blunt in front; fastigium sometimes quite narrow between antennal bases but not produced forward as a tubercle or cone..13

6a Head produced forward as a rounded tubercle with concave sides (A); slender small to medium-sized meadow katydids. Fig. 407—(CONOCEPHALINAE) 7

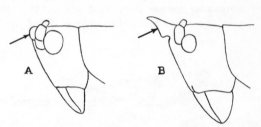

Figure 407

6b Head produced forward as a distinct cone which is usually excavated and toothed below (B); slender medium to large-sized species —(COPIPHORINAE). Fig. 407.................................9

7a Prosternum armed with rather long slender spines; body length usually more than 18 mm.; form more robust; ovipositor heavier. Fig. 408.......*Orchelium vulgare* Harris Common meadow katydid

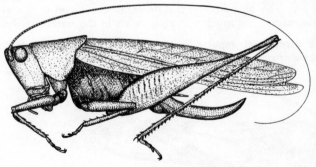

Figure 408

LENGTH: 34-36 mm. RANGE: Quebec and Ontario to Georgia and North Carolina, west to Wyoming and Texas.

Green marked with brown or pale brown. Common and widespread. Found in grasslands where it favors clumps of tall grass. The male call involves trilling alternating with quick staccato sounds, and is more varied than the calls of most crickets and many katydids.

O. *gladiator* Bruner, the Gladiator katydid, ranges from Montreal and New England to Washington and northeastern California, South to Tennessee and Kansas.

Several other *Orchelium* species are known, differing principally in details of male cerci and ovipositor.

7b Prosternum with spines very short or absent; body length usually under 17 mm.; form slenderer; ovipositor slenderer..............8

8a Male cercus long and slender (A) with internal tooth as shown; ovipositor longer than hind femur. Fig. 409......................
..........*Conocephalus strictus* (Scudder) Rapier meadow katydid

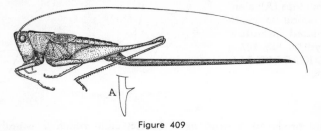

Figure 409

LENGTH: 19-45 mm. **RANGE:** New York to North Carolina, West to Arizona.

Green and brown. The extremely long ovipositor is even longer than shown, in some specimens. Found in grass.

Some seventeen rather similar looking forms are recognized from our country. The best structural differences are found in the ovipositor and male cercus, but much variation exists in the various species.

8b Male cercus not especially elongated (A) and with internal tooth as shown; ovipositor shorter than hind femur. Fig. 410...........
.......*Conocephalus fasciatus* (De Geer) Slender meadow katydid

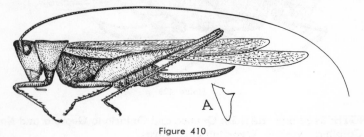

Figure 410

266

LENGTH: 14-21 mm. RANGE: Nova Scotia, Ontario, and Manitoba to Bermuda and northern Mexico, West to Wyoming and New Mexico.

Green and brown. Common in grass and weeds, especially in damp spots. This is replaced by the long or short-winged subspecies *vicinus* (Morse) in the western states. It reaches the coast in California. The male's call is weak and alternates between tiny staccato *"tic-tic-tic"* sounds and little high-pitched wavering trills.

9a Cone of head not excavated and toothed beneath. Fig. 411......
............*Bucrates malivolens* (Scudder) Bucrates katydid

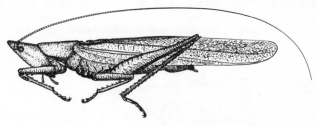

Figure 411

LENGTH: 27-53 mm. RANGE: Florida to Virginia and Texas.

Brown or green. Long or short-winged. Common in saw grass areas. Long-winged (macropterus) individuals fly easily and have been taken at lights. The male's stridulation is a soft shuffling sound, quite without ringing qualities.

9b Cone of head excavated and toothed beneath....................10

10a Tegmina reduced to short lobes, covering less than half of abdomen, and wings rudimentary if present. Fig. 412................
Belocephalus subapterus Scudder   Half-winged cone head katydid

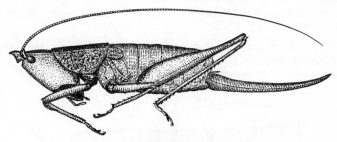

Figure 412

LENGTH: 25-38 mm. RANGE: Florida, Georgia, and South Carolina.

Pale green or brown with narrow brown stripes from fastigium to hind angles of pronotum. Commonest in December in undergrowth of open pine woods and palmetto hammocks. Sometimes found in board piles and under boards on ground.

B. sabalis Davis the Palmetto cone head katydid is a large green species common in southern Florida on scrub palmetto. Nocturnal. Males produce a low-pitched long series of "zip-zip-zip" sounds. They bite hard.

Several additional forms of *Belocephalus* are known.

10b Tegmina and wings well developed...........................11

11a Cone of head rather triangular and pointed as seen from above; roughened above, ending in a sharp downcurved hook at apex. Fig. 413...

...*Pyrgocorypha uncinata* (Harris) Hook-faced cone head katydid

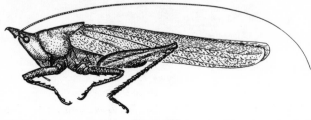

Figure 413

LENGTH: 47-50 mm. RANGE: Florida to North Carolina, Tennessee, Arkansas, Texas, Cuba, Mexico, and Central America.

Green or brown. Tegmina with scattered minute black dots. Found on grass, cabbage palmettos, mangroves, reeds, and undergrowth. Males stridulate like *Neoconocephalus*, a loud buzzing, and the stridulating period is short, from late March to before mid April.

11b Cone of head more rounded and not sharply pointed as seen from above; not roughened above, and with no sharp downcurved hook at apex...12

12a Cone of head (fastigium) much longer than wide (A) (see Fig. 420); ovipositor very long. Fig. 414..............................*Neoconocephalus exiliscanorus* (Davis) Long-beaked cone head katydid

Figure 414

LENGTH: 55-65 mm. RANGE: Connecticut to North Carolina, Mississippi, and Texas.

Green or brown. Green individuals have narrow yellow stripes along side margins of pronotal disc. Brown individuals often have minute black specks scattered on the tegmina. Taken among cat-tails, in tall reeds of tidal marshes, in briery thickets, and in corn fields. Often common locally. Males call at night but not as loudly or strongly as some other species.

The shape and coloring of the beak is distinctive for the different species. (See Fig. 420.)

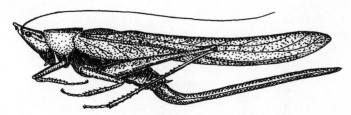

Figure 415

N. ensiger (Harris), (Fig. 415) the Sword-bearer katydid (E) is smaller and common, often in cornfields, in the East. Males call day and night, producing a monotonous series of *"tsip-tsip-tsip"* sounds.

N. robustus (Scudder), (Fig. 416) the Robust cone head katydid (F) occurs from Cape Cod to Virginia, and to the Great Lakes region. Also in California where it is well established in the Central Valley and sierra foothills. A very powerful, loud, shrill cicadalike sound

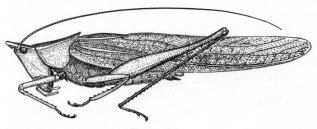

Figure 416

from the males is accompanied, at close range, by an oppressive heavy buzzing.

N. palustris (Blatchley) Fig. 417 (H) is widespread but not especially common over much of the East.

269

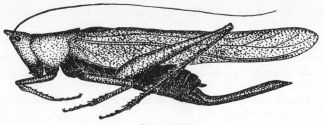

Figure 417

N. nebrascensis (Brunner) (B, D) occurs from Ontario, Tennessee, and Minnesota to the Atlantic.

N. melanorhinus (Rehn and Hebard) Fig. 418 (C) is a submaritime species which ranges from New Jersey to Florida.

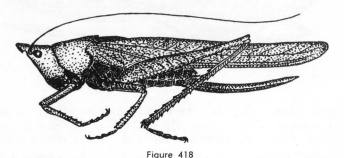

Figure 418

12b Cone of head (fastigium) (Fig. 420) wider than long to slightly longer than wide. Fig. 419.................................*Neoconocephalus triops* (Linnaeus) Broad-tipped cone head katydid

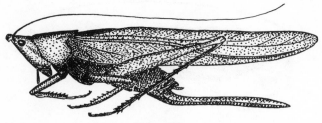

Figure 419

LENGTH: 53-56 mm. RANGE: Washington, D.C. to Florida, Texas, and California.

Green or brown. Fastigium (Fig. 420) (K) broad and with a black band beneath. Males produce a loud harsh buzzing sound. They often fly long distances to escape.

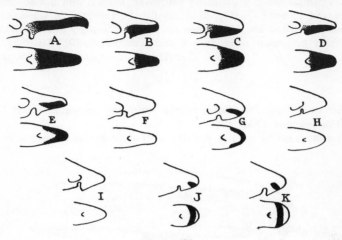

Figure 420

N. retesus (Scudder) (J) is another common widespread eastern form.

N. caudellianus (Davis) (G) is a less common eastern species which flies strongly. Males produce a slow loud resonant "*dzeeet-dzeeet-dzeeet*" sound.

N. velox Rehn and Hebard (I) is a swift-flying species of southern Florida. The call is a loud and continuous buzzing.

13a Ovipositor short, broad, flattened, and rather abruptly curved upward (A) (Fig. 421); mostly long-winged green, brownish (or pinkish) species; wings commonly conspicuously longer than tegmina; pronotum rather narrow and not shield-like—(PHAENEROPTERINAE)
....14

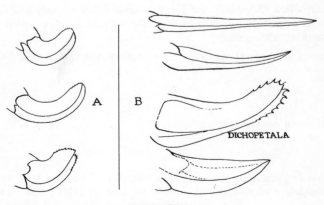

Figure 421

13b Ovipositor usually distinctly narrower, longer, and not so abruptly curved upward (B) (Fig. 421); mostly short-winged or wingless variously marked species; wings (if present) usually shorter than tegmina; pronotum often broad and shield-like—(DECTICINAE).....
........................(Treated in a separate key, page 281)

14a Extremely slender, delicate, and long-legged; wings much longer than tegmina. Fig. 422..
Arethaea gracilipes papago (Hebard) Papago thread-legged katydid

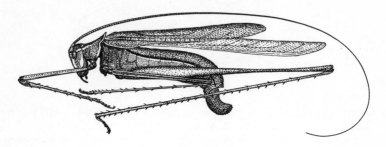

Figure 422

LENGTH: 31-33 mm. RANGE: Arizona to California.

Green, usually with a colored stripe on side. A fragile insect whose delicate colors are as hard to preserve as a complete set of unbroken appendages. The commonest Arizona species and often found on grass and weeds. Sometimes attracted to light. Males produce a weak high-pitched stridulation.

A. phalangium (Scudder), the Eastern thread-legged katydid, occurs in Georgia and Florida and is the only eastern member of the genus. Found on wire grass.

Several additional species, some short-winged, occur in the Southwest.

14b Of more normal proportions...................................15

15a Disc of pronotum concave with margins at rear raised, thickened, blackish, and crenulated; length 60 mm. or more. Fig. 423......
...............*Stilpnochlora couloniana* (Saussure) Giant katydid

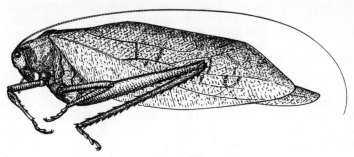

Figure 423

LENGTH: 61-75 mm. RANGE: Florida and Mexico.

Green, edging at rear of pronotal disc black. Taken on papaya and other vegetation. A very large rich green species, highly desirable for the collection, but rather uncommon.

15b Pronotum not as described above; mostly smaller species......16

16a Space between antennal bases much wider than the diameter of basal antennal segment......................................17

16b Space between antennal bases about equal to diameter of basal antennal segment, or narrower..............................18

17a Hind femur nearly as long as tegmen; ovipositor longer and not abruptly bent upward. Fig. 424...............................
...*Amblycorypha rotundifolia parvipennis* Round-winged katydid

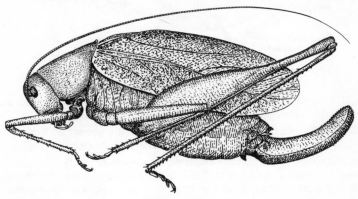

Figure 424

LENGTH: 31-34 mm. RANGE: Oklahoma, Arkansas, and Texas.

Green or (rarely) pink. This southern prairie subspecies is very distinctive in appearance and rounder-winged than more typical forms which occur into Minnesota, Michigan, and New England. In Iowa, Kansas, and Missouri the subspecies *iselyi* Caudell is found. Often common on grass, weeds, and undergrowth. The call is either a short two to four-beat sound repeated at intervals, or a long series of "*tsip-i-tsip-i-tsip*" sounds.

A. oblongifolia (De Geer) is common from Quebec to Colorado, Iowa, Nebraska, and Texas. The tegmina are at least three times as long as their greatest width. The male stridulating field is much larger than the pronotal disc.

A. floridana Rehn and Hebard ranges from Florida to Texas. It resembles *oblongifolia* but the male stridulating field is but little larger than pronotal disc.

A. insolita Rehn and Hebard is found uncommonly from Arizona to Texas and Mexico. It often has purplish spots on the tegmina. All of the *Amblycorypha* have the wide space between the antennal bases which separates them instantly from *Scudderia* etc.

**17b Hind femur short, less than two-thirds as long as tegmen; ovipositor short and abruptly bent upward. Fig. 425...................
....*Microcentrum rhombifolium* (Saussure) Broad-winged katydid**

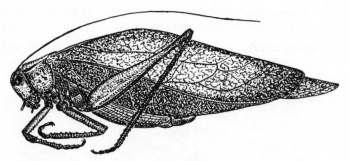

Figure 425

LENGTH: 51-65 mm. RANGE: Southern U. S. from coast to coast, north to Utah, Colorado, Kansas, Indiana, and New York.

Green. The middle of the front margin of the pronotum has a blunt "tooth." Common on many kinds of plants and trees. Destructive.

M. californicum Hebard, the California angle-winged katydid, from California, Arizona, and lower California, is smaller than *rhombifolium*, and the front margin of the pronotum is shallowly emarginate at middle. Common in oaks. Makes a clicking sound.

M. retinerve (Burmeister), the angular-winged katydid, is an eastern species which is paler green than *rhombifolium*, with the head tinged yellowish and the front margin of the pronotum straight at middle.

18a Tegmen **very wide before middle, and densely finely reticulate;** **fastigium narrow, a little raised, and with a distinct median groove.** **Fig. 426**. . . . .
. . . . *Turpila rostratum* (Rehn and Hebard) **Narrow-beaked katydid**

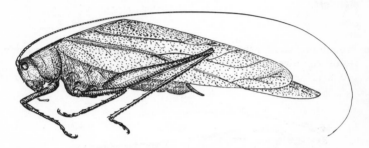

Figure 426

LENGTH: 38-39 mm. RANGE: Florida.

Green, often suffused with yellowish. Looks like a small *Microcentrum* at first glance. Several individuals have been taken from foliage of buttonwood, *Conocarpus*, and from mangrove. Males call with a "zrrp-zrrp-zrrp" low rasping sound.

18b Tegmina **narrower and not so abruptly widened before middle;** **tegmina variously sculptured; fastigium variable**. **19**

19a Front femur **more than one-third as long as hind femur; tegmen** **moderately broad. Fig. 427**. . . . .
. . . . . . *Platylyra californica* Scudder **California chaparral katydid**

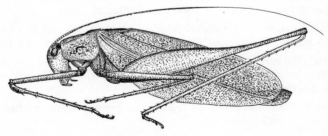

Figure 427

LENGTH: 22-24 mm. RANGE: California.

Green. Widespread and not uncommon in chaparral areas of California. On scrub oak, *Ceanothus*, etc. Often captured by hunting wasps and easy to net when in transit to the wasp's burrow. Males produce short, quick, harsh, but not very loud "*zitt-zitt*" sounds.

19b Front femur less than one-third as long as hind femur; tegmen slenderer 20

20a Pronotum "saddle-shaped"; tegmen usually with white markings; small southwestern species. Fig. 428..........................
........*Insara covilleae* Rehn and Hebard Creosote bush katydid

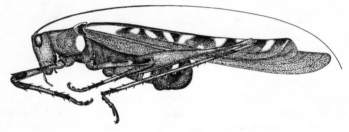

Figure 428

LENGTH: 28-30 mm. RANGE: California and Arizona to Mexico.

Green and dark green with white markings. A beautiful desert species which is restricted to creosote bush from which it may be beaten. The marks on pronotum and side of body are pearly.

I. elegans Scudder, the Mesquite katydid, is light green, darker on tegmina, and has the tegmina marked with 8 white bands. Rather common from Arizona to Texas and Mexico.

I. elegans consuetipes (Scudder) is green to brownish-yellow and lacks white marks. On various plants in California, Nevada, and Arizona.

I. juniperi Hebard, the Juniper katydid, is green, mottled and barred white. An elegant little species found in Arizona, California, and New Mexico on Juniper.

Several additional forms of *Insara* are known, some of them very uncommon in collections.

20b Pronotum not "saddle-shaped"; tegmen without white markings; widespread 21

21a Male subgenital plate (shown) long, slender, upturned, its apex usually with a V-shaped notch; eye round; middle femur not spined beneath. Fig. 429...22

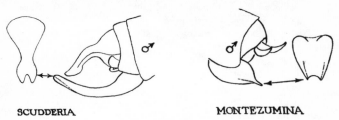

SCUDDERIA   MONTEZUMINA

Figure 429

21b Male subgenital plate (shown) short, broad, nearly straight, its apex broadly emarginate (Fig. 429); eye elongate oval; middle femur spined beneath. Fig. 430...................................
............*Montezumina modesta* (Brunner) Montezuma katydid

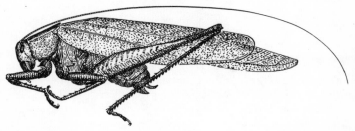

Figure 430

LENGTH: 32-33 mm. RANGE: Florida, North Carolina, and Illinois.

Green, disc of pronotum edged yellow or brownish. An uncommon species which looks at first glance like a small *Scudderia*. Specimens have been taken from floating water hyacinth, on sugar cane, and at light. Perhaps when the habits of this species become known specimens will be easier to come by for the collection.

22a Tegmina broader; first branch of median vein forked, the forks reaching the sutural margin; color green, rarely marked with brown. Fig. 431...*Scudderia furcata* Brunner von Wattenwyl Fork-tailed bush katydid

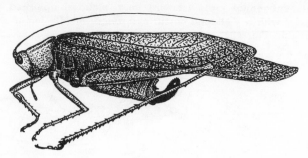

Figure 431

LENGTH: 36-40 mm. RANGE: General.

Green, sometimes tinged brownish. Common on grass, trees, bushes, especially at edges of meadows, marshes, etc. Common in towns and sometimes destructive. The call is a sharp "Zick" or a soft "zeep-zeep-zeep." Females often give a little chirp in reply to a male. Two subspecies are recognized in the South. The male subgenital plate and ovipositor are diagnostic. Figs. 429, 431.

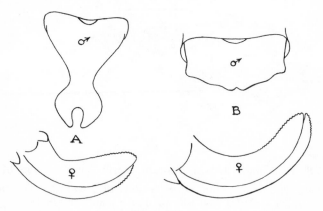

Figure 432

S. *septentrionalis* (Serville) Fig. 433 the Northern bush katydid, is smaller, uncommon, and mostly taken from forest undergrowth from Maine to New Jersey, Minnesota, and Nebraska. The last dorsal abdominal segment of the male has no downcurved process at middle. Details as in "B," Fig. 432.

278

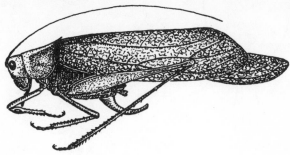

Figure 433

S. *texensis* Saussure and Pictet, the Texas bush katydid, ranges from Ontario to Florida and Texas. The male abdominal process is as in "C" Fig. 434.

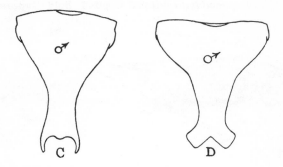

Figure 434

S. *curvicauda* (De Geer), the Curve-tailed bush katydid, from southeastern Canada to Virginia, Tennessee, and Nebraska, has the male abdominal process as in "D" Fig. 434.

S. *mexicana* (Saussure), the Mexican bush katydid, occurs from Arizona and southern California to Guatemala. The male abdominal process is shaped as in "E" Fig. 435.

279

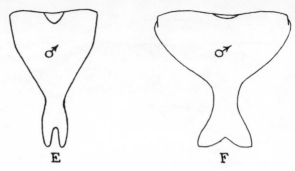

Figure 435

S. *pistillata* Brunner, the Broad-winged bush katydid, occurs from Nova Scotia to Saskatchewan and South at least to Virginia. The male abdominal process is shaped as in "F," Fig. 435.

22b Tegmina narrower; first branch of median vein joining ulnar vein; green strikingly marked with brown and black. Fig. 436........
..............*Inscudderia taxodii* Caudell Bald Cypress katydid

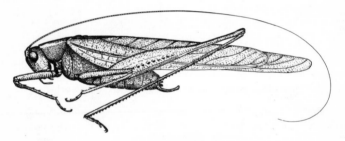

Figure 436

LENGTH: 30 mm. RANGE: Mississippi.

Green with brown and blackish on and near some of the tegminal veins. An active species taken on *Polygonum* in a cypress slough.

I. strigata (Scudder), the Striped katydid, from Florida and Georgia, measures 44 mm. in length and has a brown median stripe bordered by a black stripe on each side down the back. Otherwise green except some brown on legs and lateral margins of pronotal disc. A slender and beautiful katydid taken commonly from *Hypericum fasciculatum* and occasionally from rosemary, (*Ceratiola*), and other vegetation.

I. walkeri Hebard, Walker's katydid, is a handsome Florida species taken commonly on bald cypress, mostly from trees and sprouts standing in water. Colored about as in *taxodii* but larger, with apical tooth of male cercus much shorter, and with apex of male subgenital plate less specialized.

DECTICIDS

"CERBERUS"
FIGHTING ATTITUDE.

ECTICIDS are often called shield-backed katydids because of their enlarged pronota. Most of them are short-winged. Numerous species occur in the southwestern states, fewer elsewhere. The so-called "Mormon Cricket" is a decticid (pronounced *deck-tiss-sid*) which occurs in tremendous hordes and has often been ruinously destructive. The "Coulee Cricket" is also sometimes destructively common, but our other decticids are at most only moderately common, while many rank among our scarcest insects. A popular group with collectors, they may be taken on warm nights with the aid of lights when the males are stridulating. Females are generally scarcer in collections as they are silent and are usually found more or less accidentally.

KEY TO DECTICIDS

1a **Ovipositor moderately broad to apex and with conspicuous teeth at apex; legs and antennae extraordinarily long and slender. Fig. 437** . . . . *Dichopetala brevihastata* Morse Short-winged katydid

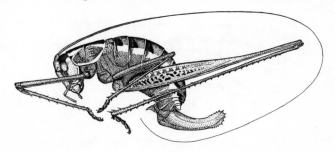

Figure 437

LENGTH: 13-25 mm. RANGE: Arizona to southwestern Texas and Mexico.

Green and/or brown, often with a pair of white stripes. A very slender delicate species, common on various low plants of the desert grasslands. Adults August to October. Best collected at night. The ovipositor, while broad, is moderately long and not very strongly bent up. The genus does not fit in very well where it is usually placed with leaf-winged katydids such as *Scudderia*, and for purposes of this handbook it seems as well to place it with the decticids. Males stridulate weakly and look and behave much like decticids.

D. oreoeca Rehn and Hebard is a similar species which occurs at altitudes of from 3,900-6,500 feet in the Big Bend region of Texas.

D. emarginata Brunner is another nocturnal flower-eating Texas species.

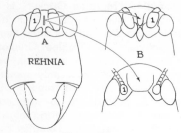

1b Ovipositor longer, slenderer, or more pointed, and with much finer teeth or no teeth at apex; legs and antennae not as long and slender....................2

Figure 438

2a Fastigium very narrow Fig. 438 (A), about one-fifth as wide as first antennal segment; hind border of pronotum strongly raised; wings usually slightly longer than tegmina; front legs with long strong spines. Fig. 439...
..*Rehnia cerberus* Rehn and Hebard   Cerberus shield-back katydid

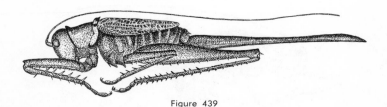

Figure 439

LENGTH: 36-75 mm. RANGE: Texas and New Mexico to Mexico.

Green with pearly white and brownish markings. Wing pale greenish-blue with four irregular rows of more or less separate black spots. A powerful, spectacular, and aggressive predaceous species which occurs adult from July to September. Males produce a harsh rapid chattering "tzi-zi-zi-zi-zi" sound.

R. spinosus Caudell, with long black spines on all of the legs occurs in Texas. Uncommon.

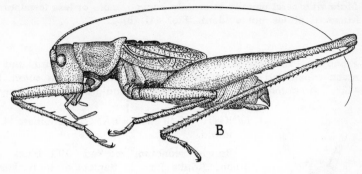

Figure 440

R. victoriae Caudell (Fig. 440 B) is similar but not as large and is less spiny. It occurs from Mexico through Texas to Kansas. The wing has a central blotch of shining black.

Rehnia are somewhat different from most of our decticids and are thought to belong to a different subfamily, the LISTROSCELINAE.

2b Fastigium wider Fig. 438 (B), one-third or more as wide as first antennal segment; hind border of pronotum usually not strongly raised; wings shorter than tegmina; front legs usually less strongly spined. 3

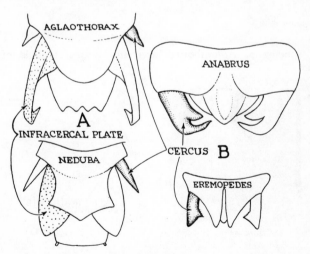

Figure 441

3a Male with cerci simple, conical, lateral; infracercal plates well developed, terminal, larger than cerci. Fig. 441 (A)................4

3b Male with cerci usually internally hooked, more or less terminal; infracercal plates not evident. Fig. 441 (B).......................5

4a Pronotum extremely large with disc roughly oval in form and not much constricted at front; brown, green, and black in color. Fig. 442....*Aglaothorax ovatus* (Scudder) Splendid shield-back katydid

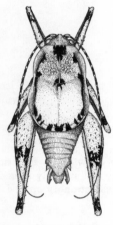

LENGTH: 26-40 mm. RANGE: Southern California.

Brown, pronotum marked with black and green. Adults June to September in bushes or trees of desert region. Male calls "zip-zip" with a pause of several seconds before repeating.

A. segnis Rehn and Hebard occurs along the eastern slope of the Sierra Nevada Mountains. It is larger and more highly colored than *ovatus*. The male calls "zic-zic-zic" with a pause, or sometime four "zic's."

A. armiger Rehn and Hebard occurs in the yucca-pinyon-juniper zone in Charleston Peak Canyon, Nevada. The male calls much like *segnis* and can be heard for almost 200 feet.

Figure 442

The species of *Aglaothorax* have the largest shields of all our decticids.

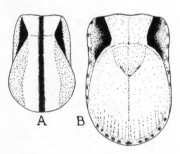

Figure 443

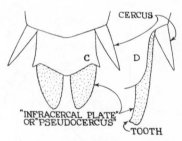

Figure 444

4b Pronotum large but not as large as above, with disc more strongly narrowed at front (Fig. 443); colors browns, grays, and black, not green. Fig. 445...
..........*Neduba carinata* Walker Carinated shield-back katydid

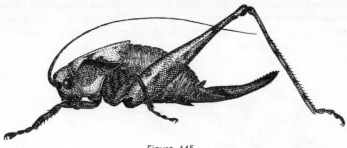

Figure 445

LENGTH: 19-39 mm. RANGE: California to British Columbia.

Brownish, the pronotum striped, mottled, or disc and lateral lobes as contrastingly colored areas. A common bush and tree-dwelling species. The male's call is a series of "tzeee-tzeee-tzeee" sounds. Male pronotum as in Fig. 443 "A," male pseudocercus as in Fig. 444 "C."

N. morsei Caudell, found from California to Washington, is smaller and has the pseudocerci long and toothed inwardly Fig. 444 (D). The tegmina are purplish-brown. The call is a diminishing series of "*tsip-tsip-tsip*" sounds.

N. diabolicus (Scudder) is a larger species found on yucca and desert shrubs at Walker Pass, California. It ranges north to Mt. Shasta. Male pronotum as in Fig. 443 "B."

5a Wing rounded, shining, opaque black.........................6

5b Wing (when present) not round, opaque, and black.............7

6a Tegmina longer than pronotum; pronotum with no strong depressions on disc, and with no strong lateral ridge. Fig. 446.........
............*Zacycloptera atripennis* Caudell Black-winged decticid

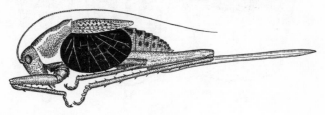

Figure 446

LENGTH: 28-68 mm. RANGE: Southern Nevada.

Gray-brown with white marks and black wings. Found in sandy areas in the Walker Lake area. Like *Rehnia* these spread their wings in a menacing manner and bite viciously when disturbed. They eat *Atriplex* flowers and car-crushed insects. The call is a long-continued rapid series of "zi-i-ik" sounds. A striking uncommon species and a great prize to collectors.

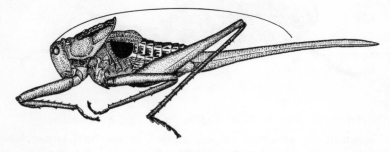

Figure 447

6b Tegmina shorter than pronotum; pronotum with strong depressions on disc, and with heavy and prominent lateral ridges. Figs. 447, 448...... *Plagiostira gillettei* **Caudell Gillette's shield-back katydid**

LENGTH: 25-68 mm. RANGE: Nevada to Utah, California and Colorado.

Yellow-brown with depressed area of pronotum greenish, metazona without white marks (A) and hind margins of abdominal segments with black spots. Wing black. A large rather slow-moving but handsome species which eats car-crushed insects and feeds on a variety of desert plants. Many specimens are more robust than the one shown.

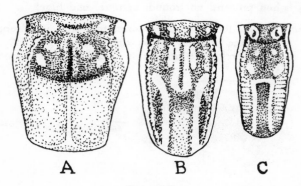

A   B   C

Figure 448

P. mescaleroensis Tinkham is similar but smaller and has the metazona of the pronotum marked with two white lines which diverge in front (B). It occurs on the Mescalero dunes of New Mexico.

P. albonotata Scudder is still a bit smaller and has the pronotum (C) much narrower with white lines on the metazona which unite in front. It is common on desert plants from Arizona to Utah and Colorado.

7a Tegmen of male (and often of female as well) longer than pronotum 8

7b Tegmen of male shorter than pronotum........................15

8a Tegmina (A) not covering all of abdomen, triangular in form and narrow at apices; cercus of male (B) long, straight, and with one large internal tooth. Fig. 449...................................
.... *Acrodectes philophagus* Hebard Timberline shield-back katydid

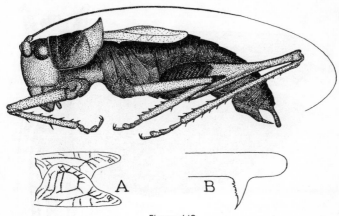

Figure 449

LENGTH: 19-25 mm. RANGE: Sierra Nevada Mts., California.

Brownish or greenish with fine black markings. The tegmina are brownish. Found uncommonly from moderate altitudes (Cottonwood Creek below Walker Pass) to 13,000 feet in Mt. Whitney-Mono Pass region. Adults at high altitudes in August. The nervous and rapid activity of this species reminds one much of the movements of common field crickets (*Acheta*). Eats lichens and is well camouflaged when motionless on a variegated rock.

8b Tegmina covering abdomen or rounded at apices, not triangular as above; cercus of male variable..........................9

9a Prosternum with paired spines, Fig. 450. 10

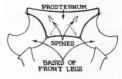

Figure 450

287

9b Prosternum s m o o t h , no
spines 12

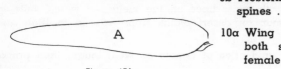

Figure 451

10a Wing vestigal in one or
both sexes; color green;
female flightless........11

10b Wing long, fully developed for flying; color mottled gray, brown,
blackish, or greenish. Fig. 452...................................
..........*Capnobotes fuliginosus* (Thomas) Brown-winged decticid

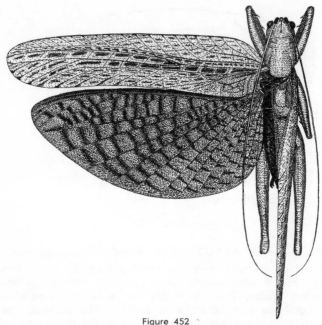

Figure 452

LENGTH: 64-72 mm. RANGE: Arizona to California, Nevada, Utah, and
Mexico.

Brownish with gray mottling; wing mostly brown. Uncommon on
mesquite and other shrubs. Males may be heard calling loudly as one
drives slowly along at night, and may be stalked and taken with lights.
Adults May to October. A fine large decticid which is partly carnivorous.

C. occidentalis (Thomas) is similar to *fuliginosus* except smaller and with
wing only faintly colored. Adults of this grayish or greenish species

are found uncommonly, mostly in the juniper-pinyon belt from California to New Mexico, Utah, and southern Idaho in July and August.

C. *bruneri* Scudder occurs in California north to Davis and Mt. Diablo. The tegmen (Fig. 451) is much narrowed in apical half.

11a Fastigium three-fourths as wide as first antennal segment, not grooved above; disc of metazona flattened; ovipositor distinctly curved upward. Fig. 453, 453A.................................
.......*Hubbellia praestans* Hebard Hubbell's shield-back katydid

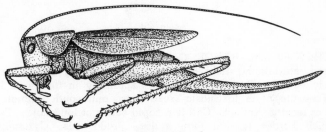

Figure 453

LENGTH: 36-85 mm. RANGE: Florida.

Green, brown on top of head and pronotum, tegmen with lower margin yellow in female, white in male. Found high in trees and thus difficult to collect. While "rare" in collections this species (like many others) is moderately common in the field. This has also been called *H. marginifera* Walker.

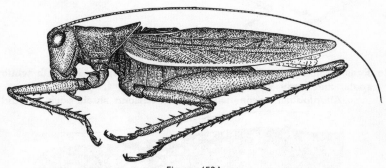

Figure 453A

11b Fastigium less than one-half as wide as first antennal segment, grooved above; disc of metazona convex; ovipositor slightly downcurved. Figs. 454, 455...
.........*Cyrtophyllicus chlorum* Hebard Green chaparral decticid

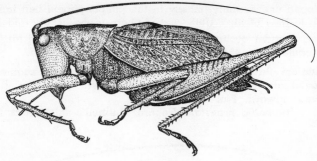

Figure 454

LENGTH: 23-60 mm. RANGE: California.

Green, stridulating field of male tegmen partly brown, tegmina narrowly edged yellow below. Occurs sparingly in trees and bushes from Yosemite north to Shasta-Yreka area, and south through Coast Range at least to Antioch. Call is a rapid series of loud notes. Females are much harder to find than males. Predaceous. *Cyrtophyllicus, Hubbellia,* and the European *Tettigonia* are very similar in most respects when compared side by side.

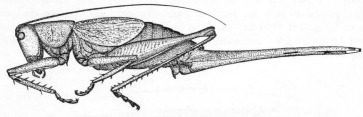

Figure 455

12a Eyes strongly convex and protuberant; tegmina green with white spots, and body with pearly markings. Fig. 456 . . . .
. . . . . *Anoplodusa arizonensis* Caudell   Arizona shield-back katydid

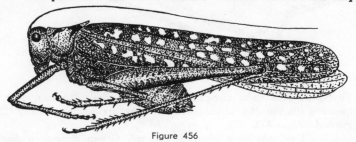

Figure 456

LENGTH: 50-55 mm. RANGE: Arizona to California and Nevada.

Largely green with brownish and whitish markings. This large, beautiful, and uncommon decticid lives on saltbrush (*Atriplex*) and on creosote bush. It has been found east as far as Florence, Arizona, north to Stillwater, Nevada, and west to Mojave, California. Adults May to August. The male calls much like *Capnobotes fuliginosus* but not nearly as loudly.

12b Eyes moderately convex and not notably protuberant; tegmina not green with white spots, body without pearly markings.........13

13a Tegmina long, with a row of markings in the median area. Fig. 457........*Platycleis tessellata* **(Charpentier) Tessellated decticid**

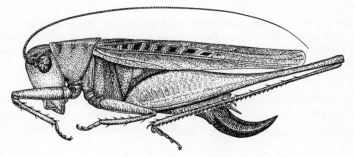

Figure 457

LENGTH: 22-23 mm. RANGE: Mediterranean, California.

Brownish with dark spots on tegmen. First noted in California in 1951. Now common in Bermuda grass of roadside ditches in Mother Lode country and in Sacramento Valley. The stridulations are very feeble. A pretty little species.

13b Tegmina long or short and without a row of markings in median area 14

14a Ovipositor slender, 11-14 mm. long, and strongly bent upward. Fig. 458 ....
Metrioptera sphagnorum **(Walker) Canadian shield-back katydid**

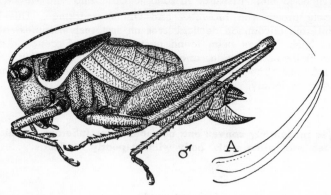

Figure 458

LENGTH: 17-31 mm. RANGE: Alberta to British Columbia and north-ward.

Pale brown marked with black and yellowish. Male tegmina either short and broad (shown) or fully developed and reaching past apices of hind femora. Female tegmina short and ovipositor (A) bent upward. Males trill softly. Adults are found in summer in meadow edges, along trails and roads, in spruce swamps, on tree trunks, etc.

14b Ovipositor broader and about 6 mm. long, feebly bent upward. Fig. 459 . . . . *Metrioptera roeselii* (Hagen) Roseli's decticid

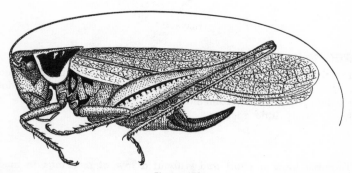

Figure 459

LENGTH: 14-25 mm. RANGE: North-central and eastern Europe, now established in Quebec.

Brown marked with green and black. Both long and short-winged individuals are found. In Quebec the short-winged form is less often taken.

15a Species occurring from Minnesota, Iowa, Missouri, and Arkansas eastward to the Atlantic. Fig. 460.............................
..*Atlanticus testaceus* (Scudder) Short-legged shield-back katydid

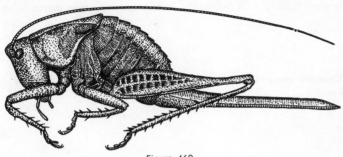

Figure 460

LENGTH: 18-48 mm. RANGE: Ontario to Kentucky, west to Minnesota and Illinois.

Brown with black on sides of pronotum and on tegmina. As shown in Fig. 461 "B" the tegmina (T) are more than one-half as long as the pronotal disc (P). Found on the ground and in low vegetation. A rather clumsy species. Adults June to September.

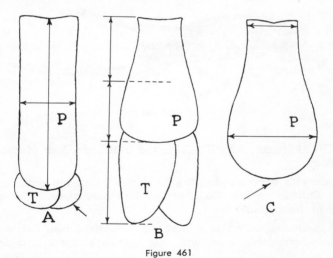

Figure 461

The nine species of U. S. *Atlanticus* are all eastern.
A. *glaber* Rehn and Hebard from Florida and Georgia has the pronotal disc nearly parallel-sided and more than twice as long as wide (A).

A. *gibbosus* Scudder from Florida to North Carolina and measures 26-63 mm. Our largest *Atlanticus* and a hard biter. As shown in "C" the tegmina are concealed beneath the pronotum (P). Fig. 461.

A. *americanus* (Saussure) from the northeast, and A. *pachymerus*, (Burmeister) from the Carolinas to Arkansas, are other common species.

15b Species occurring from the Dakotas to Texas, westward to the Pacific 16

16a Pronotum a little elongate, of rather light construction, and without well-defined lateral margins; male with tegmina visible, female concealed; no median longitudinal stripe down back; last dorsal abdominal segment of male ending in two long lobes. Fig. 462...
....*Eremopedes bilineatus* (Thomas) White-striped green decticid

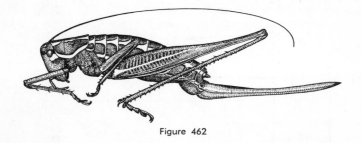

Figure 462

LENGTH: 24-51 mm. RANGE: California to Nevada, New Mexico, and Mexico.

Green with white stripes. The handsome adults are common from July to October on low desert plants. Eats road-crushed insects and foliage of desert plants.

E. *ephippiatus* (Scudder) is a similar but reddish-brown species with light-margined black tegmina. It occurs in southern Arizona.

E. *balli* Caudell from Arizona and New Mexico is smaller, dark brown, the pronotum often yellowish-brown, and the hind femur has a black stripe. The tegmen is black with the veins pale in color.

A few additional species of *Eremopedes* are known.

16b Pronotum usually shorter or of rather heavy construction, or with rather well defined lateral margins; male tegmina sometimes concealed, female tegmina sometimes visible; a median longitudinal stripe down back sometimes present; last dorsal abdominal segment of male sometimes ending in two fairly long lobes, but often not 17

17a Prosternum with a pair of conspicuous spines between bases of front legs. Fig. 463 18

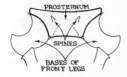

17b Prosternum without spines............ 19

Figure 463

18a Ovipositor downcurved; abdomen with a distinct pattern as shown; hind femur reaching about to tip of abdomen or a little beyond. Fig. 464.. *Apote notabilis* Scudder Northwestern shield-back katydid

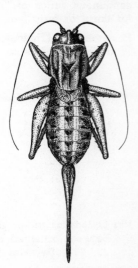

LENGTH: 33-55 mm. RANGE: Oregon to British Columbia.

Brown marked with gray and black. A large usually uncommon species of rather limited distribution.

Figure 464

18b Ovipositor straight or slightly upcurved; abdomen not marked as above; hind femur reaching far past tip of abdomen. Fig. 465.... *Pediodectes americanus* (Saussure) American shield-back katydid

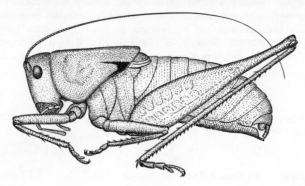

Figure 465

LENGTH: 33-80 mm. RANGE: Texas to Wyoming and east to Tennessee.

Greenish-yellow, pronotum marked blackish-brown at rear, and with three pale stripes. Adults from May to September in mesquite and other bushes. A large common nocturnal predaceous species. The continuous series of *"tsee-tsee-tsee"* sounds of the male are audible for thirty or forty feet.

P. stevensonii (Thomas), a similar but smaller common species, occurs from South Dakota and Colorado to New Mexico.

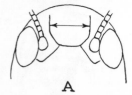

P. tinkhami Hebard, from Texas and Mexico, has a large white mark across the face.

S e v e r a l additional *Pediodectes* are known, mostly very uncommon "collectors' items," known from few specimens.

A

Figure 466

19a Ovipositor rather short, broad, and pointed; fastigium very broad between antennal bases (Fig. 466 A). Fig. 467...................
........*Decticita brevicauda* (Caudell) California grass decticid

LENGTH: 12-23 mm. RANGE: California.

Brown marked with green and black. Occurs on grassy well-drained slopes from May to August. Adept at plunging away through their jungle of grass stems.

D. balli Hebard occurs from Yosemite and Santa Cruz southward. It is similar to *brevicauda* except that males have the pronotum strongly ridged (carinate).

296

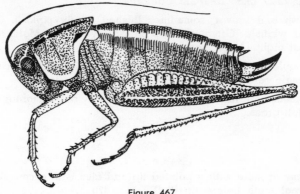

Figure 467

19b Ovipositor long and slenderer; fastigium not as broad between antennal bases..20

20a Pronotum with median longitudinal ridge sharp, smooth, and well developed. Fig. 468..............21

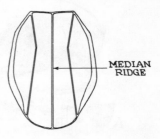

MEDIAN RIDGE

20b Pronotum with no sharp, smooth, well developed median longitudinal ridge (in specimens with rough pronotum a low rounded median ridge is visible).....................22

Figure 468

21a Cercus of male with a curving point or hook at tip but with no internal tooth before tip (A, B). Fig. 469.........................
..........*Clinopleura minuta* Caudell Gray-brown grass decticid

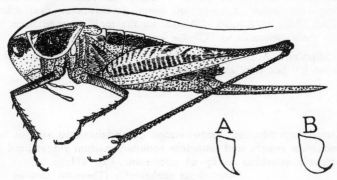

A   B

Figure 469

297

LENGTH: 15-27 mm. RANGE: California.

Grayish and brown, sometimes flushed faintly pinkish. Pronotum margined whitish. Often common in grassy areas. Males stridulate weakly at night. Male cercus as "A."

C. melanopleura Scudder, also from California, is similar except larger and male cercus as in "B."

Clinopleura are rather expert at diving away out of sight and harm's way in tall grass.

21b Cercus of male with a pointed tip and also with a conspicuous in-internal tooth before tip (B, D). Fig. 470.........................
................*Steiroxys strepens* Fulton Oregon grass decticid

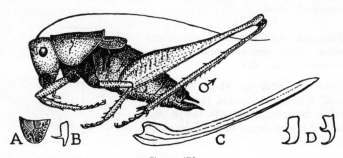

Figure 470

LENGTH: 20-37 mm. RANGE: Oregon.

Green or brown, lobes of pronotum sometimes with light margins. Sometimes common in meadows of tall grass where the males' weak whirring stridulation is heard all about in daytime. Best taken by trampling. June to August. "A" shows the male tegmen from above, "B" the male cercus, and "C" the ovipositor.

S. pallidipalpus Thomas from the western states is similar but the male cercus (D) has two internal teeth.

22a Large heavy-bodied, large-headed ground-dwelling species having pronotum rough, and with low rounded median ridge; hind femur scarcely reaching to tip of abdomen. Fig. 471................
................*Peranabrus scabricollis* (Thomas) Coulee cricket

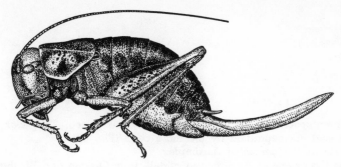

Figure 471

LENGTH: 28-50 m. RANGE: British Columbia, Alberta, to Montana and Idaho.

Dark brown or reddish-brown, margins of pronotum yellowish, legs and underside yellowish-brown. Sometimes destructively common in crops. A large, bulky, short-legged decticid.

22b Without the above combination of characters.................23

23a Large heavy-bodied ground-dwelling species having pronotum shiny, rather heavily constructed, and more than one-third as long as body length (not counting ovipositor); female subgenital plate (Fig. 473) straight across tip and with a small incurved structure at each apical angle. Fig. 472.....................................
....................*Anabrus simplex* Haldeman Morman cricket

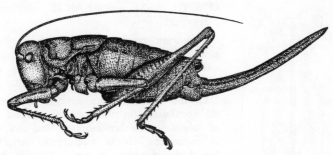

Figure 472

LENGTH: 24-62 mm. RANGE: West of Mississippi River.

Brown, yellowish, green, or black, sometimes irregularly mottled or distinctly marked. This insect has often brought heartbreak, hardship, and great economic loss in the West.

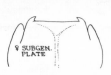

Figure 473

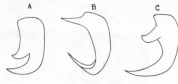

Figure 474

Three species of *Anabrus* are currently recognized. They look much alike and are separated by the male cerci (Fig. 474):

"A" shows the cercus of *A. simplex*.

"B" is the cercus of *A. cerciata* Caudell, from Oregon and Washington.

"C" is the cercus of *A. longipes* Caudell, from western Montana, northern Idaho, and Oregon to British Columbia.

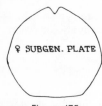

Figure 475

23b Smaller, ground or vegetation-dwelling species having pronotum more or less dull, rather lightly constructed, and one-third or less as long as body length (not counting ovipositor in female); female subgenital plate emarginate or notched at middle and lacking apical angles with incurved structures. Fig. 475........................24

24a Male pronotum with disc broadly rounded into lateral lobes; often with a black stripe down middle of back; commonly found walking about on ground; hind femora comparatively shorter and heavier. Fig. 476. *Ateloplus luteus* Caudell Black-striped yellow decticid

Figure 476

LENGTH: 19-31 mm. RANGE: California to Nevada.

Yellowish or tan, sometimes grayish on sides. Two black lines, mostly running together, forming a stripe down the middle of the back, but sometimes absent.

Of the seven known species of *Ateloplus*, all southwestern, the normal striped phase of *luteus* is the handsomest and the easiest to recognize. It is nocturnal. Adults are found in August in small desert bushes. Males stridulate weakly.

A. notatus Scudder is reddish-brown with a black stripe. It walks about on the ground at night. It is quite scarce and is found only in southern California.

24b Male pronotum with disc rather abruptly angularly rounded into lateral lobes, at least on metazona, or with distinct lateral ridges; hind femora comparatively longer and less heavy than above. Fig. 477...**25**

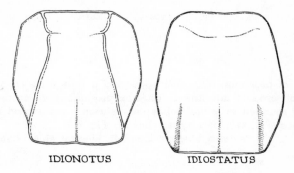

IDIONOTUS   IDIOSTATUS

Figure 477

25a Disc of pronotum (Fig. 477) appearing flat and bounded by sharp lateral ridges at sides; male cerci about as wide as long, pointed at apex, and with an internal tooth at base. Fig. 478............ ....*Idionotus brunneus* Scudder Sierran decticid

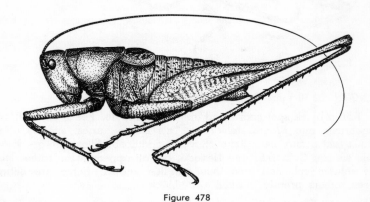

Figure 478

LENGTH: 18-19 mm. RANGE: Sierra Nevada Mts., California.

Brown, pronotum often marked with a little black. Occurs on shrubs in Motherlode region. Uncommon. As with many other insects, when the habits are better understood this may turn out to be fairly common after all.

Two or three additional species are known.

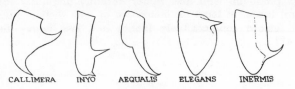

CALLIMERA   INYO   AEQUALIS   ELEGANS   INERMIS

Figure 479

25b **Disc of pronotum (Fig. 477) appearing a little rounded and round-
ing off broadly into lateral lobes on prozona, more narrowly angularly rounded to lateral lobes on metazona; male cerci of various
shapes (Fig. 479) (five types shown). Fig. 480....................
..........*Idiostatus elegans* Caudell Elegant shield-back katydid**

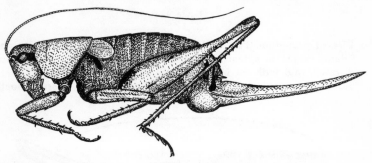

Figure 480

LENGTH: 32-50 mm. RANGE: Nevada.

Tan, a black spot near tip of abdomen in male. Feeds on sunflower,
sagebrush, and *Bromus tectorum*. This is the largest species of the
genus and occurs near Reno. Several additional *Idiostatus* are known
from sierran California and Nevada, but all appear to be rather local,
are seldom collected, and thus are litle known. Some are entirely
green, others prettily marked with black.

I. hermanii (Thomas) (Fig. 481) is an all green species taken in Plumas
County. The male cercus (A) is distinctively shaped.

I. callimera Rehn and Hebard is from Nevada. The male cercus and
dark markings at base and middle of hind femur identify it.

I. inyo Rehn and Hebard occurs from Walker Pass to the West base of
Montgomery Pass. It is small, mottled gray, and the cercus of the
male is distinctive.

302

I. aequalis Scudder occurs west of the divide in the Sierra. It is brownish with a black spot on the tegmina and the male cercus is distinctive.

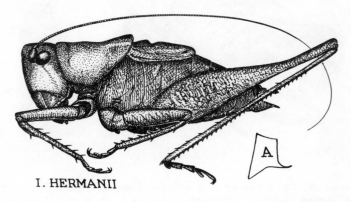

I. HERMANII

Figure 481

I. inermis (Scudder) is pale greenish and brownish with black on last abdominal segment. As usual, the male cercus is distinctive.

HUMP-WINGED CRICKETS

At first glance the insects placed here are likely to be mistaken for decticids. However the several characters separating them from katydids are fundamental. As students of nature we should feel fortunate at having these interesting insects living rather commonly in our country. Elsewhere in the world the family is known only from the type specimen of *Prophalangopsis obscura* (Walker) from India, and one other specimen of the same genus from the China-Tibet border. Males have short tegmina and call with a loud tinkling sound. At a distance this suggests tiny ringing bells to me, but up close it is a powerful shrilling sound. Females are grayish-brown bulky creatures found mostly on the ground. Fig. 482.

Cyphoderris monstrosa Uhler.....................**Hump-winged cricket**

LENGTH: 21-25 mm. RANGE: Colorado and Wyoming to Oregon and Washington, and British Columbia to Saskatchewan.

Brown with black and pale yellowish or pinkish-buff markings. The external male genitalia is as shown in "A." Found from moderate altitudes to near timber line. Males call from dusk until the nightly chill sets in. Males are usually found on branches or tree trunks, usually

Figure 482

facing down, and when located with headlamp or flashlight are easily taken. Large numbers of females ate the fruit buds off peach and cherry trees in May of 1901, in Idaho. In British Columbia they sometimes gnaw peaches, prunes, and apples in the orchards, leaving marks such as mice might make with their teeth.

C. buckelli Hebard, Buckell's hump-winged cricket, from Washington, British Columbia, and Idaho, is simliar but a little smaller and has the male genitalia of a different shape (B) as viewed in profile.

GROUND AND CAMEL CRICKETS

Belonging to this family are many of our least known orthopteroids. They are silent, secretive, mostly nocturnal, and often specialized and restricted to out-of-the-way ecological niches. At first glance many of them look pretty much alike, but some careful work with the hand lens will likely lead to surprises and many hours of fascinating collecting and study. The largest genus of camel crickets in the U. S. is *Ceuthophilus* (sounded soo-tah'-fill-us). A monograph of more than 550 pages and with more than 850 figures, by Dr. Hubbell, deals with this genus alone, and must be obtained if one wants to really go into *Ceuthophilus* in detail.

Three subfamilies are represented in our fauna: GRYLLACRIDINAE by a single species, RAPHIDIOPHORINAE including the cave crickets and the very numerous species of camel crickets, and the STENOPELMATINAE. These latter are the very common and distinctive ground crickets commonly called Jerusalem crickets. They are widespread and common west of the Rockies. The bulky abdomen is black-banded and the space between the eyes is very wide. The jaws are powerful and the legs are short with heavy spines. The Jerusalem crickets will be taken up first and then a key to the other two subfamilies follows.

KEY TO STENOPELMATUS (STENOPELMATINAE)

1a Head and pronotum without conspicuous dark markings. Fig. 483.. ....*Stenopelmatus fuscus* Haldeman Jerusalem cricket

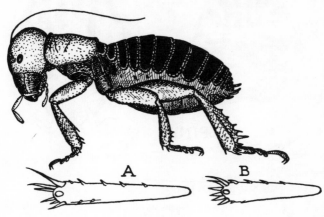

Figure 483

LENGTH: 30-50 mm. RANGE: British Columbia to Mexico and east to South Dakota and Colorado.

Brownish, abdominal segments banded black. Hind tibiae usually with four or five inner and two or three outer spines along sides. A large common, mostly nocturnal ground-dwelling insect which eats both plant and animal food. Sometimes destructive to seedling plants. Often parasitized by two or three horse-hair worms which are found curled and intertwined in the abdomen. Often parasitized by tachina flies. Some individuals have extraordinarily large head and jaws and are said to be "megacephalic." They can stridulate weakly. They bite hard but are not poisonous. The hind tibia is typically about as in "B." Some individuals have proportionally longer hind tibiae (A) and the head may at the same time be narrower as viewed from the front. If the spines at the tip of the hind tibia are unusually long the specimen is an example of what has been called S. *longispina* Brunner. As yet there is no general agreement as to whether "*longispina*" is a valid species or merely an interesting variant.

Stenopelmatus intermedius Davis and Smith ranges from California (Oakland is the type locality) to Arizona. It is similar to the above except smaller, of a more reddish-brown color, and the front margin of the prosternum is truncate or subtruncate instead of rounded. Other differences have been noted but these are hard to see.

1b Head and pronotum conspicuously marked (A, B). Fig. 484........
.........*Stenopelmatus pictus* Scudder Pictured Jerusalem cricket

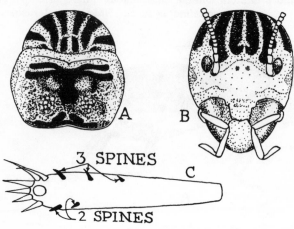

Figure 484

LENGTH: 20-30 mm. RANGE: California.

Brownish, head and pronotum patterned black, abdomen banded black. The hind tibia usually has 3 inner and 2 outer spines along sides (C). Specimens of *fuscus* and *intermedius* sometimes exhibit faint markings on the head corresponding to those of *pictus*, but they are black and conspicuous in *pictus*.

KEY TO GRYLLACRIDINAE AND RAPHIDIOPHORINAE

1a Tarsi with lobes beneath; eyes elongate-oval, located beside basal segments of antennae; ovipositor strongly upturned and pointed at tip; antennal bases far apart. Fig. 485..........................
.........*Camptonotus carolinensis* (Gerstaeker) Leaf-rolling cricket

LENGTH: 12-15 mm. RANGE: New Jersey and Indiana to Mississippi and Florida.

Reddish-brown above with darker markings, pale beneath. Our only representative of the subfamily GRYLLACRIDINAE, this interesting cricket hunts aphids at night. For concealment during daylight hours it commonly constructs a shelter for itself. A leaf is repeatedly bitten through until a loose flap is formed. The insect folds this flap over and pulls the edge down using its legs. At the same time it spins

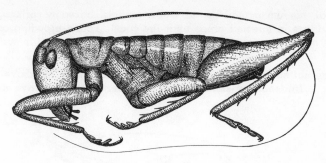

Figure 485

out silky strands from its mouth and fastens the leaf portions together. The sticky strands shrink as they dry, helping to pull the leaf edges together, and the cricket may help the process by pushing from outside with its legs. These crickets sometimes use empty bladder-nut pods as hideouts instead of rolled leaves.

1b Tarsi not lobed beneath; eyes rounder, partly above basal segment of antenna; ovipositor nearly straight to moderately upturned and usually with several small teeth at tip; antennal bases close together ....(RAPHIDIOPHORINAE)..........................2

2a Front femur more than 3 times as long as pronotum..............3

2b Front femur not more than 2 times as long as pronotum and usually considerably less...4

3a Tibiae square in cross-section, and with rows of small close-set teeth along the corner angles of the square tibiae. Fig. 486.............
..*Tropidischia xanthostoma* (Scudder) Square-legged camel cricket

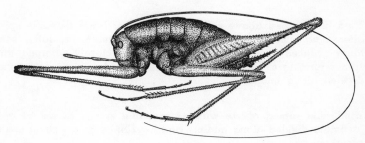

Figure 486

LENGTH: 18-30 mm. RANGE: California to British Columbia.

Brown, body darker. With appendages stretched out forward and back these lanky crickets have a maximum spread of about 8 inches.

Nocturnal, not uncommon in old wells, tunnels, boxed-in springs, and under bridges in forested areas near the coast. Found prowling on forest floor, especially near streams, at night. Adults commonest in summer.

3b Tibiae not square in cross-section, and not as spiny as above. Fig. 487..... *Hadenoecus subterraneus* (Scudder) Common cave cricket

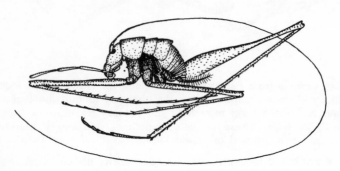

Figure 487

LENGTH: 16-20 mm. RANGE: Southeastern U. S.
Pale yellowish-brown, abdomen often with dark blotchy markings.

A fragile and very lanky cricket found rather commonly in caves. The ovipositor is nearly or quite as long as the body.

H. puteanus Scudder from Georgia and Mississippi to Pennsylvania is a similar but darker brown species usually found in and under coverings of wells. It has the ovipositor about one-half as long as the body.

4a Hind tibia armed above with pairs of rather large movable spines alternating with series of small immovable teeth, the latter sometimes reduced in number or displaced by closely grouped large spines forming a "sand-basket" at the apex; fastigium not strongly divided along midline...6

4b Hind tibia armed above with no movable spines except at apex; fastigium divided along midline and developed as a pair of conical prominences 5

5a Fastigium developed as a pair of narrow prominent cones which touch at the base; hind legs long. Fig. 488......................
........*Tachycines asynamorus* Adelung Greenhouse stone cricket

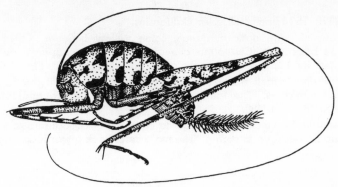

Figure 488

LENGTH: 14-16 mm. RANGE: Asia, Europe, and various localities in the U. S.

Brownish-yellow strikingly mottled with brown. A greenhouse pest which has become established in various states and very likely will turn up in additional areas. Originally it is thought to have come from China. The front tibia has a small spine between the pair of large ventral spurs at the apex.

Diestrammena apicalis Brunner is a plainer looking but otherwise similar cricket, also an adventive and found in greenhouses. It has the apex of the front tibia unarmed above and there is no tiny median spine present between the pair of large spurs located below at the apex.

5b Fastigium developed as a pair of low cones which are distinctly separated at the base; hind legs short. Fig. 489.................
.........*Gammarotettix bilobatus* Thomas Chaparral camel cricket

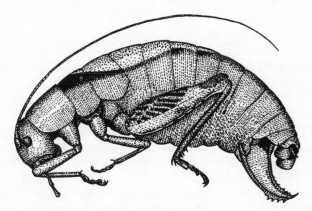

Figure 489

LENGTH: 15-18 mm. RANGE: California.

Brownish with dark markings, some yellow beneath. Often common on buckbrush (*Ceanothus cuneatus*) and other chaparral and best collected by beating. The male cerci are straight (A). Fig. 490..

G. *genitalis* Caudell from southern California has less of the dark colored markings. The male cerci are strongly curved and turn forward (B). Fig. 490.

G. *aesculus* Strohecker from Sequoia National Park, California, is common on buckeye in spring. The male cerci hook inward (C). Fig. 490.

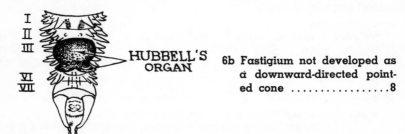

Figure 490

6a Fastigium developed as a downward-directed pointed cone.......7

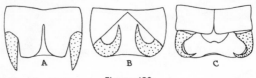

6b Fastigium not developed as a downward-directed pointed cone 8

Figure 491

7a Male with Hubbell's organ and long spines on abdomen (Fig. 491); hind tibia straight. Fig. 492......................................
.....*Pristoceuthophilus sargentae* Gurney Sargent's camel cricket

LENGTH: 11-12 mm. RANGE: Oregon.

Brownish and gray mottled yellowish and black. Under bark of a dead standing tree at 5,700-6,000 feet. Hubbell's organ overlaps the median portions of abdominal segments III and V and parts of segments II and VI.

P. *gaigei* Hubbell is a similar but slightly smaller species taken in the Olympic mountains of Washington. Hubbell's organ in this species does not overlap abdominal segment III at all, and overlaps seg-

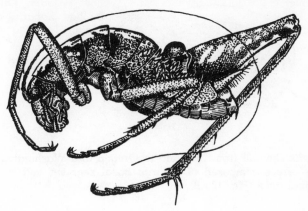

Figure 492

ment V only slightly. The function of Hubbell's organ is not definitely known.

7b **Male abdomen with low tubercles above but with no Hubbell's organ present; hind tibia strongly bowed. Figs. 493, 494** . . . .
. . . . . *Pristoceuthophilus pacificus* **Thomas Mushroom camel cricket**

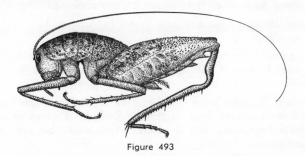

Figure 493

LENGTH: 12-14 mm. RANGE: Pacific Coast to Nevada.

Brownish, mottled darker. Common in woods, in deep duff, in open grassy meadows (in rodent burrows), under boards and similar cover. Sometimes destructive in commercial mushroom plantings. Attracted to molasses traps. Several other species resemble this, viz:

P. caelatus Scudder from the Pacific Coast area has the male cerci broadly toothed inwardly (Fig. 495 A) and the male hind femur has a long narrow thin triangular ridge beneath.

311

Figure 494

P. cercialis Caudell from Montana to Oregon and Washington has the male cercus composed of a large basal segment and a few tiny terminal ones (Fig. 495 B).

Figure 495

Figure 496

P. tuberculatus Caudell from northern California has numerous spines plus some large smooth tubercles on the abdomen (Fig. 496 C).

P. arizonae Hebard from low oak forest in Arizona has the abdomen smooth above.

P. marmoratus Rehn from southern California has the male hind tibia only slightly bowed and the hind femur has a series of small teeth beneath.

P. salebrosus Scudder from California to Washington has only a few low tubercles above, located mainly along hind edges of abdominal segments beginning with II or III. Male hind tibia similar to that of *pacificus*.

8a All tarsi 3-segmented; blind. Fig. 497..........................
.......*Typhloceuthophilus floridanus* Hubbell **Blind camel cricket**
LENGTH: 7-15 mm. RANGE: Florida.

Whitish to pale brownish. Blind. Found only in burrows of pocket-gophers in well-drained sandy soil as in "high pine-turkey oak" areas. Individuals may live for two years. Digging is done by using the head and mandibles like a hoe. By way of contrast *Ammobaenetes* dig by kicking sand back with their hind legs. Several dozen individuals of

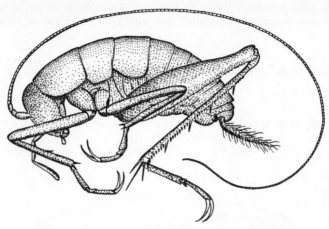

Figure 497

this blind camel cricket are sometimes found in a single extensive gopher burrow. These insects are almost surely predators on smaller arthropods which also inhabit the gopher burrows.

8b At least the middle tarsi 4-segmented..........................9

9a All tarsi 4-segmented.......................................10

9b Front tarsi or both front and hind tarsi 3-segmented.............20

10a Front tibia with a spine above, near middle. Fig. 498...........
............*Udeopsylla robusta* (Haldeman) Robust camel cricket

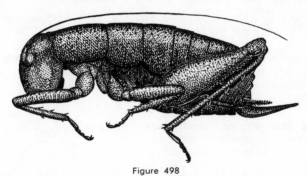

Figure 498

LENGTH: 18-26 mm. RANGE: Minnesota and Illinois to Idaho, Utah, New Mexico, and Texas.

Black, brown, or mottled brown. Common under rocks and logs, in burrows which it digs in the soil, and taken on plowed ground on

313

cloudy days or about dawn and dusk. The male hind femur is large and heavy, much as in *Daihinia* but with only small spines beneath.

10b Front tibia with no spine above, near middle..................11

11a Hind tibia with long spines crowded together above at apex to form a "sand basket." Fig. 499................................
....*Rhachocnemis validus* (Scudder) Coastal sand-treader cricket

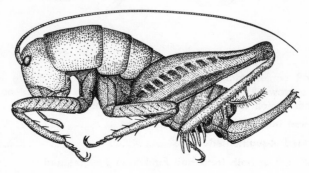

Figure 499

LENGTH: 14-20 mm. RANGE: Coastal California.

Brownish with darker transverse bands. Like *Ammobaenetes* these crickets dig into sand dunes to pass the day, emerging to feed at night. They dig by kicking with the hind legs. They are easily taken in traps baited with molasses or banana. Found as far North as San Francisco.

11b Hind tibia with no "sand basket" at apex...................12

12a Spines at apex of hind tibia subequal in length or at least with last upper spine at apex usually less than 1.5 times as long as last lower spine at apex (Fig. 501 A); small immovable teeth between large movable spines above on hind tibia few in number. Fig. 500 ....
Styracosceles neomexicanus (Scudder) New Mexico camel cricket

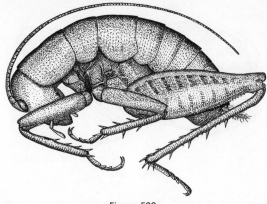

Figure 500

LENGTH: 17-20 mm. RANGE: Arizona to New Mexico and Colorado.

Brown, appendages sometimes paler. Adults in June and July in transition zone of various mountain areas. Ground dwellers.

S. *longispinosus* (Caudell) from Washington state, and S. *oregonensis* (Caudell) from the Mt. Hood area of Oregon are similar looking species.

12b Spines at apex of hind tibia un-
    equal in length, last upper spine
    at apex usually more than 1.5
    times as long as last lower spine
    at apex (B); small immovable
    teeth between large movable
    spines above on hind tibia usu-
    ally numerous. Fig. 501......13

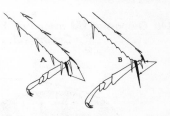

Figure 501

13a Male cercus (shown) with a heavy clublike basal portion and a
    slender flexible tip portion; hind tibia of male with a broad ventral
    tooth near base; last tergite of male much enlarged; upper surface
    of body with numerous low nodules. Fig. 502.................
    ....*Ceuthophilus nodulosus* Brunner Club-tailed camel cricket

315

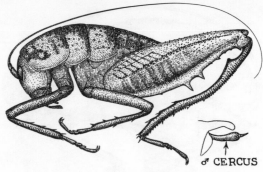

♂ CERCUS

Figure 502

LENGTH: 10-14 mm. RANGE: Texas and New Mexico to South Dakota and Kansas and Nebraska to Colorado Rockies.

Reddish-brown with darker markings. Taken under rocks in rather open country in fall and winter. Certain (robustifemoral) male individuals of many species of *Ceuthophilus* have the hind femur of a heavier structure with the spines larger, and with the hind tibia bowed. Other (gracilifemoral) males of the same species have the hind femur of a lighter build with the hind tibia straight. Such forms may be quite "different looking."

13b Male cercus tapering rather evenly from base to apex; hind tibia with no broad ventral tooth near base; last tergite of male smaller; upper surface of body rather smooth.........................14

14a Ovipositor (A) armed at tip with short blunt teeth. Fig. 503.......
............*Ceuthophilus utahensis* Thomas Utah camel cricket

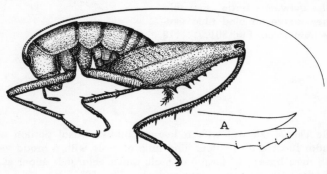

Figure 503

316

LENGTH: 12-14 mm. RANGE: Idaho to Arizona, New Mexico, Texas, and Oklahoma.

Yellowish-brown with weak pattern and transversely banded abdomen. Found in fairly open aspen and conifer wooded country under rocks or bark, in holes, etc. Invade basements and sometimes become so numerous in wells as to polute the water with their dead bodies; a health hazard.

14b Ovipositor armed at tip with longer sharp more or less hook-like teeth **15**

15a Male hind femur with a rather thin ridge-like expansion beneath which ends as a long sharp point near apex of femur, lower edge of ridge with a row of small teeth. Fig. 504.....................
........*Ceuthophilus lamellipes* Rehn **Ridge-legged camel cricket**

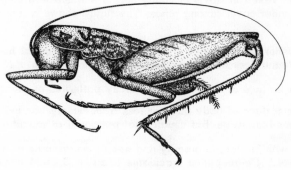

Figure 504

LENGTH: 12-15 mm. RANGE: Utah and Arizona.

Yellowish-brown with faint markings. Found sparingly in semi-desert areas. Taken in a mammal burrow and in a deep ditch made in adobe and boulders at 4,350 feet. More than 90 species of *Ceuthophilus* are known from the U. S. They are secretive and seldom noticed or collected.

15b Male hind femur not as described above.....................16

16a Ovipositor with 3 ventral teeth and a terminal hook at tip (A); hind femur heavy and heavily toothed beneath in male. Fig. 505.....
...*Ceuthophilus crassifemoris* Hubbell **Thick-leggel camel cricket**

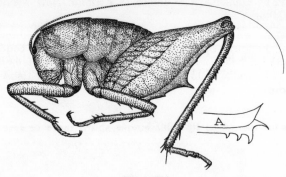

Figure 505

LENGTH: 15.5-19.5 mm. RANGE: North and South Carolina.

Brownish, often with blackish areas, a pattern more evident in paler specimens. Taken in areas of sandy soil of southeastern coastal plain, probably under cover among pines. The figure shows a robustifemoral male.

16b Ovipositor usually with 4 ventral teeth plus terminal hook at tip; hind femur less heavy and with fine teeth beneath............17

17a Upper surface of body rather distinctly patterned or maculate...18

17b Upper surface of body more or less transversely banded or with a pale median stripe, but usually not patterned or maculate......19

18a Male with 9th tergite broadly and deeply emarginate at middle (A). Fig. 506.`..*Ceuthophilus maculatus* (Harris) Spotted camel cricket

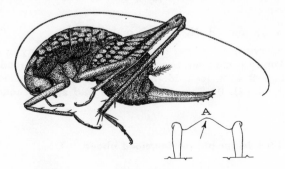

Figure 506

LENGTH 10-19 mm. RANGE: Manitoba, the Dakotas, and Nebraska to the Atlantic south to Maryland, Ohio and Arkansas.

318

Brown with pale median line and other conspicuous markings. Found commonly in drier forested areas where it remains under cover during the day.

18b Male with 9th tergite bluntly produced at middle (A). Fig. 507....
.............*Ceuthophilus brevipes* Scudder Boreal camel cricket

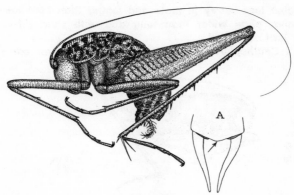

Figure 507

LENGTH: 14-15.5 mm. RANGE: Southeastern Canada and eastern U. S., south to Kentucky.

Brown with light and dark markings, darker and more mottled than *maculatus*. April to September. Often common in forested areas where it remains under cover during daytime. Farther South it requires the moisture of caves, tunnels, etc. Easily taken in molasses traps.

19a Hind tibia heavy in male and about as long as hind femur; male subgenital plate much longer than wide and consisting mostly of two long lobes (A). Fig. 508....................................
....*Ceuthophilus californianus* Scudder California camel cricket

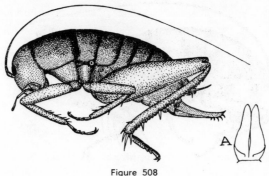

Figure 508

319

LENGTH: 14-17 mm. RANGE: California.

Yellowish to reddish-brown, pronotum often with a pale median line; usually appearing transversely banded. At first glance large specimens resemble *Styracosceles*, and small specimens resemble *C. fusiformis*. Often common in Upper Sonoran to Transitional grassland areas. Lives in the ground, in rodent burrows, under stones, boards, etc.

19b Hind tibia less heavy in male and longer than hind femur; male subgenital plate wider than long and with short lobes forming apical half. Fig. 509...
.........*Ceuthophilus fusiformis* Scudder Fusiform camel cricket

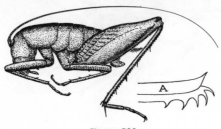

Figure 509

LENGTH: 7-11 mm. RANGE: Alberta and Manitoba to Utah, New Mexico, and Oklahoma.

Brownish varying from straw to patterned with blackish. (A) shows the ovipositor. Common in grassland areas in ground, in rodent burrows, among sedges in swales, and occurs to 10,300 feet in pine-juniper forest areas of the Rockies. Adults from March to December.

20a Hind tibia with dorsal spines long and crowded at apex to form a "sand basket." Fig. 510................................*Ammobaenetes phrixocnemoides* (Caudell) Caudell's sand treader cricket

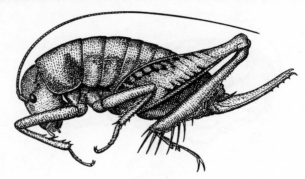

Figure 510

LENGTH: 15-17 mm. RANGE: New Mexico and Texas.

Brownish with darker areas. Occasionally destructively common (as at Pony, Texas, where they reportedly cut off plants at night). Most of the several species of *Ammobaenetes* are found on sand dunes where they eat bits of organic debris and they are mostly of no economic significance. The hind tarsi are 3-segmented.

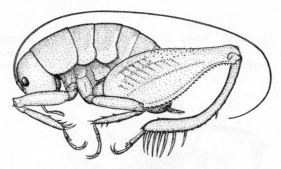

Figure 511

Macrobaenetes valgum (Strohecker), the Coachella sand treader cricket (Fig. 511), is common in sand dune areas of the Coachella Valley region of California. It is pale colored and measures 17-19 mm. Males have bowed hind tibiae. They dig energetically using the "sand baskets" of the hind tibiae to kick sand several inches. They spend their days buried deeply in the sand, emerging to mate and feed at night. The 4-segmented hind tarsi shows that this species is not an *Ammobaenetes*.

20b Hind tarsi with dorsal spines not long and crowded at apex, not forming a "sand basket"....................................**21**

21a Front tarsi 3-segmented, hind tarsi 4-segmented..............**22**

21b Front and hind tarsi 3-segmented. Fig. 512....................
........*Daihinia brevipes* **Haldeman Great Plains camel cricket**

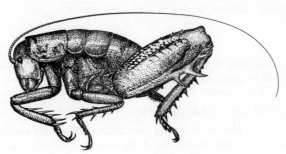

Figure 512

LENGTH: 22-24 mm. RANGE: Great Plains from North Dakota to Texas and plains areas among Rockies of Colorado and Wyoming.

Dark brown. A large heavily built cricket. The male hind femur is very powerfully built and heavily spined. The female hind femur is more like that of *Udeopsylla*. A ground-dwelling species taken under rocks, in rodent burrows, etc.

22a Hind tibia with 7 large dorsal spines (exclusive of apical spurs); middle tibia normally with 4 spines on each side above. Fig. 513..
.......*Daihinioides larvale* Strohecker Strohecker's camel cricket

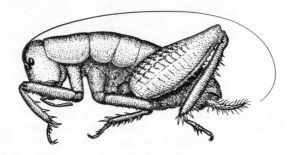

Figure 513

LENGTH: 17-23 mm. RANGE: New Mexico.

Whitish in life. Taken in company with *Ammobaenetes arenicolus* Strohecker at White Sands, New Mexico, at edges of "flats" and on dunes. They feed on *Ephedra* cones in small windrows of the flats.

D. *hastiferum* (Rehn) from New Mexico, Arizona, and Colorado, has one large tooth at middle of lower margin of male hind femur, the male subgenital plate is longer, and the insect is more heavily sclerotized. Otherwise much like the above.

22b Hind tibia with 5 large dorsal spines (exclusive of apical spurs); middle tibia normally with 2 spines on each side above. Fig. 514..
.......*Phrixocnemis truculentus* (Scudder) Truculent camel cricket

LENGTH: 18-20 mm. RANGE: Ozark Plateau and adjacent areas.

Brown, sometimes with lighter markings, sometimes suffused darker. Specimens have been taken in Arkansas in October and November from under a log in woods.

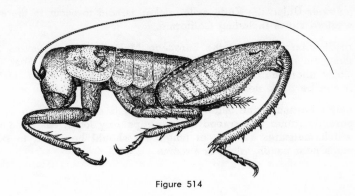

Figure 514

MOLE CRICKETS

These highly specialized crickets are seldom seen although they are often quite common. They burrow in the ground and are quick to escape when disturbed. The body is covered with a fine pile. The front legs are highly modified for digging.

KEY TO GRYLLOTALPIDAE

1a Front tibia with four dactyls, two movable; hind femur shorter than pronotum. Fig. 515...
............*Gryllotalpa hexadactyla* Perty Northern mole cricket

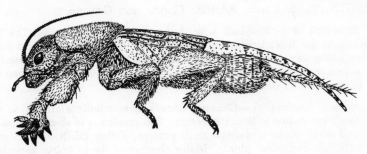

Figure 515

LENGTH: 21-30 mm. RANGE: Eastern Canada to South America.

Brown with limited blackish areas. Nocturnal. Common in muck along margins of lakes, ponds, etc. Often heard chirping in its burrows. Usually not easy to collect.

323

G. cultriger Uhler, the Knife mole cricket, is said to occur in the south-western states including California.

G. gryllotalpa (Linnaeus) the European Mole Cricket, measures 35-40 mm. and is locally established at various places in the East, especially about nurseries. It makes a churring sound in its burrows. It can be quite destructive to plant roots.

G. major Saussure, the Giant Mole Cricket, is a rarely taken but apparently rather widespread (but perhaps very local) eastern species which measures 41 mm. in length. It should be found in boggy muck near ponds, lakes, or streams.

1b **Front tibia with two dactyls; hind femur usually longer than pronotum. Fig. 516** ....
 ....*Scapteriscus acletus* **Rehn and Hebard Southern mole cricket**

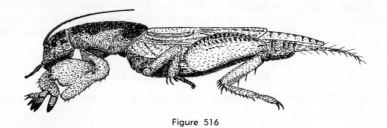

Figure 516

LENGTH: 26.4-35.5 mm. RANGE: Florida and Georgia.

Brownish to pinkish-buff with dark pattern on pronotum. The free portion of the front trochanter is very large. Vegetable gardens sometimes suffer severe damage from these insects. The calls are described as a rich gutteral "grrr" and may be heard all about at night when one is in an infested area.

S. vicinus Scudder, the Changa, occurs from southeastern U. S. and the West Indies to South America. The pronotum is shorter, broader, and often lacks a definite dark pattern. Often destructive to roots of grass and other plants. Males commonly fly to lights, especially on dark cloudy nights.

S. abbreviatus Scudder, the Short-winged mole cricket, measures 21-24 mm. It occurs in Florida, the West Indies, and Brazil. It is destructive to truck crops. The pronotum has dark markings but the tegmina cover only about one-third of the abdomen instead of about three-fourths as in *acletus*.

SAND CRICKETS OR PYGMY MOLE CRICKETS

Small burrowing crickets found commonly along sandy margins of ponds and streams. They resemble the larger mole crickets in a general way but differ from them in numerous important ways. For example at the tip of the abdomen one finds in addition to the cerci a second pair of appendages below the cerci which look much like a second pair of cerci. The function of these unusual appendages is unknown.

These nimble crickets are so small and such powerful jumpers that they seem to suddenly "disappear into thin air" when approached. We have two very interesting species belonging to a single genus.

KEY TO PYGMY MOLE CRICKETS

1a Length more than 5.5 mm.; hind tibia with four pairs of long slender plates used in swimming; hind tarsi 1-segmented. Fig. 517........
.....................*Tridactylus apicalis* Say Larger sand cricket

Figure 517

LENGTH: 6-9.5 mm. RANGE: Ontario to Florida, Mexico, and South America, west to southern California.

Brown or black with light and dark markings, variable. Common on sandy shores, bars, etc., at edge of water. These small insects are silent and the front tibiae are without hearing organs.

1b Length less than 5.5 mm.; hind tibia with one pair of short plates used in swimming; hind tarsi absent. Fig. 518...................
.................*Tridactylus minutus* Scudder Smaller sand cricket

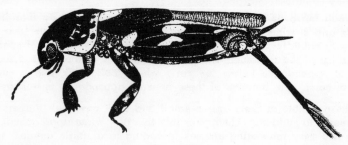

Figure 518

LENGTH: 4-5 mm. RANGE: New Jersey to Florida, Cuba, Central America, west to California.

Black or blackish-brown with light markings. Common in stubble fields and at edges of streams, ponds, etc. where sandy, and often in wet areas where there is scattered grass or weeds. Best collected by sweeping net back and forth just over area where they are seen. Individuals just suddenly "disappear" if stalked singly. In California they are found commonly North at least into Mendocino County.

CRICKETS

We have quite a number of kinds of gryllid crickets in our country, including charming singers, destructive pests, and quite a few kinds of special interest because of curiously specialized structures and habits. For example males of certain genera have special alluring glands secreting substances which are attractive to the females. In *Nemobius* the special structure is the first spine of the inner row above at the base of the hind tibia. The tip of the spine is bitten off by the female during mating. In *Oecanthus* and *Hapithus* the alluring gland is situated on top of the thorax, normally concealed by the tegmina. Females feed upon secretions of these glands as the spermatophore is being transferred to them.

Many crickets chirp or trill purely as individuals, but tree crickets commonly synchronize their trilling.

Whereas the West is particularly rich in decticids, the East has by far the better assortment of gryllid crickets, and building a good collection of these can be an extremely interesting pursuit.

KEY TO GRYLLIDAE

1a Tiny wingless subspherical forms having large antennal pits, no ocelli, small eyes, much enlarged hind femora, and usually found with ants (subfamily MYRMECOPHILINAE). Fig. 519, 520........
........*Myrmecophila oregonensis* Bruner West coast ant cricket

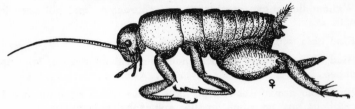

Figure 519

LENGTH: 2-3.2 mm. RANGE: California to British Columbia.

Brownish with faint markings. Common in nests of various ants. The food of these crickets consists at least in part of secretions from the ants. We have only four species.

M. pergandei Bruner, Eastern ant cricket, is similar and occurs from Maryland southward and west to Nebraska.

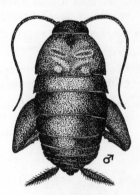

Figure 520

M. manni Schimmer, Dry lands ant cricket, occurs in arid and semiarid sections from Washington to Arizona and Mexico. It is paler in color than oregonensis.

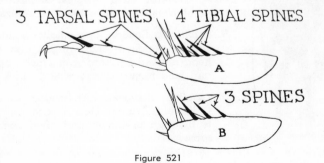

3 TARSAL SPINES 4 TIBIAL SPINES

A

3 SPINES

B

Figure 521

M. nebrascensis Lugger, Nebraska ant cricket, ranges from eastern Nebraska to Texas, New Mexico, and eastern Arizona to Mexico. The inner margin above on the hind tibia is armed with only 3 spines which increase in length toward the apex (Fig. 521 B). The other three species normally have 4 spines on the inner margin above (Fig. 521 A) and they alternate in length.

1b Without the above combination of characters, and not associating with ants...2

2a Hind tibia with rows of long spines above......................3

2b Hind tibia with tiny denticulations but without rows of long spines above 15

3a Hind tibia armed above with long spines which have no tiny denticulations and no much smaller spines between them............4

3b Hind tibia armed above with long spines which have tiny denticulations or much smaller spines between them..................11

4a Second tarsal segment compressed, base somewhat cylindrical in cross-section, minute (GRYLLINAE).............................5

4b Second tarsal segment somewhat flattened, proportionally larger, distinct, heart-shaped (TRIGONIDIINAE)........................9

5a Spines of hind tibia long and movable; small species, body length 12 mm. or less. Fig. 522...
..............*Nemobius fasciatus* (De Geer) Striped ground cricket

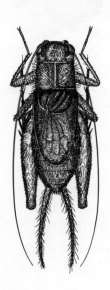

LENGTH: 7.2-11.5 mm. RANGE: Nova Scotia to Manitoba and south to Tennessee, Arkansas, and New Mexico.

Dark reddish-brown to black. Tegmina and wings long or short, often in same locality. Very common and widespread. Males call day and night with shrill high-pitched intermittent or continuous trill. Adults from July until frosts kill them. Several other species, subspecies, and races of *Nemobius* have been recognized.

N. ambitiosus Scudder is a smaller southeastern species which is short-winged and has the head marked on front with black and white, and hind femur usually with 2 black stripes.

N. carolinus neomexicanus Scudder of Oregon, California, Arizona, New Mexico, and Mexico is blackish or brown and often common in grass.

N. cubensis mormonius Scudder is smaller, short-winged, and often abundant in Bermuda grass. Nevada to Colorado and South to Arizona and Texas.

5b Spines of hind tibia usually immovable; larger species, body length 14 mm. or more...6

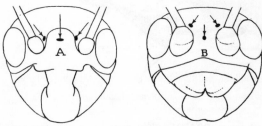

Figure 523

6a Ocelli arranged as a nearly straight transverse row (Fig. 523 A). Fig. 524.......*Anurogryllus muticus* (De Geer) Short-tailed cricket

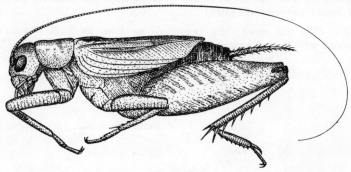

Figure 524

LENGTH: 12-17 mm. RANGE: New Jersey to Florida and Texas, West Indies, Mexico, Columbia, and Guiana.

Brownish, abdomen dark. Hind tibia extremely short, first hind tarsus much elongated and spined. Sometimes destructively common on various crops. Live in burrows which they dig. Males produce a high-pitched trilling at night, often singing from the burrow entrance.

6b Ocelli arranged as a triangle (Fig. 523 B)......................7

7a Space between antennal bases approximately as wide as diameter of basal antennal segment. Fig. 525.............................
..................*Gryllodes sigillatus* (Walker) Decorated cricket

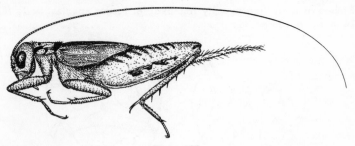

Figure 525

LENGTH: 14-21 mm. RANGE: Widespread in the tropics. Florida.

Brownish, banded and mottled darker brown. Female tegmina very short. Often common and very active. Males produce an energetic high-pitched shrilling call. Taken under bricks and between stones. In hot houses at Washington, D. C.

7b Space between antennal bases at least twice as wide as diameter of basal antennal segment....................................8

8a Hind tibia not more than two-thirds as long as hind femur, and armed with 4 or 5 spines above on each side. Figs. 526, Fig. 527..
..............*Miogryllus verticalis* (Serville) Stripe-headed cricket

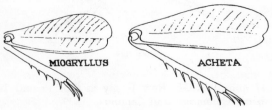

Figure 526

LENGTH: 10-17 mm. RANGE: New York to Florida, Texas, Kansas, Nebraska, and Oklahoma.

Brown to black, head usually yellow-striped. Usually short-winged. Found under vegetation, leaves, boards, in ground burrows, etc. Males produce high-pitched intermittent trills.

M. lineatus (Scudder) of southwestern United States is a similar species taken sparingly in dry desert and foothills, in cotton fields, feeding on cotton blossoms, and in grass areas in town.

8b **Hind tibia at least three-fourths as long as hind femur, and armed with 5 to 8 spines above on each side. (Figs. 526, 528)............ ....*Acheta assimilis* (Fabricius) Field cricket**

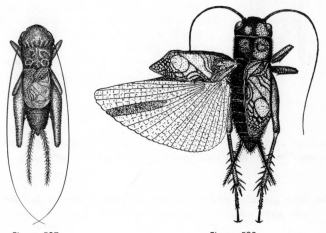

Figure 527   Figure 528

LENGTH: 14-30 mm. RANGE: General.

Brown or black, sometimes marked with orange on tegmina, etc. Variable. Many names have been applied to populations of different appearance but these are hard to tell apart with certainty. Final decisions are being sought concerning which names are valid, how many species there are, etc. Common and often destructive. Males produce an intermittent shrilling sound.

A. domesticus (Linnaeus), the House cricket, is yellowish-brown or straw colored and often enters houses and other buildings in Europe and eastern North America. It is the hearth cricket whose cheerful singing has been mentioned many times in literature.

9a **Last segment of maxillary palpus broadly lobed, appearing very large and concave; first antennal segment longer than wide; head and thorax red, tegmina brown. Fig. 529........................ ....*Phyllopalpus pulchellus* (Uhler) Red-headed bush cricket**

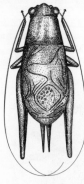

LENGTH: 6-7 mm. RANGE: New York to Florida and west to Indiana, Illinois, and Kentucky.

Head and pronotum red, pronotum with yellow on sides; otherwise black and brown. Not uncommon on low shrubs, among grass, and on young trees. Favors buttonbush, *Cephalanthus occidentalis*. A pretty and active cricket. Males elevate the tegmina like *Oecanthus* and produce a weak wavering high-pitched trill. The much enlarged maxillary palpi are black. They are often vibrated in a rapid and curious manner when the cricket is approached.

Figure 529

9b Last segment of maxillary palpus club-shaped; first antennal segment wider than long; color not red and brown.................10

10a Pale greenish-yellow species with head nearly flat between eyes, and eyes distinctly longer than wide. Fig. 530.................
.........*Cyrtoxipha gundlachi* Saussure Gundlach's bush cricket

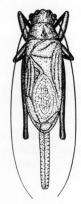

LENGTH: 5.5-6.5 mm. RANGE: Florida, West Indies, and Central America to northern South America.

Pale green, tibial spines and ovipositor marked with black. Common on tree foliage and shrubbery, especially in moist areas. Males produce high-pitched tinkling calls both day and night.

C. columbiana Caudell occurs from Washington, D. C., to Florida and Texas. It is much like *gundlachi* except ovipositor stouter and longer, extending past the tips of the hind femora, and the ovipositor teeth are blunt instead of sharp as in *gundlachi*. It is also a bit larger and stouter. Common in trees and shrubs well off the ground. At night males call in a pervasive silvery trilling chorus.

Figure 530

10b Brownish or yellowish species with head convex between eyes, and eyes about as long as wide. Fig. 531..........................
..............*Anaxipha imitator* (Saussure) Cuban bush cricket

LENGTH: 4.7-6.2 mm. RANGE: Cuba and Florida.

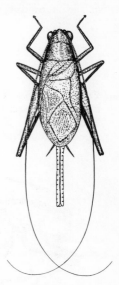

Brown, a dark brown stripe running back from eye along each side. Taken on sloping ground between hammock jungle and mangrove swamp, jumping and flying low about dead leaf litter of wild coffee. *Psychotria undata.* Common on jungle floor at Key Largo. Males produce intermittent high-pitched trills.

A. *exigua* (Say) Say's bush cricket, is common and widespread from New England and Minnesota to Florida and Texas. It is larger than *imitator* and has the ovipositor longer, fully one-half the length of hind femur. On grass and dense vegetation in damp places where the silvery tinkling of the males is heard both day and night, three distinct calls are produced by *exigua:* a slow tinkle, a fast tinkle and a trill, but

Figure 531

not by the same individual. A few additional species of *Anaxipha* are known.

11a Ocelli present (ENEOPTERINAE)..............................12
11b Ocelli absent (OECANTHINAE)..............................14
12a Male tegmen with a stridulating organ; front tibia with a hearing organ; body length under 20 mm..........................13
12b Male tegmen with no stridulating organ; front tibia with no hearing organ; body length 23 mm. or more. Fig. 532..............
.....................*Tatalisca lurida* Walker Silent bush cricket

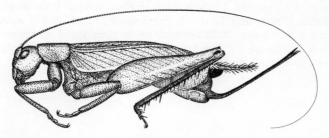

Figure 532

LENGTH: 23-30 mm. RANGE: West Indies, Florida.

333

Brown. Occasionally taken on Florida buttonwood. *Conocarpus erecta*, red mangrove, and bay cedar.

13a Front tibia with hearing organ on inner surface only; tegmina usually not covering all of abdomen; wings rudimentary or shorter than tegmina. Fig. 533......................................
........*Hapithus brevipennis* Saussure Short-winged bush cricket

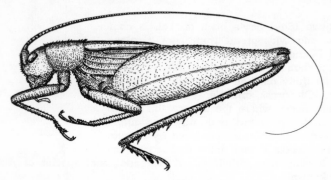

Figure 533

LENGTH: 11-19 mm. RANGE: Florida to Georgia and Louisiana.

Pale reddish-brown, male with yellow stripe on side of tegmen with black line beneath. Adults are occasionally found from July to October in tangled undergrowth of rather dry open oak and pine woods. Much commoner among fans of saw palmetto.

H. agitator Uhler, the Restless bush cricket, ranges from New York to Florida, Cuba, and Texas. It measures 9-14 mm. and is more robust than *brevipennis*. Male tegmina reach near tip of abdomen but are often mutilated by the females. Common on prickly ash, scarlet oak, and other vegetation.

13b Front tibia with hearing organ on both inner and outer surfaces; tegmina covering all of abdomen; wings longer than tegmina. Fig. 534................*Orocharis saltator* Uhler Jumping bush cricket

LENGTH: 14-16 mm. RANGE: New Jersey to Florida, Nebraska, and Texas.

Grayish-brown, often faintly striped or mottled. Often common on oaks and other trees, found hiding in a large epiphite *Tillandsia utriculata*, on *Crataegus*, etc. Often flies to escape. The calls are short rapid high-pitched trills which are heard on cloudy days and at night.

O. *gryllodes* (Pallas) is a West Indian and southern Florida species in which the pronotum has a black stripe on each side. On vegetation of various kinds, under bark, etc.

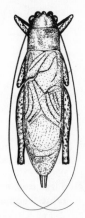

Figure 534

14a First and second basal segments of antenna unmarked or each with only a single mark. Fig. 535............................ ....*Oecanthus niveus* (De Geer) **Snowy tree cricket**

LENGTH: 12-14.5 mm. RANGE: Most of U. S. to Central America.

Pale greenish, head and bases of antennae yellowish. Basal antennal segments marked as in Fig. 536 "B." On deciduous trees and shrubs where they feed on aphids. The call is a high-pitched "*treet-treet-treet*" repeated endlessly.

O. *latipennis* Riley from eastern U. S. is as broad-winged as *niveus* in the male. The basal antennal segments (Fig. 536 A) lack distinct markings. Pale straw colored with head and antennal bases purplish-pink. Found in thickets of shrubs, vines, and tall weeds.

O. *angustipennis* Fitch from eastern U. S. has the male much narrower, basal antennal segments marked as in Fig. 536 "C," and it occurs on deciduous trees and shrubs.

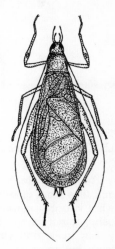

Figure 535

O. *exclamationis* Davis from eastern U. S. has the male narrow, basal antennal segments marked as in Fig. 536 "D," and occurs on deciduous trees such as oak, hickory, and beech.

O. *californicus* Saussure from western U. S. is brown to ivory with a reddish tinge on head in pale individuals, and with basal antennal

335

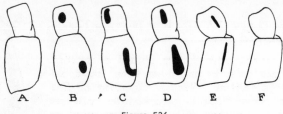

Figure 536

segments marked as in Fig. 536 "E" or unmarked (F). Found in thickets of shrubs and other low plants.

14b First and second basal segments of antenna each with two marks which sometimes run together. Fig. 537 . . . .
. . . . *Oecanthus nigricornis* Walker Black-horned tree cricket

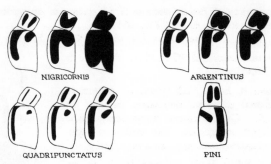

NIGRICORNIS ARGENTINUS

QUADRIPUNCTATUS PINI

Figure 537

LENGTH: 12-14 mm. RANGE: Ontario to North Carolina, Tennessee, west to Kansas and Nebraska.

Tegmina pale, head and pronotum usually with dark midline, body and legs more or less blackish. The basal antennal segments are somewhat variably marked as shown, the almost completely black segments being found on specimens from North Carolina. On tall weeds, shrubs, young trees, and vines. This and the subspecies *quadripunctatus* (below) damage raspberry, blackberry, grape, plum, peach, etc., by laying eggs in the stems.

O. nigricornis argentinus Saussure replaces the typical form from the Great Plains to the Pacific. It varies from entirely pale to weakly suffused darker on abdomen. The moderately heavy markings of the basal antennal segments vary somewhat about as shown. Mostly on weeds and small shrubs.

O. nigricornis quadripunctatus Beutenmuller occurs from Ontario to Florida and Mississippi. It ranges farther West, from British Columbia to Arizona and Texas, but there tends to be atypical and to intergrade with *argentinus*. The body is normally entirely pale and the basal antennal segments are variably marked about as shown. The narrow markings shown in the first diagram illustrate the typical Atlantic states form. The broader markings shown in the third diagram are from farther West and are much like certain *argentinus*.

O. pini Beutenmuller occurs from Connecticut to North Carolina on or about pines. Specimens are greenish or brown, the basal antennal segments marked as shown.

15a Tegmina long; wings projecting far beyond tegmina and abdomen; form long and slender; hind femur slender. Fig. 538..............
.........*Neoxabea bipunctata* (De Geer) Two-spotted tree cricket

LENGTH: 20-22 mm. RANGE: Connecticut to Kansas, Georgia, and Mississippi.

Pale pinkish-brown, female tegmina with two pairs of dark areas. The first basal segment of the antenna is unmarked and has a blunt tooth in front at apex. Usually uncommon and difficult to collect as it prefers dense tangles of wild grape vines, etc. Males produce rather low pitched mellow intermittent trills of a few seconds duration, and they sing at night. This is the only known species of the genus.

Figure 538

15b Tegmina short; wings absent; form rather broad; hind femur stout (MOGOPLISTINAE) 16

16a Male pronotum with hind margin nearly straight across; tegmina well exposed; ovipositor not widened near apex. Fig. 539......
...........*Hoplosphyrum boreale* Scudder Western bush cricket

LENGTH: 13-15 mm. RANGE: California and Lower California to New Mexico and Texas.

Brown. Found in Upper Sonoran zone under rocks and leaves or in crevices of trees. The call is a high-pitched rapid "cree-cree-cree."

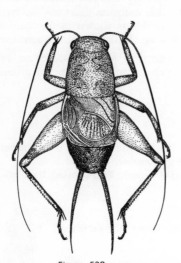

Figure 539

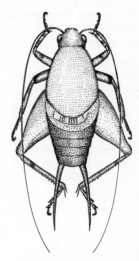

Figure 540

16b Male pronotum with hind margin broadly rounded and covering most of tegmina; ovipositor distinctly widened near apex........
............*Cycloptilium squamosum* Scudder Scaly bush cricket

LENGTH: 5.4-7.2 mm. RANGE: Texas to Florida.

Gray-brown, covered with minute silvery scales imparting a sheen. Found under bushes, among grasses and weeds, in Spanish moss, in salt marsh grass, on weeds, etc.

C. comprehendens Hebard is a similar species which occurs commonly from Nebraska and Texas to California.

C. zebra (Rehn and Hebard) from extreme southern Florida has the male tegmina strikingly marked with blackish-brown. A few additional species of *Cycloptilium* are known.

INDEX AND PICTURED GLOSSARY

A

ABERRANT: different from the usual type.
Acantherus 170
Acantherus piperatus 154
Acheta 287
Acheta assimilis 331
A. domesticus 331
Achurum hilliardi 153
A. sumichrasti 153
Acridinae 99, 104, 107, 151
Acridid grasshoppers 98
Acrididae Section 1 104
Acrididae Section 2 151
Acrodectes philophagus 287
Acrolophitus 107, 164
Acrolophitus hirtipes 105
A. variegatus 105
Actinia richardsoni 107
ACUTELY: sharply; like a point; less than a 90 degree angle.
Adenostema 94
ADVENTIVE: of accidental occurence; not a native species.
AEDEAGUS: genital organ of male insect.
AEDEAGI: plural of aedeagus.
Aeoloplides tenuipennis 209
Aerochoreutes carlinianus 145
A. carlinianus strepitus 145
Aeropedellus clavatus 159
Ageneotettix 167
Ageneotettix deorum 167
A. deorum curtipennis 168
A. sierranus 168
Agroecotettix modestus 204
A. modestus aristus 205
A. modestus crypsidomus 205
Aglaopteryx gemma 37
Aglaothorax 283
Aglaothorax armiger 284
A. ovatus 284
A. segnis 284
Agymnastus ingens 121
Aidemona azteca amrami 203
ALCOHOL: flammable liquid available in various concentrations and often used in killing and preparing insects. Some forms are very poisonous.
Alder 205
Aldrin 8
Alfalfa 109, 197, 220, 226, 233, 235, 237
ALGAE: a group of lower plants; one-celled algae sometimes grow on tetrigids.
ALLURING GLAND: gland producing a substance attractive to other individuals, especially of the opposite sex.
Amblycorypha floridana 274
A. insolita 274
A. oblongifolia 274
A. rotundifolia iselyi 274
A. rotundifolia parvipennis 273
Amblytropidia mysteca 177
A. occidentalis 176
Amitermes minimus 78
A. silvestrianus 77
A. snyderi 76
A. wheeleri 77
Ammobaenetes 312, 314, 321
Ammobaenetes arenicolus 322
A. phrixocnemoides 320
Amphitornus coloradus 175
A. coloradus ornatus 176
A. coloradus saltator 176
Anabrus 283, 300
Anabrus cerciata 300
A. longipes 300
A. simplex 299, 300
ANAL VEIN: an unbranched vein located behind the cubitus.

ANAL   INTERCALARY

Figure 541

Anaxipha 333
Anaxipha exigua 333
A. imitator 332
Anconia hebardi 151
A. caeruleipennis 151
A. integra 151
Anisolabis maritima 15
Anisomorpha buprestoides 20
A. ferruginea 21
Anoplodusa arizonensis 290
Anoplotermes fumosus 75
ANTERIOR: at or toward the front.
Anurogryllus muticus 329
APEX: the end of a structure farthest from its base or point of attachment.
APICAL: at or toward the apex or tip of any structure.
Aplopus mayeri 21
Apote notabilis 295
Appalachia 198
Appalachia arcana 205
A. hebardi 205
APPENDICULAR FIELD: large area with scarcely any veins at apical ends of wings of certain cockroaches (see Fig. 542).

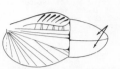

Figure 542

Apples 304
Apple trees 226
Aptenopedes aptera 192
A. sphenarioides 191
ARCUATE: curved like an arch or bow.
Arenivaga bolliana 57
A. floridensis 57
Arethaea gracilipes 272
A. phalanginum 272
Argiacris rehni 212
AROLIUM: pad-like lobe between tarsal claws.

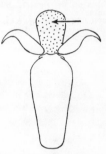

Figure 543

Arphia 113
Arphia behrensi 112
A. conspersa 112
A. granulata 112
A. pseudonietana 111
A. pseudonietana crassa 112
A. saussureana 112
A. sulphurea 111
A. xanthoptera 111
Arrowweed 230
Artemesia 94
Artemesia pycnocephala 143
Asemoplus 201
Asemoplus montanus 199
ASYMMETRICAL: having the half on one side of the midline shaped differently than the other half.
Ateloplus luteus 300
A. notatus 300
Atlanticus 293, 294
Atlanticus americanus 294
A. gibbosus 294

Figure 544

individuals of the same species have them much longer (stippled).

Figure 545

CALCARIA

Figure 546

Figure 547

INDEX

341

INDEX

CUBITUS: a longitudinal vein of the tegmen which branches conspicuously.

Figure 549

D

DACTYL: finger-like or toe-like structure.
DENTICULATION: a small tooth.
DESERT: areas of our southwest with high temperatures and low annual rainfall.

DIAGNOSTIC: enabling recognition.
DINOSAUR: giant reptile which lived long ago.
DIPLURA: order of primitive insects.
DISC: central upper portion or central portion.
DISCOIDAL VEIN: first and principal branch of humeral vein; provides framework for much of outer part of tegmen.

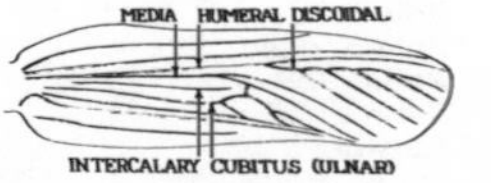

Figure 550

DISTAL: toward the end farthest from the point of attachment on the body.
DIVERGENT: spreading apart from a common base.
DORSAL: pertaining to the upper surface or back.

E

ECOLOGICAL NICHE: a particular habitat, e.g. sand dunes.
ECOLOGY: branch of science dealing with interactions between living organisms and their environment.
EMARGINATE: having the margin notched or with a portion of the margin cut out.

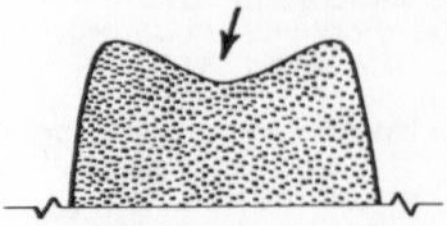

Figure 551

ENTOMOLOGIST: one who studies insects scientifically.
ENZYMES: chemical catalytic substances produced by living cells.
EQUILATERAL TRIANGLE: triangle having all three sides of equal length.
ETHYL ACETATE: $CH_3 CO_2$ $C_2 H_5$ acetic ether, a flammable liquid useful for killing insects. Use with reasonable caution and adequate ventilation.
ETHYL ALCOHOL: CH_3 . $CH_2 OH$ potable alcohol, useful in preparing insects for mounting.

EVOLUTION: the process through which complex or specialized organisms gradually develop from simpler or primitive ones.
EVOLUTIONARY: see evolution.
EXCAVATE: hollowed out.
EYES: organs used for seeing; in insects generally of two types: simple (called ocelli) and compound (paired and made up of numerous eye elements).

F

FACET: flattened place, reminding one of the angular faces of gemstones.
FAMILY: taxonomic category comprising a group of related genera; major subdivision of an order.
FASTIGIUM: front portion of head (vertex) between and above compound eyes, often with angular facets, sculptured, or produced as a ridge, point, tubercle, or cone, and useful in classification of many jumping orthopteroids.

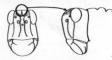

Figure 552

FEMORA: plural of femur.
FEMUR: thigh; usually the stoutest segment of insect leg, connected to body by coxa and trochanter and bearing tibia at distal end.

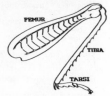

Figure 553

FENESTRATE: having veins arranged so as to leave rows of window-like spaces.

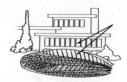

Figure 554

FONTANELLE: frontal pore (at middle of head) present in many termites.
FORMALIN: CH_2O; strong-smelling solution of formaldehyde useful as an antiseptic or preservative.
FOVEOLAE: plural of foveola; small depressions or pits in grasshoppers located at sides of fastigium.

Figure 555

FRONTAL COSTA: broad prominent vertical ridge on front of head between compound eyes and running down toward clypeal margin, often bearing median ocellus.

Figure 556

FURCULAE: paired structures at base of supra-anal plate of some grasshoppers, often distinctive in size and shape and then useful in classification of closely related species.

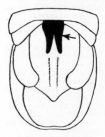

Figure 557

G

GENERA: plural of genus.
GENETICALLY: according to the laws of heredity.
GENETICS: scientific study of heredity.
GENITALIA: organs of reproduction.
GENUS: an apparently distinctive and taxonomically isolated species (monotypic genus) or a group of apparently related species sharing some character or combination of characters and commonly thought to represent a ramifying evolutionary branch (polytypic genus).
GRACILIFEMORAL: having the hind femora slender and with reduced spination where some individuals of the same species have them thick and heavily spined.

Figure 558

INDEX

INDEX

GLOBOSE: shaped somewhat like a round ball or sphere.
GREAT BASIN: semiarid region extending from Sierra-Cascade chain eastward. Characteristic plants include: Sagebrush, Creosote Bush, *Atriplex*, and *Sarcobatus*.
GREGARIOUS: occurring in groups or congregations but without social organization or castes.
GULA: sclerite forming middle portion of underside of head.

H

HABITAT: the place where a plant or animal normally lives.
HEMIPTERA: insect order in which the mouthparts form a sucking beak and in which the fore wings are thick basally and membranous apically.
HOLARCTIC: faunal region which includes Europe and North Africa, Asia, North of Himalayas, and North America North of Mexico.
HOPPERDOZERS: horse-drawn devices of various designs formerly much used by farmers in combatting destructive grasshoppers.

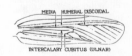

Figure 559

HUBBELL'S ORGAN: a conspicuous structure of unknown function found on the abdomens of certain crickets.
HUMERAL VEIN: the third major vein of the tegmen. The discoidal vein branches from it.

Figure 560

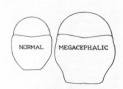

Figure 567

MEDIA: fourth major vein of tegmen.

Figure 565

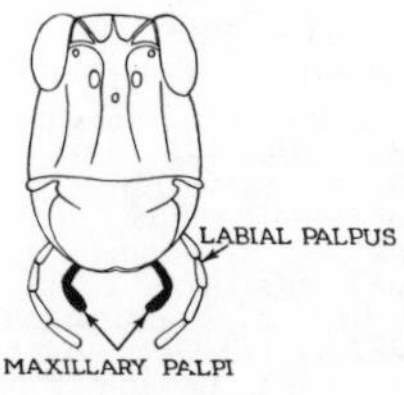

Figure 564

Figure 566

INDEX

MESONOTUM: upper portion of mesothorax.
MESOSTERNUM: bottom portion of mesothorax.

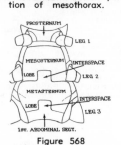

Figure 568

METANOTUM: upper portion of metathorax.
METASTERNUM: bottom portion of metathorax.

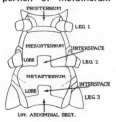

Figure 569

METAZONA: portion of pronotum behind principal sulcus.

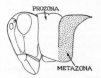

Figure 570

METHYL ALCOHOL: CH_3 . OH, wood alcohol; a poisonous kind of alcohol.
MIGRATORY PHASE: swarming or gregarious long-winged and differently colored form of some kinds of grasshoppers which arises when nymphs are crowded together during their development.
MINUTE: tiny.
MONOTYPIC GENUS: a genus having only one (distinctive) species.
MORPHOLOGY: branch of science dealing with form or shape of structures.

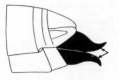

Figure 571

INDEX

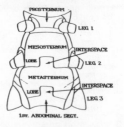

Figure 572

PROTOZOA: microscopic 1-
celled animals.
PROZONA: portion of pro-
nutum in front of princi-
pal sulcus.

Figure 573

Q

R

heavily spined where some individuals of the same species have them slender and with reduced spination.

ROBUSTIFEMORAL.   GRACILIFEMORAL.

Figure 574

S

SCLERITE: one of the body plates of an insect's external covering, bounded by sutures or membranes.
SCLEROTIZED: hardened, as when sclerites are thickened and toughened by having chitin or other chemical substances deposited in them.
SETAE: hairlike structures.
SHAGREENED: finely roughened, like shark leather.
SOCIAL: living in groups or colonies, generally with specialized castes and with a conspicuous division of labor.
SOCIAL HORMONE: a chemical substance produced by specialized termites which acts to preserve the normal ratio of specialized to unspecialized (workerlike) individuals.
SOLDIER: termite specialized for fighting in defense of the colony.
SOLITARY PHASE: sedentary or stationary form of some grasshoppers which results when nymphs develop in uncrowded circumstances. Intermediates between this and the migratory phase are often found.
SPECIALIZED: modified from the primitive type.
SPECIES: the individuals of a certain kind, able to mate freely and to produce fertile offspring of the same kind, and commonly includes an assortment of varieties, races, and subspecies.
SPERMATOPHORE: capsule containing sperm cells.

SPIRACLE: a breathing pore.
SPRING SPECIES: a species which is adult early in the year and which passes Summer in the egg stage.
SPUR OF TIBIA: calcar; movable hook-like spine at apex of tibia.
SPUR OF WING: dark marking running toward base from band, near front of wing.
STERNITE: the ventral piece in a ring or segment of the insect body.
STRIDULATE: to produce sounds by rubbing roughened areas together.
STYLE: small appendage near tip of abdomen.
STYRIFOAM: a frothy plastic substance available in blocks of various thicknesses.
SUB ANAL STYLES: short, sometimes highly modified appendages located below the anus.
SUBAPICAL: near the apex.
SUBGENITAL PLATE: sclerite covering the genital opening from beneath, often scoop-shaped.

Figure 575

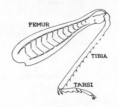

Figure 577

Figure 576

T

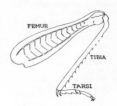

Figure 578

TROCHANTER: second segment of orthopteroid insect leg, between coxa and femur, and usually tiny.

TRUNCATE: cut squarely across.

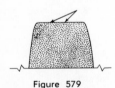

Figure 579

TUBERCLE: rounded lump or pimple.
TUBERCULATE: with tubercles on surface.

TYMPANA: plural of Tympanum.

TYMPANUM: external membrane of hearing organ.

TYPE LOCALITY: the place where the type specimen (and often the accompanying type series as well) was collected.

TYPE SERIES: all of the specimens of a new species which the describer had before him and which he considered as representing his new species, at the time he described it.

TYPE SPECIMEN: the specimen the describer had before him in naming the species and which he designated as typifying the species.

U

UPPER SONORAN: western grassland - oak - chaparral life zone below transitional, roughly equivalent to Upper Austral in East.

V

VALVE OF OVIPOSITOR: one of sclerites of ovipositor.

VARIANT: individual which differs in some minor way from ordinary appearing individuals.

VEIN: one of the major parts of the framework of a wing.

VEINLET: small vein.

VENTRAL: under, on the belly side.

VENTRILOQUIAL: illusive quality of a sound which makes it seem to come from various directions.

VERTEX: middle part of top of head, in front of occiput.

VESTIGIAL: reduced, rudimentary, nearly lost.

Volatile solvent technique 4

W

X

XYLENE: $C_6H_4(CH_3)_2$, liquid useful in mounting camel crickets and in clearing tissues generally.

Y

Z

*Since going to press a paper has been received changing the generic name *Zubovskya* to *Boonacris* for our American species.

THE SAME EVENT THAT SPELLS
"The End" FOR ONE
IS BREAKFAST FOR ANOTHER...